THE COLLECTOR'S
DICTIONARY OF CLOCKS

THE COLLECTOR'S DICTIONARY OF

CLOCKS

BY

H. ALAN LLOYD

SOUTH BRUNSWICK
NEW YORK: A. S. BARNES AND CO.

Library of Congress Catalogue Card Number: 65-24848

A.S. Barnes and Company, Inc
Cranbury, New Jersey 08512

SBN: 498 06279 1

Printed in the United States of America

FOREWORD

TO EMPLOY the word Dictionary in a title is a challenge; it implies completeness and the expectation of an answer to the query in mind.

The author feels that, thanks to the generous treatment by his Publishers in the matter of illustrations, the various types of clock are well represented; nevertheless, the reader should not look upon this as the Clock equivalent of the *Oxford Dictionary of the English Language* in thirteen volumes. If, however, he is from time to time disappointed in not finding that for which he is looking, it is hoped that this may be balanced by his finding much in this book with which he was not previously acquainted. The subject has been confined to Clocks; Sun Dials, Astrolabes, Watches and Chronometers are all separate fields and would each require a volume to themselves.

To cover nearly 4,000 years and to deal with thirteen different countries has been a tremendous task and one never before attempted. When we come to consider the short biographies of Clockmakers, as opposed to the clocks that they made, the problem becomes much more difficult, for Baillie's *Watch and Clockmakers of the World* contains 35,000 names, Professor Morpurgo's list of Italian makers has 1,000 or more names, and Dreppard's American list has several thousands of names. Obviously one has to be very selective. We can, however, console ourselves with the thought that the vast bulk of the names, at any rate since the end of the 18th century, are those of sellers of the clocks and not those of makers. For these biographies and dates Baillie, Britten, Morpurgo and Dreppard have been drawn upon. One whose name is practically un-known, and who deserves much more appreciation, is Lucien Verité. His clocks in Beauvais and Besançon Cathedrals are in all respects worthy of equal notice to those of Strasburg and, of later years, Messina and Copenhagen.

It is understandable that the country with the largest representation is England; for the other countries, headings such as Austrian Clocks, or American Clocks etc., are given, under which all the numbers of the illustrations of clocks of those countries are gathered together. This is not always as easy as it would seem, especially in the early years of the 15th, 16th and 17th centuries when the best craftsmen went from court to court in Europe. For example, Burgi was born a Swiss, but he worked in Germany and Bohemia. As far as is possible the clocks will be assigned to the country in which they were made, irrespective of the nationality of the maker. In the early years French, German, Flemish, Burgundian and Italian clocks were all very alike in design and, as these are rarely signed, dated or bear any place names, it is largely a matter of guess-work to allot them to the different countries.

That craftsmanship in design and execution still exists today is evidenced in the clocks under the headings Copenhagen, Dondi, York and the Zodiac, but apprentices are lamentably few. Against this, research into Antiquarian Horology during the past twenty years has been very active and it is hoped that the reader may have much pleasure in the results of this research recorded here.

H. Alan Lloyd

5

ILLUSTRATIONS

GEOGRAPHICAL DISTRIBUTION OF THE CLOCKS ILLUSTRATED

THE COLLECTOR'S DICTIONARY OF CLOCKS

REFERENCE NUMBERS IN TEXT
The reference numbers given thus [1] in the text refer to books and other publications quoted, which are listed on page 204.

ACANTHUS. The stylised representation of the leaves of the Mediterranean acanthus plant; adopted from Greek classical sculpture for the representation of Corinthian capitals on the columns decorating the finest clock cases from 1660 to 1700 (Figs. 1 and 322).

The dial of Fig. 1 should be compared with the dials of the clocks by John Hilderson and East (Figs. 278 and 28). The engraving is evidently by the same hand, a man whose work can be recognised, not only by its fine quality, but by the fact that his work is always asymmetrical. The flowers on the corners, for example, balance each other, but are of different species; the same applies to the design in the centre of the dial. There was, at this period, another engraver whose work appeared on the back plates (q.v.) of many good quality clocks, but whose designs are always symmetrical (*see* Fig. 257).

ACORN. A brass or turned-wood finial, sometimes on the hood (q.v.) of a clock (Fig. 2) and sometimes as a drop finial (Fig. 266).

ACORN CLOCK. A type of American shelf clock (q.v.) made in Connecticut in the middle of the 19th century, roughly in the form of an acorn (Fig. 3). These clocks are not easily found; in the example illustrated it will be noted that there is glass in the base, which is internally painted, allowing the motion of the pendulum to be seen. The makers were the Forestville Manufacturing Co. of Forestville, Connecticut.

ACT OF PARLIAMENT CLOCK. In 1797 William Pitt introduced an Act of Parliament which read, in part . . . 'For and upon every Clock or Timekeeper . . . which shall be used for the purpose of a clock and placed in or upon any dwelling

1. *Bracket clock by Edward East. London, c. 1685.* (*The late Mr W. J. Iden*)   2. *Hanging clock by William Clement. London, c. 1675-80.* (*Author's collection*)   3. *Acorn clock. U.S.A., c. 1855.* (*Mr Walter M. Roberts*)

4. *Anonymous 'Act of Parliament Clock'. 1714. (The Haberdashers' Company)*

5. *Sir George Airy's clock. 'Greenwich Mean Time' from 1870-1920. (The Astronomer Royal)*

6. *Detail of the barometric adjustment in Airy's clock.*

house, or any office or building . . . whether public or private . . . there shall be charged an annual duty of five shillings, for every gold watch or watch enamelled on gold . . . ten shillings . . . and for every silver or metal watch . . . two shillings and six pence'. The immediate effect of this was for persons to do away with their watches and clocks. The effect on the industry was so disastrous that the Act was repealed in 1798. According to Britten[1] tavern keepers introduced a large mural timepiece (q.v.) with a circular dial about 18 inches in diameter for the benefit of their customers. Since the Act was in force for a very short time, very few of these clocks were produced, or have survived. They might be called 'Tavern Clocks'.

As a result of this short innovation it has become the custom to call all large, dialled, unglazed, mural timepieces 'Act of Parliament' clocks (Fig. 4). This is quite wrong as the design dates from many decades before the Act. The earliest known to the author now hangs in the hall of the Haberdashers' Company in London; it is anonymous, the dial has been repainted and any original signature has been lost. According to an inscription on the case, the clock was given to the Company in 1714.

AIRY, SIR GEORGE BIDDELL. Astronomer Royal 1835-1881. The Royal Greenwich Observatory, Herstmonceux, is indebted to Airy for many lasting improvements and innovations, but here we are only concerned with the clock which he designed and had made for him by Messrs Dent (q.v.) and which was 'Greenwich Mean Time' from 1870 to 1920 (Fig. 5),

when it was superseded by the Shortt clock (q.v.) with its electrical impulse.

Airy's clock was the acme of mechanical horology, the last development before electricity stepped in and took control of all impulses. It was the first clock inherently sufficiently accurate to warrant adjustment for variations in atmospheric pressure. The pendulum is of steel and zinc and regulation is by a micrometer screw above the suspension, or by the addition or removal of small weights on the bob, as is done in Big Ben (q.v.). Supplementary regulation is by a bi-metallic steel and brass strip pivoted into the pendulum arbor, which can be pivoted from maximum slow to maximum fast or to any intermediate position (Fig. 7). Impulses were originally every second and there is still a sapphire contact in the crutch, but it was found that this absorbed too much energy, so that the impulse was changed to every two seconds, actuated by a thirty-tooth wheel on the escape arbor and visible through the hole in the seconds dial. The escapement is a combination of dead beat (q.v.) and pin-wheel (q.v.) The dial records minutes by the long hand seconds on the subsidiary dial on the right and the 24 hours of the sidereal day (q.v.) on the dial on the left.

For the barometric correction, bar magnets are fixed along each side of the bob (these are scarcely discernable in the photograph), and a horseshoe magnet, pivoted and counter-poised and placed below the bob is actuated by the pivoted lever, which has a plunger at one end resting on the open surface of the mercury in the barometer (Fig. 6). The rise or fall in the mercury level varies the distance of the horseshoe magnet from the bar magnets fixed to the bob, affecting its influence on them.

ALARM CLOCK. A clock that can be set to make a warning sound at any pre-selected time. The alarm clock is the oldest and original form of monastic and domestic clock. Before the mechanical clock was invented clocks were mostly driven by water (q.v.) and with some of these an arrangement could be made whereby, at a given time, a ball or balls could be released to fall with a clatter into a pan. The earliest form of mechanical clock was a turret clock (q.v.) made by a blacksmith. It had no dial and only struck one blow at each hour, and even if it had had a dial the general public would not have been able to read it. Fig. 8 shows a very early German example of an alarm clock of the 14th century. The cord of the weight on the right is wound round a second small drum to which a crank is attached and this shakes the small bell with a stone inside. The bell is released each hour and will ring until the weight has unwound the whole of the cord. Fig. 9 shows a slightly later development (*circa* 1400). Here again the alarm is released each hour to awaken the sexton so that he may ring the monastery bell for the appropriate chapter. The cord drum turns once an hour and the shoulder on the great wheel lifts the lever restraining the saw-tooth wheel, which then, under the influence of its own weight, turns the rod carrying the hammer backwards and forwards by means of the pallets (q.v.) fixed to it. When this wheel has made one complete turn, the shoulder seen on it will lock against the release lever.

This clock is most interesting because its construction proves definitely that it was made, primarily, for use at night. It will be noticed that there are sixteen touch knobs (q.v.) to correspond with the greatest number of hours of darkness at the

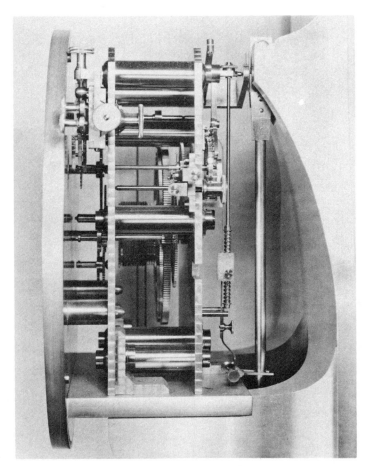

7. *Detail of escapement and movement of Airy's clock.*

8. *Early Gothic alarm clock. 14th century. (Mainfränkisches Museum, Würzburg)*

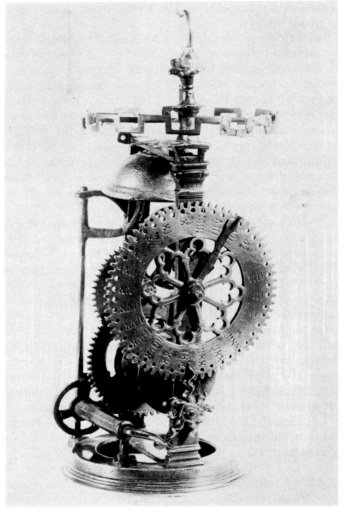

9. *Early Gothic alarm clock. c.* 1400, *from the Church of St Sebaldus, Nuremberg. (Germanisches Museum, Nuremberg)*

10. *Monastic alarm clock. 15th century. (Captain A. Simoni)*

11. *Drum clock with alarm attachment.* 16*th century. (Ilbert Collection, British Museum)*

winter solstice (q.v.). The pinion on the end of the great wheel arbor (which carries the cord drum) has three studs which take into forty-eight teeth on the wheel carrying the hour hand, so that this latter makes one revolution in sixteen hours. All previous descriptions of this clock assume a pinion of four studs giving a twelve-hour period of revolution, it was when the author removed the dial that the three-stud pinion was discovered.

The next step was to be able to select the hour at which the alarm was released, this was done by placing a hole at every hour mark in the toothed wheel carrying the hour hand; later some clocks had these holes made at every half hour (Fig. 10). A peg was then inserted into the hole which, when the clock reached the selected time, tripped the alarm release; the alarm then rang itself out. In the 16th century little travelling clocks (q.v.) sometimes had a separate alarm movement which could be clipped on to the clock proper, the alarm trip would be set off at the selected hour, as the hour hand passed the trip (Fig 11).

ALARM AND CANDLE CLOCK. An electric clock that rang an alarm and set a tea kettle boiling was hailed a few

12. *Alarm and candle clock.* 16th century. (*Science Museum, London*)   13. *Anonymous Italian altar clock.* 17th century. (*Mr Edward Brooks*)

years ago as an interesting innovation, but nearly 400 years ago, about the middle of the 16th century, a clock was devised which, at a selected hour, sprung open the lid of a box which released a flint set to strike a steel plate, thus causing a spark which ignited a small pile of tinder in a tray. This then lit a candle whose wick was lying in a horizontal position near to the tinder. The candle holder then sprang upright and this upward motion assisted the candle flame to burn, thus illuminating the clock. This arrangement is seen in Fig. 12; the candle is missing from the holder, which is seen in an upright position behind the steel striking plate. The flint lock was renewed about 1700. (*See* under CAPOBIANCO.)

ALMACANTAR. A small circle of the sphere parallel to the horizon; stars having the same almacantar have the same altitude. Sometimes described as parallels of equal altitude (Fig. 341 and 441).

ALTAR CLOCK. Towards the latter half of the 17th century and in the first half of the 18th, wooden clock case design was frequently influenced by the architectural shapes of current altar reredos design. This term 'Altar Clock' occurs in German terminology, but not in English. One of the rare cases of this type made in England is seen in Fig. 28. A typical Italian altar clock is seen in Fig. 13; in this instance we have quite a large case housing a very small movement, the converse of English practice where the movement nearly always fully filled the case. The illustration shows an astronomical clock (q.v.); the large outer disc revolves once a year and shows, against the pointer at the bottom, the date, the fixed feasts of the Church and the position of the sun in the zodiac (q.v.). The moon's age is read off a pointer under the XII, and its phase is visually indicated.

No minutes are marked, the time is read, to the nearest quarter of an hour, from the short single hand.

AMPLITUDE. The degree to which the sun rises or sets wide of due east or west. Also the extent of the arc of swing of a pendulum.

ANGULAR MEASUREMENT CLOCKS. In order to find

14. *Clock designed by Flamsteed for direct angular measurement.* 1691. (*National Maritime Museum, Greenwich*)

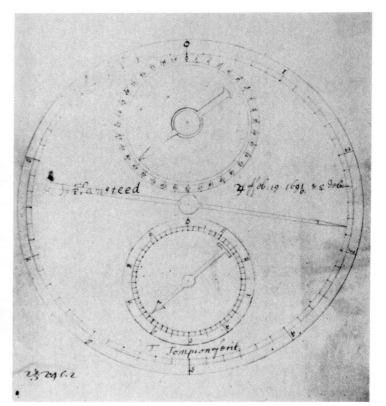

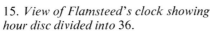

15. *View of Flamsteed's clock showing hour disc divided into 36.*

16. *Flamsteed's original design for the direct angular measurement clock. (The Astronomer Royal)*

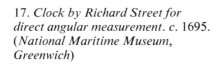

17. *Clock by Richard Street for direct angular measurement. c. 1695. (National Maritime Museum, Greenwich)*

18. *Dial of Richard Street's clock.*

the position in the heavens of a celestial body at any time, the angle between the observer, the pole and the body is ascertained, and this is known as angular measurement. The astronomer takes the time of transit of the body across his telescope and ascertains the difference between the time of that transit and the last noon. This amount of time he converts into degrees of arc of the Earth's rotation at the rate of 1° of arc equalling 4 minutes of time, since the Earth's rotation through 360° takes 24 hours, or 1,440 minutes.

John Flamsteed, the first Astronomer Royal (1675) had the idea of making a clock from which the angular measurement could be ascertained direct from the dial, instead of having to convert from hours and minutes of time. The dial of this clock is seen in Fig. 14. The clock was made with a pendulum beating $\frac{2}{3}$ second, so that the circle replacing the hour hand had thirty-six divisions, showing 360° for each 24 hours. The degree ring marked 1-36 can be seen in Fig. 15. In Fig. 14 the other side of this ring has been engraved I to XII twice over for use with the clock when its original purpose had been forgotten and an attempt had been made to run the clock on mean time, with a 1 second pendulum and the hour ring making 2 × I-XII daily. Taken in conjunction with the 1-36 ring the 'minute' hand records 10° of arc for each revolution, or 360° for the thirty-six revolutions. Each degree is divided into six parts of 10 minutes of arc each and again the 'seconds' hand records 10 minutes of arc each revolution, each minute of arc being sub-divided into six parts of 10 seconds of arc each. Thus the observer can read directly off the dial the position of the body in longitude, or its right ascension as it is called.

Fig. 16 shows Flamsteed's original drawing for the clock he had Thomas Tompion (q.v.) make for him, the only difference being that Flamsteed had the hand recording the degrees on the upper subsidiary dial whereas the clock, as made, had a disc behind the dial showing through an aperture. Flamsteed

19. (*Left*) *Back plate of a clock by Windmills with 'Apron' pendulum cock. c.* 1690. (*Mr James Oakes*)

20. (*Right*) *Long case clock with arabesque marquetry.* (*The late Mr George Hutchinson*)

prescribed a $17\frac{3}{10}$ inches pendulum which beat $\frac{2}{3}$ of a second and in his drawing the clock is showing 23° 2·4′ 6·2″ of arc. The drawing is signed J. Flamsteed Feb. 19th, 1690/1, and it will be noted that Tompion, besides putting his own name at the bottom of the dial has also engraved Flamsteed's name and the date 1691. Flamsteed's first two clocks were given to him by his friend Sir Jonas Moore (*see* under THOMAS TOMPION) because, although Flamsteed was given a salary of £100 p.a., he was not given any instruments or assistance; these he had to find for himself. Later, after Sir Jonas Moore's death, the Government laid claim to these two clocks and a long wrangle ensued, only to be finally settled in Flamsteed's favour by his widow. It will be seen that with the present clock Flamsteed took no chances.

Another clock which is believed to have been made for use either with mean time or for direct angular measurement is seen in Figs. 17 and 18, it will be noted that the extreme edge of the dial is marked I to X, as was the case with the Flamsteed clock, and that these divisions are again divided into sixty and sub-divided into thirty, or 2 minutes of arc divisions. With a $\frac{2}{3}$ second pendulum this would allow a fairly accurate reading to 1° of arc. The clock is at present fitted with a 1 second pendulum to record mean time; the reading will still be only approximate since there are no mean minutes marked, the nearest being the $\frac{1}{8}$ hour (or $7\frac{1}{2}$ minute) marks on the inner side of the chapter ring. It would seem that the clock's primary purpose was to record angular measurement directly. The author thinks that this clock may be the 'Black clock on the stairs' mentioned in the inventory of Newton's effects found

after his death in his house in Jermyn Street. The maker of the clock, Richard Street (q.v.), is known to have been employed by Newton; he made the clock Newton presented to Trinity College, Cambridge. Both angular measurement clocks are now in the Octagon Room at Greenwich.

ANOMALY. The position of a celestial body in its orbit.

APOGEE. When a celestial body is at the point of its orbit farthest from the Earth.

APPLIQUÉ. Brass decorations fastened on to the case of a clock, most frequently on to mantel clocks (Fig. 322). In some early examples they cover portions of the case cut out to facilitate the emission of sound. In these cases they were later superseded by frets (q.v., Fig. 321).

APRON. As the word suggests, something that hangs down. The decorative panel below the door of a hanging clock (q.v., Fig. 2). The term is also used to denote a decorative panel sometimes fixed to the pendulum bridge of early bracket clocks (q.v., Figs. 19 and 90).

ARABESQUE. A late type of marquetry consisting of scroll work, intersecting leaves and fantasy patterns (Fig. 20).

ARBOR. A shaft that carries wheels and pinions.

ARCH, BROKEN. A type where the arch springs from a diameter less than the width of the case. Found in both long case (q.v.) and bracket (q.v.) clocks (Figs. 21 and 22). The bracket clock illustrated was made by Henry Fish (*circa* 1760). He was the son of Henri Poisson who came to London as a Hugenot

21. Bracket clock with broken arch case in Vernis Martin, by Henry Fish. London. c. 1760. (Author's collection)   22. Long case clock in oak case by Josiah Emery. London, c. 1790. (The late Mr Percy Webster)   23. Bracket clock with plain arch by Edward Baker. London, c. 1815. (The late Mr Percy Webster)

refugee. The case, decorated with coloured and varnished engravings, is very delicate and most unusual; especially as the insides of the case and doors are also decorated.

ARCH, PLAIN. A type where the arched top springs direct from the sides of the case (Fig. 23).

ARCHER, HENRY. Archer was originally a member of the Blacksmiths' Company; according to Baillie he was admitted as 'english forrin' in 1628. He became a founder member of the Clockmakers' Company in 1632, being the first Warden of the Company; and at a Court held on 12th October, 1632, Henry Archer was appointed Deputy Master 'until Mr David Ramsay returned forth of the Country or untill his opportune occasions fitt him to take the same place upon him againe.'[3] David Ramsay does not appear to have been very active in the service of the Company and Henry Archer presided over most of the Courts held during Ramsay's year of office. Archer was, however, never Master of the Company.

Figs. 24 and 25 show a table clock by him; the bottom plate, especially the foliated decoration of the ratchet for the setting up of the spring, shows French influence and the hunting scenes around the case are definitely continental, either French or

24. (*Left*) *Table clock by Henry Archer, London, c. 1635. (Messrs Sothebys)*

25. (*Right*) *Bottom plate of Henry Archer's clock.*

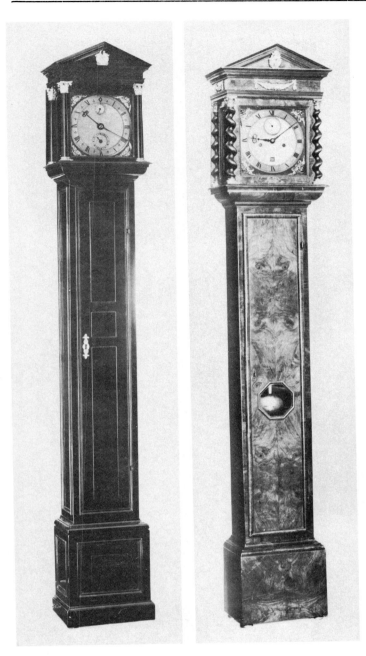

26. Long case clock by Johannes Fromanteel. London, c. 1675/80, with architectural hood and ebonised panelled trunk. (Lord Harris)   27. Long case clock by Edward East. London, c. 1670, in lignum vitae *veneered case. (The late Mr W. J. Iden)*

German. The term 'english forrin' need not necessarily mean that Archer came here from abroad, for any one living some way from London, say East Anglia, was regarded as 'Forrin'. The small hinged doors seen on the right and left in Fig. 24 are there to enable one to see how far the fusees (q.v.) for going and strike had run down.

ARCHITECTURAL CASE. In the early days of English clockmaking it would seem that the making of clock cases was put into the hands of cabinet makers; only later did case makers appear as specialists. There are practically no surviving records of clock case makers, the author can only recall having twice seen names mentioned. The early cases followed the fashion of contemporary furniture with plain lines, panelled

and with a classical portico top, often supported by columns (Fig. 26). Later these columns were twisted in the Restoration style (Fig. 27) and, occasionally, the case had a broken pediment (Fig. 28).

ARIES, 1ST POINT OF. Formerly the sun was at the 1st point of Aries in the zodiac (q.v.) at the Vernal, or Spring Equinox (q.v.), that is the day when the sun crosses the ecliptic in its apparent passage from the Winter to the Summer Solstice (q.v.). Due to the Precession of the Equinoxes (q.v.) the Vernal Equinox is now in the constellation Pisces. From custom it is still called the 1st Point of Aries.

ARNOLD, JOHN (1736-1799). Arnold's chief claim to fame is that he, together with Thomas Earnshaw (q.v.), simplified the design of the marine chronometer with which John Harrison (q.v.) won the £20,000 prize for making a timepiece sufficiently accurate to enable mariners to ascertain their longitude when at sea. He is also noted for making a watch so small that it could be fitted into a ring; this ring watch was bought by George III in 1764 and is now in the Usher Collection in Lincoln. Arnold is included in this book because he made two Regulators (q.v.) for Greenwich Observatory in 1774, which were fitted with ruby pallets and for a time provided the time standard of the country (Figs. 29 and 30). As will be seen, the Regulator was

28. Architectural (altar) clock by Edward East. London, c. 1665, with tortoiseshell veneered columns. (Mr J. Huddleston)

29. *Regulator No.* 1 *made by John Arnold, London, for Greenwich Observatory.* (*The late Mr W. J. Iden*)   30. *Gridiron pendulum in Arnold's No.* 1.   31. *Drum clock with astrolabe dial, with its travelling case. German, anonymous, c.* 1550. (*Dr Eugen Gschwind*)

provided with a gridiron pendulum (q.v.), and had Graham's dead beat escapement (q.v.). The hour is read through the slot in the dial, the long hand records minutes and the small subsidiary dial, seconds.

ASPECT. The angular relationship at any time between the positions of two celestial bodies, e.g., the sun and the moon (Fig. 165).

ASTROLABE. An instrument for taking the altitude of heavenly bodies, from which time and latitude can be ascertained. It consists of a disc suspended by a ring and having a rotatable diametrical rule or alidade, with sights, turning within a circle of degrees for measuring the altitude of the sun or stars. The back plate is engraved with a circular map of the stars. The rete (or net) (q.v.) is a fretwork plate cut out to show the relative positions of the stars to one another and to the sun's position in the zodiacal circle[4] (q.v.). In Fig. 31, a drum clock of the 16th century, the alidade is replaced by the clock hand.

ASTROLOGICAL CLOCK. Occasionally a clock designed purely on astrological lines is found, one such German clock is seen in Fig. 32. The dials are: top right, the hours I-XII, top left, the age, phases and aspects of the moon, centre, the Italian

32. *Brass table clock designed for astrological use. c.* 1620. (*Hessisches Landesmuseum, Kassel*)

hours (q.v.) 1-24, bottom right, the day of the week and its planetary god and at bottom left is marked four times over 20, 40, 60—Juventus (Youth), Virilitas (Manhood), Senectus (Old Age) and Mors (Death). Between the dials is engraved Aenea (Copper), Ferrea (Iron), Argentea, (Silver) and Aurea (Gold); on the side of the case is engraved:

Fata viam invenient
Sic ubi fata volunt
Ludite forma fugit, ludite vita perit
Fugit volatilis aetas.

This may be translated as:

The fates will find a way
So where the fates wish
Play, beauty flies away, play, life perishes,
Youth flies away on wings.

ASTRONOMICAL CLOCKS. This term is applied to any clock which shows any celestial phenomenon. The delineation of the phases of the moon and the apparent position of the sun in the zodiac (q.v.) were the first to be indicated. The earliest mechanical clock to have astronomical indications is that by Giovanni Dondi, begun in 1348 and finished in 1364. Next comes the first clock in Strasburg Cathedral (*circa* 1352-1354). All that we know for certain of this clock is that it was about 34 feet high—this has been ascertained from plug marks in the wall of the Cathedral—and that it was surmounted by a cock that crowed.[5] Many other examples of astronomical clocks will be found in this book (*see under* DONDI, CAJETANO, HAHN, OLSEN, SCHWILGUÉ and WATSON.

ASTRONOMICAL DIAL. *See* DIAL.

ASTRONOMICAL HOURS. Astronomers work on sidereal time (q.v.), that is time by the stars. The sidereal day is that time which elapses between two successive transits of a selected star across one's meridian. When measuring the length of the solar day, on which the mean day is based, account has to be taken of the time taken to cover the distance travelled by the Earth whilst it is making its daily revolution; this varies every day (*See* EQUATION OF TIME). The nearest star is so vastly farther away than the sun that this distance in sidereal reckoning becomes a point, and the length of the sidereal day is constant; 3 minutes 56 seconds less than the mean day of 24 hours (Fig. 33). Astronomers started their days at midday until very recently, when they changed and started at midnight in accord with civil time.

ATKINSON, DR ROBERT d'E. Dr Atkinson, who is the Chief Assistant at the Royal Greenwich Observatory, Herstmonceux, will be remembered by horologists in posterity as the designer of the clock in York Minster, erected to commemorate all airmen who fell in the 1939-1945 war. The clock was made in the Observatory workshops under Dr Atkinson's supervision. Its principal feature is a sun which reproduces the risings, settings and meridian transits of the sun, as seen at York. The central dial is a planisphere which revolves in a sidereal day (q.v.), with a sun which travels slowly along the ecliptic (q.v.). The clock (Fig. 34) is designed for 54°N, but the south pole is taken as the centre of rotation and the north pole is projected to infinity; hence the horizon is convex instead of the usual concave delineation. The ecliptic is projected into a circle which leads to a horizon which is circular, as would be seen by an

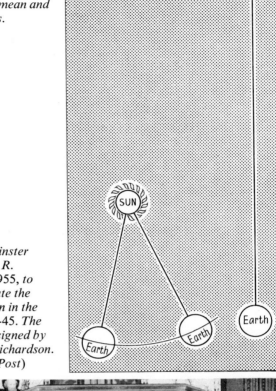

33. *Diagram illustrating the difference in length between the mean and sidereal days.*

34. *York Minster clock by Dr R. Atkinson, 1955, to commemorate the fallen airmen in the war of 1939-45. The case was designed by Professor Richardson. (Yorkshire Post)*

35. *Movement of the York Minster clock. Note the large hollow arbor of the Sun's effigy to enable it to revolve eccentrically around that bearing Earth. (Yorkshire Post)*

airman. The Earth is a fixed disc in the centre, painted to resemble the neighbourhood of York, with the Minster in the centre, as seen by an airman flying over York and facing south. Below the main dial are, on the right, three dials for hours, minutes and seconds of mean time, and on the left similar dials for sidereal time, or 'Local Hour Angle Aries' in navigational terminology. The rear dial (not illustrated) carries a depiction of the circumpolar constellations and has a silver annulus round the edge, divided into hours of right ascension (q.v.), which are divided into 5 minute divisions. Local sidereal time can be read off a pointer fixed at the top. In Fig. 35 can be seen the large hollow bearing carrying the effigy of the sun, which enables it to revolve eccentrically around the arbor carrying the Earth. The case of the clock was designed by Professor Richardson, P.P.R.A.

ATMOS CLOCK. In 1913 a Paris engineer, J. E. Reutter, had the idea of using atmospheric pressure changes to wind up a clock. This principle had already been put into practice by James Cox in 1765 (q.v.), although it is probable that Reutter knew nothing of this. Reutter's experiments were successful, but lack of suitable materials prevented the development of the idea at that time. The present clock employs changes in temperature instead of changes of atmospheric pressure to wind itself, and relies only on a fall of temperature, whereas Cox's clock was wound by either a rise or fall of pressure. Ethyl Chloride (C_2H_3Cl), a compound highly sensitive to temperature changes is used, and this is contained in a metallic bellows within the brass case seen at the back of the clock (Figs. 36 and 37).[6]

AUGSBURG CLOCKS. Augsburg in Bavaria was one of the principal centres of clock production in Germany during the Renaissance (q.v.). Augsburg clocks are usually very decorative and of high quality; they are rarely signed, but some bear the

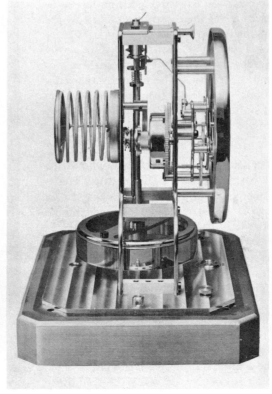

36. *Atmos clock, self-winding through changes in atmospheric temperature. c. 1940. Swiss manufacture. (Jaeger-Le Coultre)*

37. *Movement of the Atmos clock.*

38. (*Left*) *Anonymous Augsburg clock. 16th century.* (*British Museum*)

39. (*Above*) *Anonymous lion clock, Augsburg. 16th century.* (*Gershom Parkinton Collection, Bury St Edmunds*)

town stamp, AG (Agustae). Fully to describe Augsburg clocks would require a vast book, so numerous are the variations of design. Often religious motifs were used (Figs. 153 and 223); at other times animals were the basis of the design and in these the eyes usually moved in harmony with the escapement (Figs. 38 and 39, *see* also under BLINKING EYES). Fig. 38 shows a griffin placed on a case which is a very fine example of the cabinet makers' craft. Here the hours are shown on the vertical dial and the quarters on the smaller horizontal dial. The eyes move with the escapement and at the hour the beak opens and the wings flap. This fine example was in the British Museum, but unfortunately it was destroyed during the war of 1939-1945.

40. *Typical Augsburg clock. Early 17th century.* (*British Museum*)

41. *Back view of Fig. 40.*

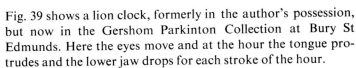

42. *Movement of a typical Augsburg astronomical clock.* (*Professor Hans von Bertele*)

43. *Movement of a typical Augsburg astronomical clock, expanded to show the epicyclic gearing.* (*Professor Hans von Bertele*)

44. *More elaborate Augsburg clock. Late 17th century.* (*Ilbert Collection, British Museum*)

Fig. 39 shows a lion clock, formerly in the author's possession, but now in the Gershom Parkinton Collection at Bury St Edmunds. Here the eyes move and at the hour the tongue protrudes and the lower jaw drops for each stroke of the hour.

Figs. 40 and 41 show two views of a type of which many were made; the example shown is from the early 17th century; from Fig. 40 it will be seen that the clock has been converted to pendulum. The double-ended hand with the effigy of the sun shows sidereal time on the outer ring of 2×12 hours, while the hand with the effigy of the moon shows lunar time, or the hour of the day in a month of $29\frac{1}{2}$ days. These hands also show, as the eccentric circle of the ecliptic (q.v.) makes its yearly revolution over the dial, the position of the sun and the moon in the zodiac (q.v.), which is read off the edge of their respective hands. The tail of the sun hand shows the astrological hour (q.v.) as the astrological day started at midday and the civil at midnight. The phases of the moon are seen through an opening in the disc carrying the moon hand, and the age of the moon can be read off the circular scale on the disc carrying the sun pointer. Beneath these hands is the hand for the Nodes (q.v.). It takes the usual German form of a dragon and can be distinguished as a black mark below the astrolabe (q.v.) facing between the two XII's. The rest of the dial is an astrolabe, and shows the position of the sun in the heavens, as well as that of the moon and certain well-known stars whose positions are engraved on the arms of the rete (or net) (q.v.). The auxiliary dial on the left shows the year of the solar cycle (q.v.) and the dominical letter (q.v.) for the current year. The auxiliary dial on the right appears to be for ornament only.

These Augsburg clocks were usually made to strike I-XII, or I-XXIV at will and the small subsidiary dial, top left, is for setting the strike for twelve or twenty-four. The purpose of the small dial on the top right, marked 1-8 has yet to be elucidated. Turning to the dial on the back (Fig. 41) the outer ring is a six months' calendar engraved with the various Saints of the day. This is engraved with the other six months on the back and therefore has to be reversed every six months. At some time an alteration has taken place and the winding hole and square introduced, for this would effectively stop the reversal of the calendar disc. Next comes the $2 \times$ XII of the mean day; within this chapter ring is an adjustable ring marked 1-24 for the Italian hours (q.v.). The inner dial is to show the length of daylight and darkness, but the dark shutter that would gradually slide over the silver dial as the days shorten, is missing (Fig. 246). The hand of the subsidiary dial on the left revolves once a week and indicates the day of the week, together with a representation of the planetary deity of the day. On the right the hand revolves once a year and indicates the current sign of the zodiac, which is divided into 30° and marked with both the physical and planetary delineation of the sign in question. The cherub head spandrels (q.v.) are interesting as they may be regarded as the forerunner of this type of spandrel, which was adopted by all the best English makers in the third and fourth quarters of the 17th century.

These clocks converted sidereal to mean time by a standard type of gearing, of a complicated differo-epicyclic kind, which is too technical to be discussed here. The ratios used are believed to have originated with the Arabs and were later adopted by the German makers; owing to the disturbances due to the Thirty Years Wars, these details were lost. Cajetano (q.v.) in 1792 wrote his *Neues Raedergebaeude* in which he claims the invention of this type of gear, no doubt honestly, whereas he was really only rediscovering that which had been lost.[10] Figs. 42 and 43 show the movement of another Augsburg clock of about the same date, both assembled and taken apart. Finally Fig. 44 shows a more elaborate type of Augsburg clock.

AURELIANO. This is the name by which Father Aurelius aS. Daniele was known. He was an Augustinian Friar in the Imperial Court Monastery in Vienna, and a teacher of mathematics. He designed and constructed the clock seen in Figs. 45, 46, 47 and 48, and now in the Bavarian National Museum. There is no information regarding the case.

In the dial is a blued steel celestial globe with the four main colures (q.v.) and the zodiacal band (q.v.); the revolution of this globe is adjusted for the Equation of Time (q.v.) so that the sun's image (not distinguishable in the illustration), will always cross the meridian at the same time as the solar hand in the main dial is indicating noon. The next dial on the left, with a figure of Apollo in the centre, shows the astronomical hours (q.v.) I-XXIV on the inner ring, and the Italian hours (q.v.) 1-24 starting at sunset, on the outer ring. The dial on the opposite side, with a figure of Chronos, or Time, in the centre, shows 'common' or French hours (q.v.) $2 \times$ I-XII on the inner ring and the Babylonian hours (q.v.) 1-24 starting at sunrise, on the outer ring. The two small central dials indicate the times of sunrise and sunset. The two dials below this series show, left, the declination (q.v.) and right, the lengths of daylight and darkness throughout the year for the latitude of Vienna. Below the

45. *General view of Aurelius aS. Daniele's astronomical clock,* 1770. (*Bayerisches National Museum, Munich*)

dial, on the left, is a hand which actuates a rack for adjusting the day of the month which should appear through a slot beside the VII on the left of the central chapter ring, but which, in the photograph, is missing. Beside this appears a letter a, b, c, or S through the slot, indicating the three common years and Leap Year (Schalt Jahr). At bottom right is a lunar globe which shows the moon's phases. In slots on the right of V to the right of the chapter ring appear the dominical letter (q.v.), the year of the solar cycle (q.v.) and the epact (q.v.). Above the centre of the inner dial appears the current year (the photograph was taken in 1946). To the left, through two slots are shown the day of the week and its planetary sign, in the photograph, Friday and

46. *Detail of the dial of Aureliano's clock*

Venus. In a corresponding position on the right, but partially hidden, the Indiction (q.v.) appears.

Taking the dial proper, the hour is indicated by an ornate hand, which can just be seen pointing between the III and the IIII on the right, and the minute by another openwork steel hand pointing towards the V on the left. The hand carrying the sun makes one revolution in 365¼ days, thus providing for leap year. The signs of the zodiac are beautifully engraved and each is divided into 30° at the base. On the outer edge of this ring the months are shown in their relation to the zodiacal divisions. The Nodal hand (q.v.), which makes one revolution in an anti-clockwise direction in 18⅔ years, is expanded at each end into

four divisions, the two outer carrying the effigy of the sun and the two inner, that of the moon. This hand indicates the limits within which a partial eclipse (q.v.) can take place. A further hand points to X and X having a hollow rectangular centre capable of sliding along the central axis to indicate the moon's apogee and perigee (q.v.). The hand with the effigy of the moon, which should make one revolution through the zodiac in a lunation, was missing at the time that the photograph was taken.

As already mentioned, of the case we have no details. Surmounting it is a figure of Victory with her two trumpets, and below, on the right, are cupids holding mathematical instruments. On each side of the dial are figures representing

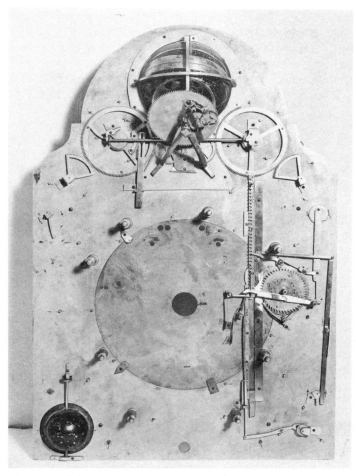

47. *View of the mechanism for the Moon, the equation and the dials above the central dial.*

48. *View of the movement proper and the calendars. This section fits on to the main dial plate through the lugs and studs seen.*

49. *The original crowing cock of the First Strasburg Cathedral Clock*, 1354. (*The late Mr R. P. Howgrave-Graham*)

Astronomy and Mathematics and below them, ring sun-dials. Around the base are figures of the twelve signs of the zodiac.[6] A full description of the clock was published in 1770 in which the title page states that the clock was made with Aureliano's own hands. It bears the imprint 'Gedruckt mit von Ehelischen Schriften.' Another fine equation clock by Aureliano is to be found in the Federal Furniture Repository, in Vienna.

AUTOMATON CLOCKS. Any clock that has an image of a man or beast of which the whole or part moves is called an automaton clock. Whilst there were many figurines in motion in some of the early Arab water clocks (*See* under WATER CLOCKS), the first introduction of automata into a mechanical clock was in the first Strasburg clock of 1354. (*See* ASTRONOMICAL CLOCK.) Preserved in the museum at Strasburg is the cock that crowned the whole edifice and which flapped its wings and crowed; also in the museum are the train (q.v.) and bellows which operated it (Figs. 49 and 50). In addition there was believed to have been a figure of the Virgin and Child, before which the three Magi passed every hour. Originally it was thought that the crowing of the cock was connected with St Peter's denial of Our Lord, but the view now more generally

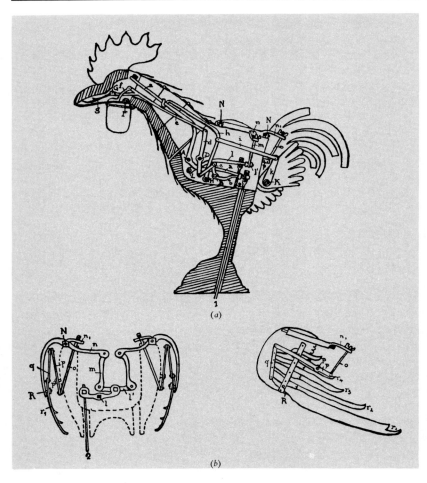

50. *Diagram of the mechanism of the Cock of the First Strasburg Cathedral Clock* (*Leonard Hill Ltd, photograph from* Some Outstanding Clocks over 700 years 1250-1950) 51. *Wooden clock with automata. Early* 17*th century.* (*Historisches Museum, Bamberg*)

accepted is that it signifies vigilance and that it derives from the cocks as a symbol for Mercury.

A late 16th- or early 17th-century wooden automaton clock from the Black Forest is seen in Fig. 51. Here the apostles process before the Christ (or Virgin and Child) and the Jack (q.v.) strikes the bell every hour.

AUXILIARY DIAL. A dial that gives a subsidiary indication to the main indication of a clock, e.g., a dial showing the day of the week or month, or a dial for Rise and Fall (q.v.) or Strike/Silent (q.v.).

BACK PLATE. This reference is only made to mantel clocks, as naturally the back plate of a long case clock (q.v.) is hidden against the back board of the case and is not a suitable object for decoration (Fig. 112). Early wooden mantel clocks usually had solid wooden doors, so there was a reason for leaving the back plate plain (Figs. 52 and 161). In Fig. 52 the signature, and a Tudor Rose on the locking plate (q.v.), and some rather delightful flowers on the pendulum cock, constitute the entire decoration. Later the back doors had a glass panel and it was worth while spending time and money on the decoration of a back plate that could be seen (Figs. 90 and 25). The early floral designs (Fig. 183) gave way to more conventional patterns (Fig. 169) the quality of which gradually deteriorated, until back plate decoration practically disappeared in the third quarter of the 18th century (Fig. 53).

BAIN, ALEXANDER. Bain was the first to utilise electricity as a motive force for a clock and was also the first to transmit electrical impulses to a series of dials. His first Patent, No. 8783, provided for an ordinary key-wound seconds pendulum as a master, but in 1843 his Patent showed an electro-magnetically driven pendulum (Fig. 54). He buried carbon and zinc plates in the ground, the moist earth serving as an electrolyte; contact was made by a sliding bar half way down the pendulum rod and actuated by an electro-magnetically driven pendulum, the bob of which was a coil swinging between two permanent magnets.

BALANCE. A wheel fixed on the top of, and at right angles to, the escapement arbor (q.v.) of a clock as an alternative to the foliot (q.v.), the rate of oscillation of which was governed by the force, weight or spring, employed (Fig. 55; this is the balance of Burgi's Experimental clock No. 1. *See* under BURGI). After the invention of the balance spring (q.v.) it was the spring and not the driving force that controlled the rate of oscillation, and hence the rate of going of the clock.

BALANCE SPRING. In the early days of clocks there was no time standard, the rate of oscillation of the balance, and hence the going rate of a clock, depended on the strength of the main driving spring, or weight; and regulation was frequently made by setting up or letting down the mainspring, or altering the amount of the weight. In 1657 Christaan Huygens (q.v.) invented the pendulum and so brought to static clocks a method

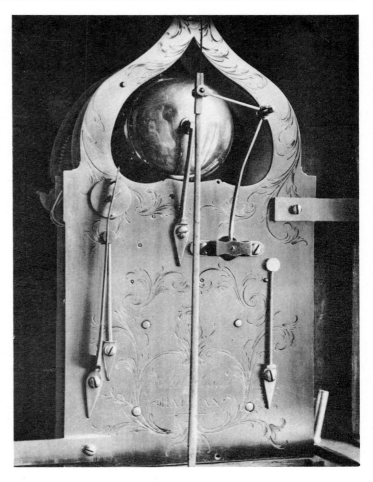

52. *Back plate of a clock by Edward East. London, c. 1665. Note that the pillars still retain the baluster form of the horizontal table clock. (Author's collection)*

53. *A late 18th-century back plate. Very slight decoration.*

54. *A wall electrical clock by Alexander Bain. c. 1850. (Science Museum, London)*

55. *A 16th-century type of balance with hog's bristle adjustment. (Hessisches Landesmuseum, Kassel)*

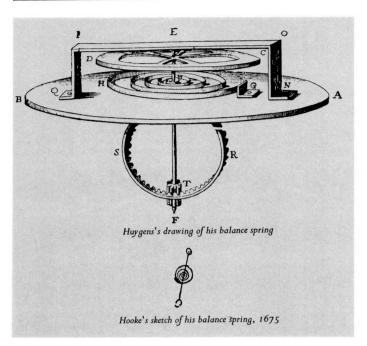

Huygens's drawing of his balance spring

Hooke's sketch of his balance spring, 1675

56. *Top, Huygens' design for a balance spring from the* Philosophical Transactions, *London, 25th March 1675. Bottom, Hooke's design for a balance spring.*

of control for the rate independent of the driving force. The search for a similar controlling element for portable clocks and watches was at once begun, but with somewhat disputed results. In 1675 Christaan Huygens published his invention of a balance spring in the *Journal des Savants* of Paris, which was repeated in the *Philosophical Transactions* of the Royal Society of London for 25th March, 1675. Huygens spring had several turns and pirouetted by means of a pinion (Fig. 56); Dr Hooke (q.v.)

at once claimed that he had invented a similar spring in 1658, and then had a watch made by Thomas Tompion (q.v.), incorporating his spiral spring, and had the watch engraved 'R. Hooke inventit 1658, T. Tompion fecit 1675'. There is no further evidence to support Hooke. He had so many ideas that he started to develop and then never completed or published that when someone else later had the same idea, quite independently, Hooke would lay prior claim. Hooke's spring differs materially from that of Huygens in that his has only two or three turns and has no pinion to cause pirouetting. Whatever the truth may be regarding the attribution of the invention, the fact remains that it was Hooke's type that was generally adopted and developed. The author has never seen a spring coupled with Huygens' name except in a planisphere (q.v.), designed by him in 1682, and made by J. van Ceulen of The Hague and now in the Leyden Museum (Fig. 382). The movement of this planisphere has been photographed for the first time for the author, from which it transpires that Huygens did not use his own design of balance spring. There is no pirouette (Fig. 58). The heavy balance appears to derive some support from a suspension spring held by a pin between two cheeks (Fig. 57).

BALDEWIN, EBERHART. Baldewin comes to our knowledge as Court Clockmaker to Landgraf William IV of Hesse in the middle years of the 16th century. He is known by the clock illustrated in Figs. 59, 60 and 61, which was made between the years 1559 and 1561, and a celestial globe made in 1575, both of which are in the Hessisches Landesmuseum, in Kassel. He made a somewhat similar astronomical clock later which the Landgraf William IV presented to the King of Saxony, and which is now in the Staatliche Physicalisches und Mathematiches Salon in Dresden. William IV, in conjunction with his

57. *Movement of Huygens' planispherium with balance spring, 1682. (Museum for the History of Science, Leyden)*

58. *Another view of Huygens' planispherium movement.*

59. Two of the four faces of Baldewin's astronomical clock, Kassel, 1561, showing the dials of the Primum Mobile, Mars, Mercury and Venus. (Hessisches Landesmuseum, Kassel)

60. View of the time movement of Fig. 59. Note the use of Cardan shafts for off-centre drives.

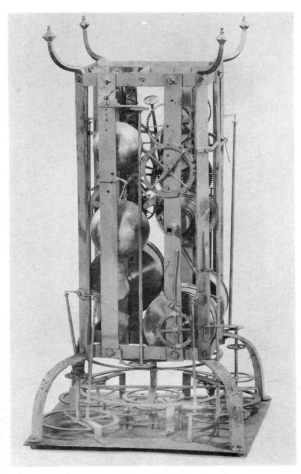

61. Movement for the planetary dials of Venus, upper, and Mercury, lower. Note the use of roller bearings in the latter.

astronomer, Andreas Schoener, calculated afresh the positions of the chief stars; the Alfonsine Tables, drawn up for King Alfonso X of Castille in about 1272 being by then out of date. A large volume entitled *Astronomicum Caesarium* was produced in Ingolstadt in 1540 by Petrus Apianus, containing volvelles, i.e., rotating paper discs from which the position of the planets can at any time be ascertained. William conceived the idea of having a clock made which should give, mechanically, the same information and Baldewin was entrusted to make it. The case and the engraving were the work of Hermann Diepel of Giessen.

Fig. 59 shows two of the four sides of this clock, each with two dials showing respectively the motions of the five planets, the sun and moon, sidereal time, mean time, and the lengths of the day and night; the whole being surmounted by a celestial globe split in two at the ecliptic (q.v.), with an effigy of the sun travelling in the division so formed from east to west in a sidereal day. At the North Pole there is a mean time dial. Fig. 59 shows the dials of Venus and Mercury (left) and those of Mars and the Primum Mobile (q.v.) (right). Fig. 60 shows an interior view and Fig. 61 the back of one of the double planetary dials. The portion of the movement between the two bottom plates has a series of trains (q.v.), the final wheel of which makes one revolution in 24 hours and from which are driven the various planetary dials through cardan shafts (q.v.), a very early application of this invention. In Fig. 61, showing the trains for the dials of Venus and Mercury, the early introduction of roller bearings in the train of Mercury, below, should be noted.[6]

BALL AND CLAW FOOT. The representation of an eagle's claw grasping a ball was used in some of the best early English

mantel clocks. Fig. 62 shows a clock by Edward East (*circa* 1665). The back plate of this clock is seen under BACK PLATE.

BALL CLOCKS. Many readers, especially those resident in London, will remember seeing a clock in the window of a well-known clockmaker in Pall Mall, in which a small steel ball runs along a series of grooves in an inclined plate; when the ball reaches the end of its traverse, the plate tips to the opposite inclination and the ball reverses its direction (*See* CONGREVE CLOCK). This idea of having a rolling ball as a time standard originated in the late 16th century, based on Galileo's law that rolling bodies on an inclined plane will cover a given distance in the same time. That a rolling ball could thus be used as a time standard to replace the foliot or balance (q.v.) was grasped by the Viennese clockmaker, Christof Margraf, who took out a patent on these lines in 1595.[7] Many variations are to be found in Grollier de Servière's book *Recueil d'Ouvrages Curieux*, published in Lyons in 1719. An anonymous clock, very much on the lines of one illustrated in the book referred to is seen in Fig. 65. The ball takes 1 minute to travel down the spiral and is restored to the top by a spring. A very elaborate example is seen in Figs. 63 and 64, a clock by Christolph Rohr of Leipzig, dated 1601. At the end of the descent the ball enters the inclined tube seen in Fig. 64 and falls into a cup attached to an endless chain running inside the vertical tube. Another cup is fixed to the chain at the upper end of the tube, and this will descend to receive the ball on the termination of its next journey. There is only one ball and the time taken for one descent and the restoration of the ball to the top of its track is 1 minute. The tall vertical shaft operates the carousel every 3 hours.

62. *Early architectural clock with ball and claw feet by Edward East. London, 1665. (Author's collection)*

63. *A rolling ball clock by Christolph Rohr of Leipzig. 1601. (Herzog Anton Ulrich Museum, Brunswick)*

64. *Movement of Christolph Rohr's clock.*

BALL DRIVE. Towards the middle of the 17th century one Radeloff (q.v.), who was a pupil of Burgi (q.v.), built clocks with heavy balls as a driving force. This would give a portable clock the advantage of a constant driving force, as is the case in weight-driven clocks, which, however, must be static. This method of drive would overcome the variation in driving force experienced in spring-driven clocks, in spite of the use of the fusee (q.v.). According to Professor Bertele in his *Uhren*, only three of these ball driven clocks are known to have survived.[7] One is in the Rosenborg Castle in Copenhagen, one in the National Museum in that city and the third, which is illustrated, is in Dr Bertele's collection (Figs. 66 and 67). The balls are stored in an upper gallery (Fig. 67), the one actually driving the clock during its descent is bearing against one of the wires of the cage fixed to the movement and so providing the motive force. When the active ball finishes its 4-hour descent it falls through a trap into a container in the base and a trip then opens a door in the upper gallery, allowing the next ball to take its active place. When all the six balls have performed their function at the end of 24 hours, they have to be replaced by hand in the upper gallery. This exact timing has the disadvantage that the owner must make two steps to 'wind' the clock, one when the fifth ball has finished its descent and another after the sixth ball, or else be on the spot exactly at the expiry of 24 hours. All these ball-driven clocks are fitted with cross-beat escapements (q.v.), and should not be confused with Ball Clocks (q.v.).

BALLOON CLOCKS. A type of clock with a waist, popular towards the end of the 18th and the beginning of the 19th centuries (Fig. 68).

65. *A rolling ball clock of the type shown by Grollier de Servière.* (*Museum for the History of Science, Florence*)

66. *Clock with ball drive and cross beat escapement by Radeloff.* (*Professor Hans von Bertele*)
67. *View of Radeloff's clock showing the ball drive and the reserve balls ready to fall.*
68. *Balloon clock. London, late 18th century.* (*The late Mr Percy Webster*)

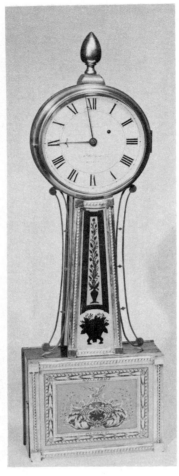

69. *Long case month equation clock by Graham's successors, Colley and Preist. London, c. 1752 (Author's collection)*

70. *Banjo clock by Aaron Willard, Boston, U.S.A. (Smithsonian Institution, Washington, D.C.)*

BANDING. An inlaid strip of veneer around a panel or door (Fig. 69).

BANJO CLOCK. An American design and probably the most elegant clock ever designed in the States. It was introduced by Simon Willard of Connecticut about 1800 (Fig. 70). Carl W. Dreppard in his *American Clocks and their Makers* asserts that the original case design was not Willard's and that the patent he took out was only for the type of movement he designed to go into the Banjo case. The author does not pretend to have any opinion on this matter; he leaves it to his American friends to discuss.

The Banjo developed into many forms, mostly degenerate; an elaboration can be seen in the Girondel (q.v.). The Banjo clock is one of the most popular clocks with American collectors; this has led to 'the supply being equal to the demand', consequently extra care should be taken when making a purchase.

BANKING. The termination of an oscillation of the balance or pendulum by its coming into contact with a limiting body.

BARKER, WILLIAM. A clockmaker of Wigan, Lancashire, who was admitted a Freeman of Wigan in 1751.[8] He was a very competent maker, his most notable achievement being the clock illustrated in Figs. 71 and 72. The astronomical dial shows the position of the sun in the heavens each day, the shutters on either side rise and fall as the length of the day changes; these are read against the inner circle carrying the words Barker, Wigan. It will be noticed that this scale starts with the inscription 'No Night'; this refers to the fact that astronomically night does not commence until the sun is 18° below the horizon, so that during the few days each side of Midsummer Day we never have more than twilight. The next scale gives (left), the amplitude (q.v.), and (right) the declination (q.v.). In the centre is the lunar globe showing its phases, with pointers indicating the time of high tide at Dover, London, Hull and Bristol. Below the lunar dial is the hand for the equation (q.v.).

The main dial is interesting for its admixture of ecclesiastical and political commemorations. The long slender hand goes round once a year and points to the various Sundays in the Church of England calendar, next comes the civil calendar and against each day is the name of the Saint commemorated, interspersed with the record of the dates of the Gunpowder Plot, the execution of Charles I and the restoration of Charles II. Along

71. *Dial of Barker's clock, Fig. 72.*

72. *Astronomical clock by Barker of Wigan, Lancashire, c. 1780.*

73. *Barograph by Yeats, Dublin, c. 1880. (Royal Dublin Society)*

74. *Clock with double basket top by John Shaw, Holborn. London, c. 1685. (The late Mr W. J. Iden)*

the inner edge of the chapter ring are marked the signs of the zodiac (q.v.), each divided into 30°. At the low point of the dial is shown the Dominical Letter (q.v.) with a pointer to delineate the one current. On the corners of the base will be noted 'brick-work quoins' (q.v.). The author has only seen this decoration on Lancashire cases. The centre of the dial is decorated with a scroll and the motto 'The man is yet unborn who duely weighs an hour'. This motto on somewhat similar scrolling appears on a long case clock by Peter Fearnley of Wigan.[9]

BARLEY TWIST. A term applied to twisted columns popular at the Restoration Period and frequently found on the hoods of long case clocks (q.v.) and sometimes on bracket clocks (q.v., Figs. 1 and 27).

BARLOW, EDWARD (1636-1716). *See* RACK AND SNAIL STRIKING.

BAROCCI, GIOVANNI MARIA AND GIOVANNI BATTISTA. These craftsmen of Pesaro made a series of fine clocks in the second half of the 16th century. It is probable that the clock seen in Titian's portrait of the Duchess of Urbino in the Pitti Palace, Florence, is by them. A marvellous spring driven clock was made for Pope Pius V; this can, perhaps, be identified with a table clock in the form of a tower signed 'Johannes et Maria Barotus Urbinus fecit MDLXX', which was in the Bernard collection in Paris.[16]

BAROGRAPH. An instrument for recording mechanically changes in atmospheric pressure. First made in 1765, by Alex-

ander Cumming (q.v.); a later example made about 1880 by Yeats of Dublin, and now in the Royal Dublin Society, is seen in Fig. 73.

BARTOLOMEO, GIOVANNI. Apprenticed to Gaspare of the Ubaldini; on the death of his master he completed the public clock in Sienna in 1399.[16]

BARTOLOMEO DI GNUDOLO. Together with Giovanni Evangelista of Piacenza began the clock for Bologna in 1444. This was an astronomical clock (q.v.) with automata (q.v.). After seven years hard work, the clock was finished in 1451; in 1482 it was out of order, but had been restored by 1492 more or less to its original state. This clock did not embody the bold conception of Bessarione, but continued to show the Earth as the centre of the Universe. It is very important to remember that Copernicus came to Bologna in 1489, stayed till 1500 and saw the clock, which may have made him think that if the sun was the centre of the Universe, the whole conception of the Universe would be revolutionised. This may have inspired him to write his *Tratto sulle rivoluzioni dei corpi celesti*.[16]

BASE. *See* PLINTH.

BASKET TOP, DOUBLE. Towards the end of the 17th century the rectangular bracket clock case was surmounted by a flattened wooden dome, known as a basket top. Later, in order to achieve a greater degree of decoration, this was replaced by a metal top, usually of cast and chased brass of open-

75. *Bracket clock with metal basket top by Johannes Fromanteel. London, c. 1685. The clock has three trains and is of split plate construction.*

76. *Bracket clock with wooden basket top by Joseph Knibb, London, c. 1670. Note the early form of shallow basket, the skeleton dial and that every minute is numbered, another early feature after the introduction of the pendulum. (Mr James Oakes)*

77. *Bracket clock with deep wooden basket top by Samuel Watson, London, c. 1695. (Mr W. Stopher)*

78. *Bracket clock of the inverted bell type by George Antrim. London, c. 1715. (The late Mr Basil Brooks)*

79. *Bracket clock of the true bell type by Benjamin Stewart. London, c. 1810. (The late Mr Percy Webster)*

work design. Finally, towards the end of the century, a few double basket top cases were made (Fig. 74).

BASKET TOP, METAL. The flat metal top to bracket clocks which followed the wooden basket (q.v., Fig. 75).

BASKET TOP, WOOD. After the architectural style of case (q.v.), the fashion was for the case to be surmounted by a flattened wooden dome, known as a basket top. The earliest form (Fig. 76) was much flatter than that adopted later (Fig. 77).

BEADING. A small half-round moulding found on clock cases.

BEAUVAIS CLOCK. *See* VERITÉ.

BECKETT, SIR EDMUND *See* BIG BEN.

BELL, INVERTED. After the basket topped clock (q.v.)

came the bell top. If this has the upper part concave and the lower convex, it is known as an inverted bell (Fig. 78). The clock illustrated was made by George Antrim, Clockmaker to George I. The front plate bears a scratched inscription relating to Sophia Dorothea, the wife of George I whom he never brought to England, and who was kept a semi-prisoner at the Castle in Celle, in Hannover. She died in 1726.

BELL, TRUE. As opposed to the inverted bell (q.v.) the true bell has the upper part convex and the lower part concave (Fig. 79).

BERTHOUD, FERDINAND (1729-1807) Born at Neuchatel in Switzerland, he came to Paris as a youth and settled there. He is a maker of great renown and produced many fine clocks and regulators. He followed John Harrison (q.v.) in the chronometer field, but never succeeded in equalling Harrison's results. He was also a most prolific writer, his best known books being *Essai sur l'Horlogerie* 1763, *Traité des Horloges Marines* 1773, and *Histoire de la Mesure du Temps* 1802.

BESANÇON CATHEDRAL CLOCK. *See* VERITÉ.

BEZEL. A circular metal ring holding the glass of a clock.

BIEDEMEIER CLOCKS. In Austria the period roughly corresponding to our Regency Period and perhaps for ten to fifteen years thereafter, is known as the Biedemeier Period. The clocks of this period are noted for their delicacy of line and general lightness of construction (Fig. 80).

BIG BEN. Much literature has been written about Big Ben, the clock in the Tower of the Houses of Parliament in London, and in view of its world-wide popularity, much more will, no doubt, be written about it. In 1844, Mr Charles Barry, the architect for the then new Houses of Parliament, incorporated in his design a clock tower with four faces. The clock was not actually made until 1854 and not erected until 1859. The intervening period was one of a long series of squabbles and failures. Sir George Airy, Astronomer Royal (q.v.), was instructed to draw up a specification and his demands were so exacting that the horological trade was up in arms. The two most difficult clauses called for the hour to be correct to within a second and for the clock to telegraph a record twice a day to Greenwich.

B. L. Vulliamy (q.v.), Clockmaker to the Queen, submitted a design, but this was criticised as a glorified church clock and the matter was thrown open to competition. Mortified, Vulliamy withdrew. The clock he designed was eventually made for Somerton Hall in Suffolk. Only two firms submitted designs, Edward Dent of London (q.v.) and Whitehurst of Derby. Matters stagnated, and in 1851 the Astronomer Royal, Airy, called in an amateur for consultation, Edmund Beckett Denison, a barrister and a Q.C., later Sir Edmund Beckett and still later, Lord Grimthorpe. Previous designs were discarded and Denison's own design and Dent's estimate for it were accepted. Dent died in 1853 and the clock was finished by his stepson, Frederick, who had taken the name of Dent. For five years after completion the clock remained at the maker's works, since the tower was not ready to receive it. During this time Denison invented his double three-legged gravity escapement, which was a variant of another gravity escapement designed by a lawyer, J. M. Bloxam, Q.C. (q.v.). Denison's escapement was

80. *Viennese wall clock of the Biedemeier period, by Gluecksstein, Vienna, c.* 1830. (*Dr A. Sobek, Vienna*) 81. *General view of the Westminster Tower clock.* (*Ministry of Works, London*)

first used in a clock made for Leeds Town Hall and the escapement of the Great Westminster Clock was changed as a result of the good performance of the Leeds clock.

There was also trouble with the bells. The first 14-ton bell cracked and had to be broken up. The architect had omitted to consult Denison regarding the installation of the big bell and only good fortune and ingenious improvisation enabled it to be installed at all. During a debate in the House of Commons on a hot summer's day in 1857 the question of a name for the big

82. *Movement of the Westminster Tower clock.* (*Ministry of Works, London*) 83. '*Big Ben*'. (*Ministry of Works, London*)

84. *Binnacle clock. (Ilbert Collection, British Museum)*

was for a hand 9 feet long, and re-designed the minute hand. The hour hand was then made of gun-metal and the minute hand, 14 feet long, of sheet copper with internal reinforcing strips. The pendulum is 14 feet long and beats 2 seconds. How pennies are put on and taken off a platform on the pendulum to regulate the clock is a popularly known fact.[142] Fig. 81 shows an exterior view of the clock, Fig. 82 the main movement and Fig. 83 the big bell.

BINNACLE CLOCK. A clock for use at sea which shows the nautical watches (Fig. 84). The minute hand goes round in half an hour when one bell is struck. The small hand goes round 3×8 hours in the 24-hour day, striking one to eight at the hours. There is no provision for the Dog Watches; the clock is by Morris Tobias, who took out a patent No. 3584 on 6th July, 1812.

BIRDCAGE CLOCK. 1). In the latter part of the 18th century there arose a fashion for small mechanical singing birds to be placed in snuff boxes. These in a larger form were sometimes placed in gilded cages that had a clock in the base, with the

85. *Birdcage clock, French. Late 18th century. Enamelled dial on the bottom of the cage. Base decorated with enamelled scenes and porcelain figures. (Chateau des Monts, Le Loche, Switzerland)*

86. *Gold birdcage clock with dial in the side of the base. Watch movement, releasing the song every hour. Musical box in the base. Decorated with pearls and diamonds. (Chateau des Monts, Le Loche, Switzerland)*

bell was discussed, and the first Commissioner of Works, Sir Benjamin Hall suggested St Stephen's Bell; now Sir Benjamin Hall was a big man and known as 'Big Ben', but the nickname was also, at the time, applied to anything big and hulking and it was the nickname of a popular burly prize-fighter, so that we cannot say whether, when a back-bencher suggested Big Ben, he had in mind Sir Benjamin Hall or just a bulky object. The name thus given originally to the big bell of 14 tons has come to denote the clock itself.

Although the French for nearly a century had a turret clock (q.v.) on a horizontal bed (the former church of Notre Dame, Versailles, had such a clock dated 1766), this layout and the general treatment of the whole as an engineering project, was new to this country. Once installed the clock would not go and it was found that the cast iron hands, designed by the architect, were too heavy. Denison kept the hour hand design, which

dial showing as the cage hung above (Figs. 85, 86).

2). The type of frame used in turret clocks (q.v.) up to the mid-19th century, where the going and striking movements are housed in rectangular iron frames adjoining each other. (*See* Fig. 141). It was generally considered that Big Ben (q.v.) was the first turret clock with a horizontal bed laid out on engineering lines, but a clock in the church of Notre Dame, Versailles, had a turret clock with a horizontal bed as early as 1766.

BISSEXTILE. The Continental expression for Leap Year. The Roman calendar progressed forward daily from the 1st of the month until the 13th or 15th, according to the length of the month, which date was called the Ides. They then began to count backwards from the 1st of the following month. Leap Year day was the day after 23rd February and 23rd February was the sext of the Kalends of March, or six days before 1st

March, hence Leap Year day was known as the bissext or second sext; hence the term bissextile for Leap Year.

BLACK FOREST CLOCKS. From about the middle of the 17th century the peasantry in Baden, around Furtwangen, near the Swiss border, began to make clocks of wood as a winter occupation. In style they resembled the iron gothic clocks (q.v.). The only metal parts were the verge and its pallets (q.v.), and the pins that were set in a vertical wooden wheel replacing the teeth of the crown wheel (q.v.). The driving weight was a conveniently sized stone. The date 1640 is usually assigned to this beginning and today Black Forest clocks are turned out in numbers, all bearing the date 1640. About 1730 a striking train (q.v.) was introduced, the bells being of glass. In Fig. 87 it will be seen that a pillar framework held the whole together. A later variant was the cuckoo clock (q.v.).

BLINKING EYE CLOCKS. Those in which the eyes in the representation of a human or animal head are connected with the escapement (q.v.) and move to and fro in harmony with it. This feature is mainly connected with Renaissance clocks on the Continent, but in Fig. 393 it was embodied in a clock made in England. In the lion's mask, in the fret above the dial, in Fig. 394 will be seen two holes. These were to show the blinking eyes of the lion when the verge pallets (q.v.) lay across the crown wheel (q.v.) above the top plate of the clock in its original

88. *Augsburg table clock with farm yard scene. The peasant points to the hour with his staff. The cow's eyes blink with the escapement.* (*British Museum*)

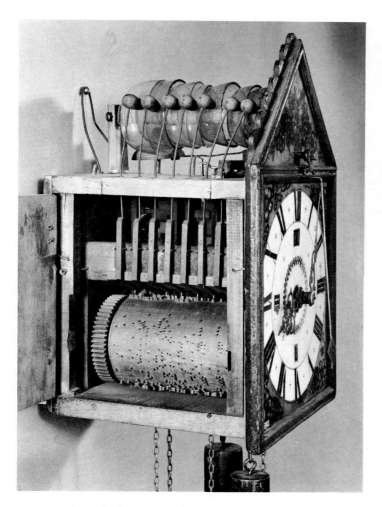

87. *Wooden Black Forest clock with glass bells. Late 18th century.* (*Deutches Museum, Munich*)

89. *Cast iron Negro blinking eye type clocks. Anonymous, U.S.A., mid-18th century.* (*Mr Walter M. Roberts*)

condition. Fig. 88 shows a clock made in the form of a farmer and his milkmaid, the latter milking a cow. The cow's eyes will move with the escapement (q.v.) and at the hours the milkmaid draws a shot of milk for each hour struck. The milk goes into a little pail supplied and comes from a small supply poured into the rump of the cow from time to time. The hour is pointed out by the farmer with his stick on a horizontal dial. The clock is German. Other examples will be seen in Figs. 38 and 39. The blinking eye clock came into favour again in the middle of the 18th century in the United States; the figures in Fig. 89 are made of cast iron.

BOB. The weight on a pendulum rod.

90. *Back plate of a bracket clock by Samuel Watson. London, c. 1695, with facetted pendulum bob and apron pendulum cock. (Mr W. Stopher)*

91. *Dial of clock by Johannes Fromanteel. London, c. 1665, with bolt and shutter maintaining power. (The late Mr W. J. Iden)*

92. *Fine Louis XIV clock on boulle pedestal. Early 18th century. (Wallace Collection, London)*

BOB, FACETTED. The early small bobs used with the verge escapement (q.v.) were sometimes finished with polygonal surfaces which were numbered in order to allow the checking of the extent to which the bob was turned during regulation (Fig. 90).

BOB, FALSE. A small disc suspended from the front end of the pallet arbor (q.v.) of a verge escapement (q.v.) and showing through a slot in the dial. This enabled a clock to be started or stopped from the front instead of having to turn it round and open the door at the back (Figs. 74 and 94). When a verge clock has been converted to anchor escapement (q.v.) this false bob is usually removed and a small engraved plate inserted to fill up the slot. If it is left, the fact that the clock has been converted will be indicated by the very narrow arc of swing of the false bob.

BOB, LENTICULAR. *See* DIAL REGULATING.

BOLT AND SHUTTER. A method whereby a small auxiliary force, known as Maintaining Power (q.v.), is brought to bear on the going train (q.v.) of a clock to keep it going during the period of winding, when the weights or spring are inoperative. In order to ensure that the winder did not forget to apply the maintaining power, it was frequently the practice to cover the winding holes with small shutters which, when pushed aside to insert the winding key, brought into action the maintaining power (Fig. 91).

BOOK CLOCK. In the latter half of the 16th and in the early 17th century there arose a fashion of making clocks in the form of small books. (*See* HANS KIENING.)

BOULLE, ANDRÉ CHARLES (1642-1732). The name of the French inventor of a technique for the decoration of furniture whereby inlays are introduced of gilded brass, silver and sometimes tin or pewter in most complicated designs. Some-

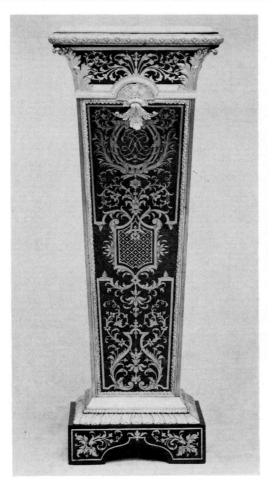

93. Pedestal in counter boulle. Compare with Fig. 92. (Wallace Collection, London)

94. Bracket clock by George Graham, London, c. 1715, with its original bracket, in which is a drawer for the key. (The late Lord Leicester)

times the inlay is in a tortoiseshell base. Clocks in cases of this type, mostly French, are sometimes erroneously called Boulle clocks; the style was very popular and many imitations arose in the 18th century (Fig. 92).

BOULLE, COUNTER. When the base material of a Boulle clock (q.v.) becomes the inlay material, e.g., brass in tortoiseshell is Boulle, tortoiseshell inlaid in brass is counter Boulle (Fig. 93, compare with Fig. 92).

BRACKET CLOCK. Originally a term applied to a clock standing on a bracket specially made for it, and fixed to a wall. Now a general term for all clocks that are designed for setting on mantels (Fig. 94). The bracket usually had a drawer for keeping the winding key.

BREAK ARCH. *See* ARCH, BROKEN.

BREGUET, ABRAHAM LOUIS (1747-1823). A French clock- and watchmaker of the highest renown. As in the case of Berthoud (q.v.), Breguet was born in Neuchatel, of French parents, and was apprenticed to a French clockmaker at the age of sixteen. He never wrote anything and so we only know of him from his work. Anything Breguet made was exquisite, whether in clocks or watches, the greater part of his output being of the latter. He excelled in making very complicated pieces, and rarely produced two alike, except for a series of single-handed watches known as Subscription Watches. His prices were high, commensurate with his work; today in the sale rooms prices for his productions run into thousands of pounds.

One of his best known productions is his 'Pendule Sym-

pathique' which has on the top of the case a small grip into which a specially designed watch can be placed. The clock then proceeds to correct the regulation of the watch and to set the hands correctly; it is capable of adjusting an error of up to $7\frac{1}{2}$ minutes and since the watch can be placed in position every 24 hours, when retiring, the error to be counteracted will certainly be within this limit. One of these clocks is in Buckingham Palace; it was made for the Prince Regent in 1814.[143] Another clock in the Palace is a long case (q.v.) with two movements side by side, one for mean time and one for the equation (q.v.). There are two gridiron pendulums (q.v.), one in front of the other, but only one driving weight. This was bought by George IV in 1825.[144]

A portable clock with chronometer escapement hitherto unrecorded is seen in Figs. 95, 96, 97. This is numbered 11, and is dated 1785-1790. From Fig. 95 it will be seen that it records hours, minutes and seconds and that it has a pivoted detent escapement of the John Arnold (q.v.) type, which is probably due to the great friendship between the two. The heavy vertical balance beats seconds with safety action, the letters M/A provide for Marche/Arrêt, a locking device. The balance spring is flat with Breguet's typical clamp (Fig. 96). The bi-metallic curb is steel/brass and the amount of compensation is variable, as is also the effective length of the vibrating portion of the spring. The whole of the compensation is mounted on a quadrant which is keyed to a pinion taking into another quadrant. In Fig. 95 it will be seen that the balance runs in front of a calibrated curve. The arbor of the vertical balance rests on the intersecting circumferences of two pairs of wheels.[147] Another

95. *Portable clock No. 11 by Breguet, Paris, c. 1785/90. Front view showing detent escapement.* (*National Maritime Museum, Greenwich*)   96. *Rear view of Breguet No. 11, showing balance spring compensation*   97. *Side view of Breguet No. 11.*

98. *Breguet portable carriage clock No. 2864, with music, alarm and date, suspended to imitate a lyre clock. Sold in 1814. (Chaux de Fonds Museum, Switzerland)*

example of Breguet's fine workmanship is seen in Fig. 98. Here is a travelling carriage clock with music, alarm and date, the whole suspended in an ormolu mounted stand simulating a lyre clock (q.v.). This clock, No. 2864, was sold by Breguet to his London representative in 1814. It has a ruby Graham cylinder escapement.

BRIDGE. A support having two feet as opposed to a cock (q.v.), which has only one (Fig. 280).

BUHL. *See* BOULLE.

BULL, RANDOLPH. A noted clockmaker of the 16th century. He was keeper of His Majesty's Great Clock in His Majesty's Palace of Westminster in the time of King James I. There is a watch by him in the British Museum.[27]

BUN FEET. Flat circular brass feet found on early English clocks, both long case (q.v.) and mantel (Figs. 27 and 75).

BURGI, JOST (1552-1632). Burgi was another famous clockmaker who was born in Switzerland, but who made his reputation outside that country. (*See* BERTHOUD and BREGUET.) Born in Lichtensteig in Toggenburgh, he entered the service of the Landgraf William IV of Hesse in 1578, being still there at the time of William's death in 1592. In 1604 he was appointed Imperial Clockmaker to the Emperor Rudolf II in Prague.

Burgi has been recognised as an outstanding genius for centuries, and celestial globes by him are to be found in the Conservatoire des Arts et Métiers in Paris, and in the Hessisches Landesmuseum in Kassel, but his clocks have not become so well known. It is only in recent years that Burgi's real contribution to accurate time measurement has been appreciated, due to the painstaking researches of Professor Dr Hans von Bertele of Vienna. As mentioned in connection with the work of Eberhard Baldewin (q.v.), Landgraf William IV was a very

99. *Burgi's experimental clock No. 1. Kassel. c. 1589. (Hessisches Landesmuseum, Kassel)* 100. *Movement of Fig. 99 showing remontoire action.*

keen astronomer and Burgi was constantly striving to give him clocks that would enable him to get better results. The following notes will give a rough idea of how Burgi tackled the problem of giving his patron more accurate clocks.

Professor von Bertele found two clocks at Kassel and one in Dresden which he designated Burgi Experimental 1, 2 and 3. In the first Burgi introduces two improvements—a three-months

going period and a remontoire (q.v.). Fig. 99 shows the front of the clock and Fig. 100 the movement (q.v.); it is a combination of weight and spring drive. The rectangular box is filled with lead pellets to allow for an exact adjustment of weight. During 24 hours this box descends the rack and rests upon the knob on the right-hand upper arm of the V lever seen. This releases a spring which turns the wheel behind the V and, by means of the

101. *Burgi's experimental clock No. 2. Before 1600. (Hessisches Landesmuseum, Kassel)* 102. *Movement of Burgi's experimental clock No. 2.* 103. *Cross beat escapement of Burgi's experimental clock No. 2.*

104. *Table clock by Burgi, c. 1591. The lid opens to show a lunar dial and by means of a pair of bevelled wheels both solar and lunar dials are kept going whether the lid be open or closed. The dial in front shows mean time and the length of day and night, that on the side is for the setting of the alarm and for setting the solar dial. (Hessisches Landesmuseum, Kassel)*

105. *Burgi's rock crystal clock. Prague, c. 1615. (Kunsthistorisches Museum, Vienna)*

studs on it, raises the V to restore the weight box to its original position. At the same time it turns the star wheel on the right one tooth for the day of the week and advances the pointer on the left one tooth forward; this indicates how many times the remontoire has functioned. The clock, which has an ordinary verge escapement (q.v.) and hog's bristle regulation (*See* under BALANCE), has a going period of three months, as Burgi was trying to cut down the loss of time incurred in regular daily winding, which was the rule at that time. His next step was to introduce a modification of the verge escapement and this Dr Bertele has named the 'Cross Beat' escapement (q.v.). This appears in the Experimental Clock No. 2 (Fig. 101). The chief point of this escapement was that it allowed for much closer adjustment of the pallet contact with the escape wheel. The design is quite revolutionary, the clock is spring driven and has a spring-driven remontoire situated above the top plate. To keep the new escapement from prying eyes, and also as a means of protection for its arms, it is shrouded on a circular tray (Figs. 102 and 103). A better view of the contact of the pallets with the escape wheel is seen under Cross Beat Escapement (Fig. 200). It will be noted that the design which we now associate with Burgi, a movement consisting of a few large wheels, is now taking shape (Fig. 102). The wire round the arbor of the great wheel leading to the remontoire can be clearly seen. Tycho Brahe talks of a clock made for him for use in his observatory at Uranienborg, on the island of Hevn in the Sound between Denmark and Sweden, which showed hours, minutes and seconds and which had only three wheels, the largest being of 2 feet 7 inches diameter and having 1,200 teeth.[11] While there is no maker indicated we can, by reference to Experimental Clock No. 2 fairly ascribe the authorship to Burgi. For the details of Experimental Clock No. 3, *see* CROSS BEAT ESCAPEMENT.

Fig. 104 shows a fine table clock by Burgi, now at Kassel.

106. *Daniel Buschmann's clock with 'Sundial' hours. Augsburg, c. 1660. (Bayerisches National Museum, Munich)* 107. *Dial of Buschmann's clock.*

This has dials on top of and underneath the lid, as well as in the body of the case. By means of bevelled gearing both clocks on the lid are kept going whether the lid be open or closed (*See* also Fig. 429). However, Burgi's greatest achievement in the way of clocks is the famous rock crystal clock now in the Kunsthistorisches Museum in Vienna (Fig. 105). This was taken out of its case, probably for the first time in centuries, by Professor Bertele, and Burgi's signature was found. The further development of the cross beat escapement found in this clock gave proof that the earlier unsigned clocks were, in fact, the work of Burgi.[6] The accuracy achieved by the crystal clock led later horologists to believe that it was, in fact, a pendulum clock many years before Huygens (q.v.) and the clock was so catalogued in the 'Treasures of Vienna' Exhibition held in London some years ago. It was this erroneous description that led to the clock being more closely examined, with the results described.

Burgi was also a great mathematician; Kepler is reported to have said of Burgi that he will pass into history with as great renown in his field as has Dürer in the field of art.[12] He is known to be the first mathematician to have compiled and used a system of logarithms.[12]

BURR. A term applied to veneer cut across a diseased formations of a tree, often producing patterns of considerable beauty.

BUSCHMANN, DANIEL (*circa* 1640-1712). Daniel was one of a family of clockmakers which, for several generations, worked in Augsburg. Baillie lists seven,[13] fathers, sons and

brothers. Daniel and Hans (q.v.) were the most important, a clock by Daniel is seen in Figs. 106 and 107. The design of the dial is most interesting. Presumably the maker wished the hour hand to follow the line that would be taken by the gnomon of a sundial. It will be noticed that the hours are irregularly spaced so that there must be a cam regulating the travel between each hour. The hour hand presumably travels the rest of the circle above the dial between the hours of 6 p.m. and 6 a.m. It will be noted that the arch of the case will just protect the long hand. The subsidiary dials indicate (left), the day of the week with its deity, (centre), the quarters with a continuous movement of the hand indicating the minutes, and (right), outer ring the day of the month as indicated by the hand and inner ring the age of the moon; the phases being shown through the aperture. Baillie lists a David Buschmann, but no Daniel, however, this piece is definitely signed Daniel Buschmann Aug, on the back plate.

BUSCHMANN, HANS. Working mid-17th century. Hans was probably the most famous of all the Buschmann family. Fine clocks by him are in many European museums, including the Kunsthistorisches Museum of Vienna, the Bayrisches National Museum, Munich and the Herzog Anton-Ulrich Museum in Brunswick. He became the first known clockmaker to have attempted to make a spring-driven clock go for one year with one winding, in the years 1651-1652, that is before the invention of the pendulum (q.v.). This first known year-clock is seen in Figs. 108, 109, 110, and 111. The clock shows the hours and, on a small subsidiary dial, the quarters. At the top there is a lunar globe with a small horizontal dial for the moon's age. In the

108. *Early spring-driven year clock by Hans Buschmann. c. 1651 (Herzog Anton Ulrich Museum, Brunswick)*

109. *Back view of Fig. 108.*

110. *Remontoire action of Fig. 108.*

111. *Movement of Fig. 108.*

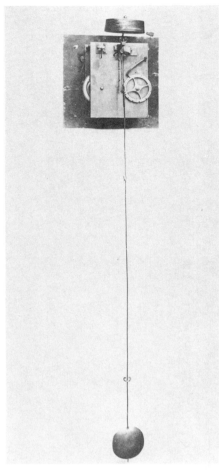  

112. *Butterfly nuts above the pendulum suspension and on the pendulum rod in a clock by Joseph Knibb, London, c. 1680. Note the straight sided Knibb type bell.* (*The late Mr W. J. Iden*)   113. *Early Gothic clock with buttress pillars and open moulded caps, c. 1450.* (*Private Collection in Austria*)   114. *Later Gothic iron clock in which the caps in the buttress pillars are closing up. c. 1500.* (*Private collection*)

base there is an annual calendar dial, of which the hand is missing. On the back is the dial for the days of the week with their planetary deities and below a dial marked 1-365 to indicate the degree to which the spring has run down. In the base (Fig. 110) is seen the mainspring which rewinds the movement proper every 24 hours (Fig. 111), through the rack seen in Fig. 110, which is governed by the four-bladed fly. Thus the actual going of the time recording part of the clock is not dependent on the year mainspring, but on the subsidiary mainspring, which, being wound every day, should maintain an equal force throughout the year, and should give results equal to a weight-driven clock.

BUTTERFLY. A winged nut for regulation, sometimes placed above the pendulum suspension and sometimes on its length (Fig. 112). In the illustration both applications are shown. This refinement is most frequently found in clocks by Joseph Knibb (q.v.) (*See* CRUTCH).

Also a method of making electrical contact in a Hipp clock (q.v.).

BUTTRESS PILLARS. German—Strebpfeilen. Found in early iron gothic clocks (q.v.) of Continental make. They are the main pillars supporting the clock in which the idea is conceived of a buttress supporting a wall. The moulded caps represent the changes in profile of a buttress as it progresses in height; in early types the moulded caps are quite open, as time progresses they close up (Figs. 113 and 114).

CAJETANO, DAVID a S. An Austrian Augustinian Friar in the Imperial Monastery in Vienna, who, judging from his work, lived about 1730-1810. He was a mathematician and horologist of the highest order and in 1769 completed the clock illustrated in Figs. 115, 116, 117 and 118, which is now in the Vienna Clock Museum. This clock is described in detail in a book published in Vienna.[14] The clock, as shown in Fig. 116, shows mean astronomical time, i.e., the day starting at noon, and by correlating this with the names of cities given in the base of the dial and their longitudes as inscribed against the cities' names, mean time at any of the places listed can be calculated. The subsidiary dials, starting at the bottom and going anticlockwise, show mean civil time (q.v.), i.e., the day starting at midnight, the position of Mercury in the zodiac (q.v.), the day of the week with its planetary sign, the moon's sidereal position and the nodes (q.v.), Jupiter's position, the epact (q.v.) and the golden number (q.v.), the indiction (q.v.), the position of Saturn, the Solar cycle (q.v.) and the dominical letter (q.v.), the position of Mars, the synodic revolution of the moon (q.v.), the moon's anomaly (q.v.) and the position of Venus in the

HOROLOGIUM ASTRONOMICO·SYSTEMATICUM·

115. Astronomical clock by David a S. Cajetano, Vienna, 1769 (photo R. J. Bohl, Vienna Clock Museum)

116. Detail of the dial of Cajetano's clock.

117. Detail of the mechanism of Cajetano's clock with the trains for all the planetary and other subsidiary dials *118. Detail of the mechanism of Cajetano's clock for perpetual calendar and equation movement.*

zodiac. Above the central dial are four apertures for indicating the current year from 1769 to 9999. The outer periphery has four circles traversed by a long hand in 365¼ days, thus allowing for leap year. Outside these is a ring with the signs of the zodiac placed at the dates in the respective months when the sun enters that sign. Of the other hands, that with the sun's effigy indicates the place of the sun in the zodiac, but its true position is not its mean position as it takes 7 days 23 hours 57 minutes 2 seconds longer to travel from the 1st point of Aries (q.v.) to Libra than from Libra to the 1st point of Aries, due to the Earth's eccentric orbit. For the moon there are four hands; and finally there is the hand for the nodes (q.v.).

The dial in the arch is astrological, it also gives the length of daylight and darkness, the Italian hours (q.v.), the declination (q.v.), the times of sunrise and sunset, the aspects (q.v.) of the sun and moon and a nodal hand, from which eclipses can be forecast (q.v.). The dial at the rear, not illustrated, has a perpetual calendar, including leap year and the equation of time (q.v.). In 1793 Cajetano wrote a book dealing with differential and differo-epicyclic gearing, but these complex gears will not be considered here.[15]

CALENDAR APERTURE. That portion of the dial which is cut away, either as a rectangle or a circle, and through which the day of the month, or the month of the year appears successively (Fig. 76).

CALENDAR, GREGORIAN. The mean year in the Julian Calendar (q.v.) of 365¼ days is 11 minutes 14 seconds longer than the tropical year (q.v.) and over the centuries this error accumulates; it first became noticeable in the calculation of the date of Easter Sunday. By 1545 the date of the Vernal Equinox (q.v.), or the first day of spring, had become 11th March instead of 21st March; an error of ten days. In 1582 Pope Gregory XIII decreed that the calendar should be corrected to restore the Vernal Equinox to 21st March by causing the day after 4th October to be called 15th October. Instead of having a leap year every four years, to get a closer approximation it was decided to omit leap year in those centennial years that are not divisible by 400, so that there are only ninety-seven leap years in 400 years. The effect of this change on horology was to introduce much complication into the construction of perpetual calendars which were designed to indicate mechanically the movable feasts of the Church. (*See* SCHWILGUÉ and JENS OLSEN.)

The change was accepted in 1582 and 1583 by most European Catholic countries; the Protestant countries came in a good many years later. In England the change was made in 1752, by which time the discrepancy had amounted to eleven days; the day following 2nd September became 14th September, but without interruption of the continuity of the week. There was much opposition due to ignorance; the common people thought that they were being robbed of eleven days of life, and riots took place under the slogan 'Give us back our eleven days'.

In the Middle Ages the end of the year came on 25th March (Lady Day or the Feast of the Annunciation), the effect of the change was that 25th March had become 5th April. In order to avoid much complication the end of the financial year 1752/3 was not altered, but became 5th April, and has so remained ever since. On the Continent New Year's Day had been fixed on 1st January and in 1752 it was so adopted in England. In the interim period dates were known as Old Style and New Style and between 1st January and 25th March days were written with the two years, e.g., 21st February 1694/5.

CALENDAR INDICATION. The average calendar indication which shows through an aperture in the dial of a clock or which is indicated by a hand moving once a day, consists of a freely turning wheel engraved 1-31 with thirty-one saw-like teeth. This is fixed behind the dial, and a pin on a wheel, which turns in the ratio of 1:2 in relation to the hour wheel, engages one of the teeth at any selected hours of the day, usually between 10 p.m. and midnight, and pushes the engraved ring one date forward. During this period the ring is locked, but otherwise it is free and can be adjusted backwards or forwards as desired. With calendars which are not designed as perpetual, the date has to be adjusted by hand for the short months and February.

CALENDAR, JULIAN. The calendar of today has its origins in the Calendar of the City of Rome, the origins of which are lost in obscurity. There were many alterations to the number of days in the various months and their names were changed from time to time to gratify the whim of various rulers. In the year 46 B.C. Julius Caesar decided to bring order out of chaos, and in order to get 1st January, 45 B.C. into its correct position the year 46 B.C. had 445 days and was known as the Year of Confusion. The length of the year was set at 365 days with an intercalary day every four years, which was to be the day after the sext of March (*see* BISSEXTILE). The number of days was set for each month as we know them today.

With the regular intercalation of one day in every four years the problem of making a perpetual calendar recording the movable feasts of the Church was much more simple than it is now, yet Giovanni Dondi (q.v.) who achieved this in 1364, was the only one known to have done so.

CALENDAR, PERPETUAL. A Perpetual Calendar is one that will record correctly the day of the month irrespective of the number of days in any month and which will take into account leap year; to do this one wheel has to have a period of revolution of four years. An example is seen in Figs. 119 and

119. *Dial of perpetual calendar clock by Helm of Ormskirk, c. 1780. (The Rev. N. V. Dinsdale)*

120. *Perpetual calendar motion work of Fig.* 119.

121. *Giovanni Dondi's perpetual calendar for Easter. Padua, 1364. This is based on the Julian calendar.*

120, a clock by Helm of Ormskirk. The hand for the day of the month in the arch of the dial is fixed to a wheel of thirty-one teeth and is moved daily by a claw, which cannot be seen in Fig. 120. Once a month the pin on this wheel engages with one of the forty-eight teeth of the larger wheel which therefore turns once in four years. On the arbor of this wheel is fixed the notched plate seen in Fig. 120, which turns anti-clockwise. In the thirty-one day months the pin seen against the rim of the plate checks the movement of the other end of the cranked lever and only allows the gathering claw to move the date hand one tooth; the shallow slots into which the pin enters on thirty-day months allow for a correction of two days. Three of the deeper slots allow for the correction for February and the fourth only allows for a correction of two days for February in leap year. The photograph was taken in the first days of December, after the November adjustment.

CALENDAR, PERPETUAL FOR EASTER. To record mechanically in perpetuity the varying dates on which Easter

Sunday falls has only been done four times in the whole history of horology. First in 1364 by Giovanni Dondi (q.v.) of Padua, in Italy, second by Jean Baptiste Schwilgué (q.v.) in the third Strasburg clock in 1842, third by Charles Ungerer of Strasburg in the Messina Clock of 1933 and fourth by Jens Olsen (q.v.) in his Copenhagen Clock of 1955.

With the Julian Calendar with its leap year regularly every four years, the problem was fairly simple. Dondi placed Easter Sunday as the first Sunday after the first full moon after 7th March. In his day, in the first year of the lunar cycle, (q.v.) Easter Sunday was 5th April and in the 19th, or last year of the cycle, 17th April. Dondi therefore calculated dates for Easter in the nineteen years of the lunar cycle and engraved them on a chain of nineteen links (Fig. 121). The other movable feasts are so many days before or after Easter, so that their dates can easily be calculated. The dominical letters(q.v.) for the solar cycle (q.v.) start with f, so Dondi made a second chain with twenty-eight links. These two chains turn together one link on 31st December each year. The third chain is for the Indiction (q.v.) which does not concern us here.[6]

With the coming of the Gregorian Calendar (q.v.) with the omission of three leap years every 400 years, the problem became much more complicated. Fig. 122 shows the mechanism for the perpetual calendar in the third Strasburg clock, by Schwilgué. It is much too complicated to be dealt with here.[6] A similar method was used by Charles Ungerer in the big clock he made for the Cathedral at Messina[145] and finally, a somewhat simplified version was used by Olsen in Copenhagen (q.v.).

CALYX. The cup or whorl at the base of a flower, often used as a decoration for clocks (Fig. 123).

CAMERINI. A Turin clockmaker who made and signed a clock with a pendulum dated 1656, which is a year earlier than

122. *Schwilgué's perpetual calendar based on the Gregorian calendar (Oeuvre de Notre Dame, Strasburg)*

123. *The floral calyx as a decorative motif on a French Gothic clock*, 1533. *Note the pomegranate finials to the turned columns on each side of the dial.* (*Mr K. Kellenberger, Winterthur*)   124. *Clock with pendulum, dated* 1656, *by Camerini, Turin.* (*Science Museum, London*)   125. *Night clock by Pietro Tommaso Campani. Rome,* 1683. (*Ilbert Collection, British Museum*)

the invention of the pendulum by Christaan Huygens (q.v.). This clock, which shows no sign of conversion from balance to pendulum, is now in the Science Museum, London (Fig. 124).

CAMPANI, GUISEPPI. Published in Rome in 1660 his *Discorso di Guiseppi Campani intorno a' suoi muti oriuoli . . . .* His brother Pietro Tommaso (q.v.) claimed the invention of silent clocks and wrote a letter to this effect. In the Mathematical Salon of Dresden there is a microscope by Campani which was used by Boettiger, the inventor of Dresden china. There is also a collection of his optical instruments in the Hessisches Landesmuseum in Kassel, Germany.[16]

CAMPANI, MATTEO. In 1655, two years before Huygens *Horologium*, Campani wrote to Louis XIV, in latin, that Pope Alexander VII had asked him to apply the pendulum to clocks. He is reported to have made a clock to run *in vacuo* which he offered to the Grand Duke Ferdinand II of Tuscany. He also invented a clock with two pendulums, which, however, was not a success. He published in 1673 the *Proposizione d'oriuoli giustissmi . . . invenzione utile a navaganti per prendere le longitudini, came anche ai geografi ed astronomi . . . dell' inventore Matteo Campani de gli Alimeni,* which shows that he essayed to solve the problem 'of the Longitude'.[6]

CAMPANI, PIETRO TOMMASO. Pietro Tommaso Campani invented a silent 'escapement' for a night clock in which he converted reciprocal into rotary motion, resulting in continuous instead of intermittent, motion and, since there is no escapement as such, the clock functioned in complete silence (Figs. 125 and 126). The pendulum hangs from a curved arm connected with a weighted bar at one end and at the other, an

eccentrically placed disc on the hub of the escape wheel, if we may so call it. This arm is set in motion by the forked piece fixed to the top of the pendulum. Once going, the weighted bar gives the impetus to the balance wheel. Modern attempts to get this clock going to time have not been very successful.[16] The clock is signed 'Petrus Tomas Campanus Inventor Roma, 1683'.

126. *Silent escapement arrangement of Campani's clock.*

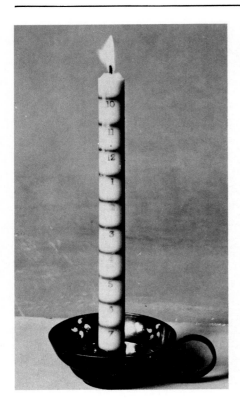

127. *A candle clock.* (*Science Museum, London*)

CANDLE CLOCK. An early method of time measurement was to notch a candle at intervals which, it was estimated, would take an hour to burn down, when protected from extreme draughts by a horn shield or other device. Sometimes a metal pin was inserted at each hour mark so that it fell into the holder as each mark was passed, giving an audible record. (Fig. 127). (*See* ALARM AND CANDLE CLOCK).

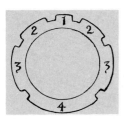

128. *Locking plate for canonical striking from a MS by Benvenuto di Lorenzo della Volpaia.* (*A. Simoni, La Clessidra. Rome, January, 1955*)

129. *Print of a carillon clock by Jeremias Sauter. Salzburg, 1704.* (*Germanisches Museum, Nuremberg*)

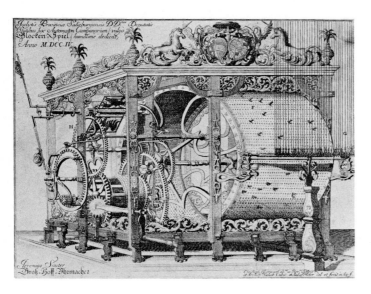

CANONICAL STRIKING. In a recently discovered manuscript of the latter half of the 15th century by Benvenuto della Volpaia (q.v.) there is shown a clock with a locking plate (q.v.) cut according to Fig. 128. This clock apparently struck the Canonical hours; Prime 3, Tertia 2, Sexta 1, Nona 2, Vespers 3 and Compline 4.[17] Fig. 239 shows in the right centre a 'contraption', the use of which has not yet been discovered, and the author submits that it may be for some such similar use.

CANOPY. A structure designed to support a bell (Figs. 332 and 247).

CAPITAL. The top portion of a column which provides the actual supporting surface; usually decorated in the manner of the classical Greek forms.

CAPOBIANCO, GIOVANNI GIORGIO OF SCHIO. A renowned Italian maker of the first half of the 16th century, who was also a goldsmith, designer and mathematician. He made an alarm for the famous Consul General Andrea Alciati and another for Cardinal Matteo Schnier (1511), which also lit a candle. He also made many other important pieces, both large and small, for various patrons in Italy and abroad.[16]

CARDAN SHAFTS. A method of drive where the two centres are not in line. Invented by Giralamo Cardanus (1501-1576) only about twenty years before their utilisation by Eberhart Baldewin (q.v.) (Fig. 60).

CARILLON. A set of bells that can be rung mechanically. One of the earliest surviving carillons is in the Clock Museum at Utrecht, dated 1542. Fig. 129 shows a print of a carillon from Salzburg by J. S. Bross, dated 1704, but we have the record of Dasypodius (q.v.) that in making the second Strasburg Clock in 1574, Isaac Habrecht (q.v.) utilised three of the carillon drums from the first clock of the 14th century.[18] We can, therefore, say that a carillon in a clock dates from the 14th century. The earliest known in England was made by Nicholas Vallin (q.v). in 1598 (Fig. 465).

CARRIAGE CLOCK. *See* TRAVELLING CLOCK.

CARTEL CLOCK. A wall clock of French origin dating from the middle of the 18th century, usually with a gilded bronze

130. (*Right*) *A cartel clock in the French style by Gale Holland. Coventry, c. 1765.* (*Messrs Ayer, Bath*)

131. (*Left and Right*) *Two clocks with caryatid columns. Second half 18th century.* (*Mr Ronald Lee*)

132. *James Ferguson's drawing of a planetary hour clock, once in his possession, showing the Celestial Spheres.* (*Edinburgh University Library*)

ornamental case (Fig. 130). The false bob (q.v.) enables the clock to be started without taking it off the wall.

CARTOUCHE. A tablet or scroll applied to a case (Fig. 62). A small plate affixed to the dial plate with the maker's name engraved thereon. Not infrequently this small plate hides the real maker's name.

CARYATID. A supporting decorative column on bracket clocks (q.v.) which takes the form of a stylised female figure, either in the whole or in the upper part (Fig. 131).

CELESTIAL SPHERES. In the Ptolemaic conception of the Universe the sun, the moon, the planets and the stars were all assumed to revolve around the Earth, each in its own orbit. There was a mechanical conception of a series of transparent spheres on to which the effigies of the sun, moon and planets were fixed. Since it was not possible to make transparent spheres in those days, spheres were built up of a series of metal bands (latin 'armilliae', hence armillary spheres), carrying the various celestial effigies. There were nine of these, the sphere, or orbit, of the moon, Venus, Mercury, the sun, Jupiter, Mars, Saturn, the Firmament of the fixed stars, then the Chrystalinium at rest and supporting the whole universe and finally the Primum Mobile (q.v.), the originator of all movement which moved slowly in a contrary direction, later recognised as the precession of the equinoxes (q.v.). Fig. 132 shows a drawing by James Ferguson, a renowned astronomer of the 18th century, of a 17th-century clock, now in the British Museum, and which he once owned. It will be noted that immediately encircling the Earth are the zones of Air and Fire (Ignis). For the inscriptions on the main column of the clock *see* ASTROLOGICAL DIAL.

CEULEN, JOHANNES VAN (d. *circa* 1715). A celebrated Dutch maker at The Hague. He made watches with balance

133. *Bracket clock by Johannes van Ceulen. The Hague, c. 1680.* (*Frederiksborg Museum, Denmark*)

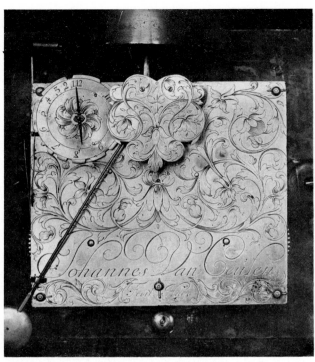

134. (*Left*) *Back plate of van Ceulen's clock.*

135. (*Right*) *Bracket clock by Grant, Fleet St, London, with chamfer top. c. 1810. (The late Mr Percy Webster)*

136. *Highly decorative clock made for the Chinese market. Anonymous. Second half 18th century. The lotus flowers open and shut alternately, and the waterfall plays. (The late Mrs Basil Ionides)*

springs and a pendulum clock for Christaan Huygens (q.v.). Huygens appears to have worked with him whilst living at The Hague, as he worked with Thuret (q.v.) whilst living in Paris (Figs. 133 and 134). In the Museum for the History of Science in Leyden there is a planispherium (q.v.) designed by Huygens in 1685 and made by van Ceulen (Figs. 382 and 383).

CHAMBER CLOCK. A term usually applied to those early iron clocks that were first made sufficiently small to be used domestically. They were frequently the work of locksmiths or gunsmiths rather than that of blacksmiths who made the large turret clocks (q.v.).

CHAMFER TOP. A top with stepped profile, as in Fig. 135, a clock by Grant of Fleet Street, London (*circa* 1810). The nice enamel dial has been spoilt by careless usage; damage has also been done around the winding hole.

CHANDELIER CLOCK. Occasionally in the late 17th and 18th centuries clocks were fitted in the bottom of objects suspended from above, as in Bird Cage clocks (q.v.). In the Rosenborg Castle in Copenhagen, King Christian IV of Denmark had a chandelier into the bottom of which a clock was fitted. This is now in the Holy Ghost Church in Copenhagen.

CHAPTER RING. The hour circle in a clock. The name probably derives from the earliest clocks in monasteries, which only struck once at each hour; the sexton then rang the bell to summon the monks to the various Offices or Chapters at the appropriate hour.

CHEEKS. The wooden battens fixed inside at the top of the sides of a long case clock (q.v.) on which the seatboard (q.v.) of the movement (q.v.) rests.

CHINESE CLOCK. See SU SUNG'S CLOCK.

CHINESE MARKET. In the latter half of the 18th century a lucrative trade sprung up between English clockmakers, mostly in London, and wealthy potentates in the East, mainly in China. Several makers were engaged in this trade, James Cox of

137. *Sunflower clock with waterfalls set above a musical box. Anonymous. Second half 18th century. (The late Mrs Basil Ionides)*

138. *Anonymous clock with lapis lazuli columns and cascading waterfalls, set on lion feet. Second half 18th century. (The late Mrs Basil Ionides)*

London being one of the principal. To satisfy the demands of the buyers the clocks had to be very ornate, complicated and highly decorated (Figs. 136, 137 and 138). In Fig. 136 whilst the flower in the centre, which is decorated with coloured paste, is open, that on the top of the clock remains closed, at the hour the central flower will retract and the upper one open. The twisted glass rods give the impression of falling water. In Fig. 137, known as the 'sunflower' clock, the chief effect is the apparent cascading as the glass bars turn. It is mounted on a musical box. In Fig. 138 there is again the cascading effect and a panorama passes before the onlooker, showing in the aperture below the dial. Fig. 139 shows an English clock superimposed upon a Swiss musical movement. The clock is interesting as it shows a very early example of English enamelling, it is signed and dated W. Craft Invt. et fecit 1779. A pastoral scene is displayed and actuated in the lower part of the clock.

CHIPPENDALE CLOCKS. A term loosely applied to long case clocks (q.v.) of which the pediments are scrolled or fretted after the style of Chippendale. Some clock case designs, both

139. *English clock placed upon a Swiss musical box, made for the Chinese market. An early example of English enamelling, signed and dated W. Craft, 1779. (Chateau des Monts, Le Loche, Switzerland)*

140. *Two long case clocks of the so-called Chippendale style; the one on the left was made in the U.S.A., late 18th century.*

long case and bracket (q.v.), appear in Chippendale's book of designs, but these meet with severe criticism from contemporary case makers as being quite impractical (Fig. 140). On the left is seen an American version of a Chippendale clock. The lack of proportion in the base and the turned feet will be noticed.

CIRCLE OF 360°, ORIGIN OF. The oldest known civilisation is that of the Sumerians, whose first inscriptions date from about 3500 B.C. They had a system of numeration based on 10 and 6; they counted up to 10, then to 6×10. Sixty then formed another unit and they went up to 10×60, or 600. With this again as a base they went up to 60×60 or 3,600. Here they thought that they had reached finality and the word for this was *sar*, which means circle, the whole or totality.[63] Although frequently thought of as the origin of the 360 degrees in the circle, this is not so; this was derived from space measurements in the celestial sphere which were eventually converted into time measurements. The Sumerians had a year of twelve months, each of thirty days and this division they applied to the celestial sphere, resulting in the creation of the zodiac (q.v.).[65] This circle

of 360 units was later adopted to measure the daily rotation, the day being divided into twelve hours, each equal to two modern hours, each of which was divided into thirty parts, so that the division of the circle provided the division of the day.[78]

CIRCULAR ERROR. Galileo (q.v.) in his first observations concluded that the period of swing of a pendulum was the same irrespective of its amplitude (q.v.). This is not quite correct, the isochronism (q.v.) of a pendulum is affected by its amplitude (q.v.) and this error is known as circular error. (*See* CYCLOIDAL CHEEKS.)

CIVIL TIME. 2×12 hours starting at midnight.

CLEMENT, WILLIAM (1638/9-1704). William Clement was born in February 1638/9 in Rotherhithe and worked there as an anchorsmith and a blacksmith. At an unspecified date, but which might be 1670, he moved to the parish of St Saviours, Southwark; in a Surrey Quarter Sessions for April, 1671 he is recorded as William Clements, late of Rotherhithe, Anchorsmith.[20] Clement is a man to whom insufficient regard has been paid until of late. He entered the Clockmakers' Company in 1677, and as he was already free of another Company, he entered as a 'Brother'. He was Master in 1694.

Huygens (q.v.) invented the pendulum in 1657 and this was combined with the verge escapement (q.v.) as currently then in use. Although the substitution of the pendulum for the balance or foliot (q.v.) showed an enormous improvement in timekeeping, horologists soon came to realise that it was far from perfect. Further, the verge escapement required a swing of about 40°, so that long pendulums with a long period were not practical, as the methods of limiting the swing needed by a verge escapement had not then been thought of. The search then began for a pendulum with a long period and a small arc. Unfortunately, we have no record of many of the various attempts that may have been made, except some entries in the Minutes of the Royal Society, concerning experiments by Dr Robert Hooke (q.v.). Fig. 141 shows a turret clock (q.v.) with

141. *William Clement's turret clock made for King's College, Cambridge, in 1671. Generally accepted as the original example of the anchor escapement. Clement was an anchor smith before he became a clockmaker. (Science Museum, London)*

anchor escapement (q.v.) dated 1671 and now in the Science Museum, London, which has no signs of having been converted from a verge escapement. This clock, which is signed and dated by William Clement, was originally made for King's College, Cambridge and the College records show that Clement paid a visit to Cambridge in 1670 and that the clock was delivered and paid for in 1671, price £42. For many decades authors have attributed this invention to Robert Hooke, each copying from the other without research. The only basis for such an attribution is a statement in Henry Sully's *Règle Artificielle du Temps* of 1727, pp. 263-264, some half century after the event and by a man who was not born at the time, to the effect that there had been a dispute as to the authorship of the invention between Clement and Hooke, and that he considered that Hooke might have been the inventor. This has since developed into 'Hooke was the inventor'. It may be noted that neither of Hooke's biographers gave him credit for the invention; on the other hand, John Smith in his book *Horological Disquisitions* 1694 and William Derham in his *Artificial Clockmaker* 1696, both give Clement the credit for the invention, and he is now generally accepted as the true inventor. Stress is laid upon this point because the invention of this escapement, with its restricted arc of swing of 3° to 4° is as important to horology as the invention of the pendulum itself, and it is the basis of all subsequent improved escapements. The shape of the escapement, closely resembling the flukes of an anchor, can be seen in Fig. 141, and as Clement was originally an anchorsmith,[20] the shape of the pallets (q.v.) may well have been inspired by his former trade. Indeed, it is the author's opinion that this trade connection weighs heavily in favour of the claims made on his behalf.

There is a clock in Wadham College with an anchor escapement which is not signed or dated, but which is believed to have been made by Joseph Knibb (q.v.) and for which the maintenance accounts go back to 1670.[21] This is one year earlier than the date on Clement's clock, but we must remember that Clement would certainly have intended applying the escapement when he visited Cambridge in 1670 to quote for the clock he made them; there is an item in the College accounts of £1. 10s. 0d. for his travelling expenses in that year. Joseph Knibb was made Free of the Clockmakers' Company in London in 1670, and would be 'au fait' with the latest developments, of which he availed himself, as did all the principal clockmakers of London. There is no record of Clement ever trying for a patent or other form of monopoly for his invention;[22] he died in 1704, and was buried in St Saviours, Southwark, now Southwark Cathedral, on 4th November.

CLOCK. A mechanical device motivated by weights or springs, that records the passing of time visually and, at selected intervals, audibly. The author disagrees with the use of the word clock for electric devices which are nothing more than the equivalent of the electric meter in the cellar indicating the current consumed in terms of time, instead of units of electricity.

COCK. In a clock the bracket that supports the pendulum is known as a cock. This has two feet; in a watch, or elsewhere in a clock, a cock is a bracket with only one foot and a bracket with two feet is known as a bridge (Fig. 280).

142. *An early astronomical clock by Edward Cockey of Warminster. Mid-18th century. 10 ft. 6 in. tall. (Mr R. Cooper)*

143. *Late astronomical clock by Cockey embodying the equation of time. c. 1770. (Ilbert Collection, British Museum)*

COCKEY, EDWARD. A very fine maker who lived in the middle part of the 18th century in Warminster, in Wiltshire, and about whom very little is known, except that he made three, and possibly four, magnificent astronomical clocks, with dials 20 inches square or more, and standing 10 feet high. The earliest, now in private possession, is seen in Fig. 142 and the latest, Fig. 143, was in the Ilbert Collection and is now in the British Museum. A third was made for Her Majesty's Drawing Room in St James's Palace and a detailed description of it is to be found in the British Museum, Kings MS. 277. These clocks all show the hours, minutes, days of the month, month of the year, the sun's place in the ecliptic (q.v.) and the age and phases of the moon; in addition, the last one (Fig. 143) shows the equation of time (q.v.), the days of the week and the Sundays of the Church of England.

It had been thought that owing to the long period of time covered by these clocks, as indicated by their styles, that there were two Edward Cockeys, father and son. Mr Bellchambers, who has made special study of West Country clockmakers, has

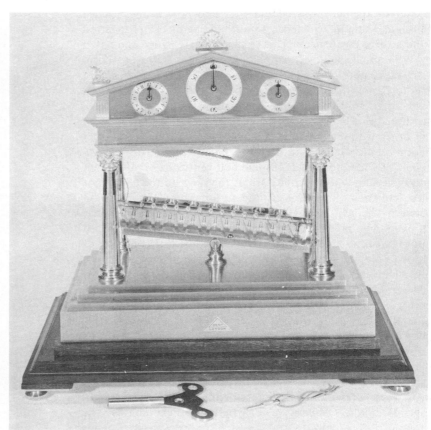

144. *Congreve's original weight-driven clock*, 1808. (*Officers' Mess, Royal Artillery, Woolwich*)   145. *Spring-driven Congreve clock.* (*Horological Journal*)

established that there was only one Edward Cockey and that he was born in 1701 and died in 1786.

A watch of hall mark 1735 is known, and a bracket clock is in the Gershom-Parkington Collection in Bury St Edmunds, which the catalogue dates to the mid-18th century. In view of the elaborate nature of the astronomical clocks it is surprising that a greater number of examples of a more ordinary nature have not survived; Cockey cannot have 'burst' into these elaborate pieces 'just like that'. The Cockey family were mainly bell founders and pewterers.

COLURES. The two principal meridians that pass through the poles and the solstices (q.v.), and the poles and the equinoxes (q.v.) respectively.

COMTOISE CLOCK. *See* MOREZ CLOCK.

CONGREVE, WILLIAM. An artillery officer who later became Comptroller of Woolwich Laboratory. In 1808 he devised his rolling ball clock, one of which has been a centre of attraction in the window of a well-known clockmaker in Pall Mall for many years. His original design was weight driven, but later models were all spring driven (Fig. 145); the clock he presented to the Prince Regent is now in the Rotunda at Woolwich (Fig. 144). As far is as known, Congreve had no knowledge of the various 16th-century types of ball clock (q.v.).

CONTRATE WHEEL. A wheel in which the teeth are cut at right angles to the plane of the wheel (Fig. 146).

COPENHAGEN CLOCK. *See* OLSEN, JENS.

CORBEL. A wall bracket originally designed to support a wall clock (q.v.). Derived from the architectural term (Fig. 94).

CORINTHIAN COLUMN. A decorative column used in both long case (q.v.) and mantel (q.v.) clocks, capped with a reproduction of the classical Greek Corinthian capital. Used in high quality clocks in the English classical period (1660-1700), but rarely found on Continental clocks (Figs. 1 and 26).

146. *Clock by Nicholas Vallin, London, c. 1590, showing clearly a contrate wheel. (Banff Museum)*

147. *Clock signed 'Roubillard, London', c. 1825, with coup perdu escapement.* (*Mr Bernard Hawkins*)

148. *Detail of the coup perdu escapement.*

149. *James Cox's clock self-winding with changes in atmospheric pressure. The jars should contain mercury. London, 1760.*

CORNER PIECES. *See* SPANDRELS.

CORNICE. The topmost moulding in a clock case.

COSTER, SALOMON. A noted Dutch maker who worked for Huygens (q.v.) and was entrusted by him with the making of the first pendulum clock. John Fromanteel (q.v.) was sent to him to learn the art of making pendulum clocks. There was at one time in the Rijksmuseum in Amsterdam a small, single-handed, spring-driven pendulum clock in a wooden case, the back of which was nailed, when this was removed the inscription 'SAMUEL COSTER—HAGHE met privilege 1657' was revealed.[23] This was therefore a clock made in the same year as Huygens assigned to Coster the rights of his invention. Was this the original Huygens pendulum clock? This clock has not been found since the Museum was reconstituted.

COUNT WHEEL. *See* LOCKING PLATE.

COUP PERDU (LOST STROKE). A clock, usually of French manufacture, in which a pendulum of approximately $10\frac{1}{2}$ inches, beating $\frac{1}{2}$ seconds, nevertheless registers seconds by its seconds hand on the seconds dial. The clock illustrated in Figs. 147 and 148 is signed 'Roubillard, London'; however it is undoubtedly a French design. One arm of the escapement is mounted on a small pivoted arm which is offset by a counterweight. When in its closed position it registers with the impulse pallet and forms a continuation of its 'dead' face. As each pin on the escape wheel drops it falls on to the top face of this pivoted arm, carrying it to the lowered position. Thus obstructed, the pin passes the impulse face and is held on the 'dead' face of the impulse pallet. The pivoted arm is released and is returned by the counterweight to the open position and,

on the return swing of the pendulum, can give impulse and escape; thus the escape wheel of sixty pins only advances once for every alternate swing of the pendulum. (*See* ESCAPEMENT, GALILEO.)

COX, JAMES (d. 1788). An eminent London maker in the middle of the 18th century. He made many elaborate clocks for the Chinese market (q.v.), but his principal claim to recognition is that he was the first to employ the principle of a change in atmospheric pressure or temperature to provide the motive force of a clock. (*See* ATMOS CLOCK).

Cox's clock made *circa* 1760 is seen in Fig. 149. Mercury is placed in the lower bowl and supports a column of mercury which expands or contracts from the upper bowl. By means of rocking arms not seen, a rack, very ingeniously pivoted, winds up a wheel by both rise and fall of pressure. The modern Atmos clock (q.v.) only winds up on a fall of temperature.[6]

CRAIG, EDWIN. One of a Northern Irish family of several brothers, one of whom became well known in politics as Lord Craigavon. He started life in the army and on his retirement was active in local county government, he was also an ardent yachtsman. Towards the end of his life he interested himself in the making of a 'free pendulum' clock embodying quite different principles to those of other makers.

He set himself the problem of converting reciprocal into rotary motion, and from the latter to the lifting of two small balls which were then rolled across two small platforms, one on each end of an arm projecting from the pendulum rod near its point of suspension (Figs. 150, 151 and 152). The retaining arm releases the ball when it is at its dead point (q.v.), on the right in Fig. 150. Thus the pendulum receives an impulse from a very

150. *Edwin Craig's free pendulum clock*, 1940.

151. *Rear view of Craig's clock*.

152. *Another of Craig's methods for converting reciprocal into rotary motion.*

small constant force when it is at its dead point. Fig. 151 shows a rear view of the clock, at the top can be seen one of the devices Craig used to overcome the inertia of the dead point when converting reciprocal into rotary motion. Fig. 152 shows another of these devices. One of Craig's clocks is in the Science Museum, London.

CRESTING. A carved wooden decoration surmounting the hood (q.v.) of a long case clock (q.v.), popular with the more expensive clocks during the third quarter of the 17th century. These usually carried a wooden ball as a finial (q.v.), placed centrally (Fig. 283).

CROMWELLIAN CLOCK. The term is a misnomer, these clocks were made long before and long after the Cromwellian period. (*See* LANTERN CLOCK.)

CROWN WHEEL. The escape wheel with saw-like teeth of the verge escapement (q.v. Fig. 246).

CRUCIFIX CLOCK. During the 16th and 17th centuries clocks embodying religious themes were frequently made. The crucifixion was a popular subject. At the base of the cross would be shown the Virgin Mary, St John and perhaps Mary Magdalene, as in Fig. 153. The hour is recorded by a band encircling the globe at the top of the cross, the going and striking trains (q.v.) being in the base. The example shown is exceptional in that it has an alarm which has to be cocked before winding and setting (Fig. 154). The base of the crucifix is pierced to show the hour selected for the alarm and there are holes in the flat top below the figures to allow the insertion of a pin to turn the dial to the selected hour. Fig. 155 shows the base plate with the cranked arm, ending in a hand and the four setting marks for the hog's bristle regulation (q.v.) of the balance.

153. (*Left*) *Crucifix clock, Augsburg, mid-16th century.* (*British Museum*)

154. (*Right*) *Alarm movement of Fig. 153. A most unusual addition to a Crucifix clock.*

155. *Back plate of Fig. 153 showing 'hand' for bristle regulation.*

156. *Back plate of a clock by Joseph Knibb, London, c. 1680, showing the crutch to receive the pendulum rod.* (*Mr James Oakes*)

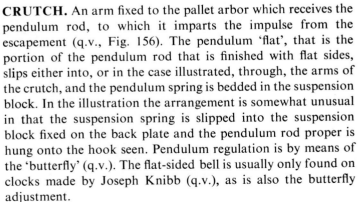

CRUTCH. An arm fixed to the pallet arbor which receives the pendulum rod, to which it imparts the impulse from the escapement (q.v., Fig. 156). The pendulum 'flat', that is the portion of the pendulum rod that is finished with flat sides, slips either into, or in the case illustrated, through, the arms of the crutch, and the pendulum spring is bedded in the suspension block. In the illustration the arrangement is somewhat unusual in that the suspension spring is slipped into the suspension block fixed on the back plate and the pendulum rod proper is hung onto the hook seen. Pendulum regulation is by means of the 'butterfly' (q.v.). The flat-sided bell is usually only found on clocks made by Joseph Knibb (q.v.), as is also the butterfly adjustment.

In another type of crutch the arms are replaced by a pin which then enters into a slot in the pendulum rod itself (Fig. 197).

an extra hour's influence to three of them. Beginning with Saturn, the farthest away, as the ruling planet for the first hour of Saturday and going in an anti-clockwise direction we find that three from Saturn gives the sun as the ruler of the first hour of the next day, Sunday, then the moon for Monday and so on (Fig. 162). Some dials have the ruling planet marked for each

from this radiate lines on which signs are marked. The signs indicated are Trines △ 120°, Quartiles □ 90°, Sextiles * 60°, and Conjunction ☍ 180°. From these lines the approximate aspect or angular relation of the moon to the sun can be determined, when read in conjunction with the outer dial bearing the effigy of the sun, which makes one revolution a year, the sun's position in the zodiac (q.v.) being read off above the XII.

DIAL, ASTRONOMICAL. Any dial which shows some form of celestial movement. The simplest form shows just the

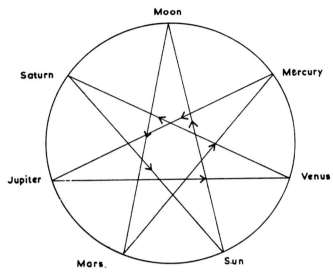

162. *Diagram for ascertaining the planetary deities for the days of the week.*

hour of the day of the week (Fig. 163), or else a table painted inside the clock door (Fig. 164). In Fig. 163 the mean hours are shown commencing at 12 midnight by the straight hand and the astrological hours by the short wavy hand. This is incorrectly fixed; it should be at 180° to the mean time hand, as the astrological day started at midday.

Also to be found frequently and mostly without the separate marking of the planetary hours, is a dial as seen in Fig. 165. The inner disc has an opening for the phases of the moon and

163. *Astrological dial showing the planet influencing each hour of the day. The short wavy planetary hand should be at 180° to the hour hand, as there is a 12 hours difference between the mean and astrological hours. (Professor Hans von Bertele)*

164. *Table of the planetary influences for day and night. (Rosenborg Castle, Copenhagen)*

phases of the moon (Fig. 123). These dials progress through all stages up to the most complicated (Fig. 116).

DIAL, AUXILIARY. A dial which is used to indicate some detail subsidiary to the main purpose of the clock, which is to record hours and minutes. The seconds dial, the day of the week dial, the strike/silent dial (Fig. 167), and the pendulum regulation dials (q.v.) are all auxiliary dials.

DIAL, CLOCK, INVENTION OF. *See* DONDI, JACOPO.

DIAL, EQUATION. A clock dial designed to register automatically the difference between the solar or sundial time, and mean time due to the Equation of Time (q.v.). One finds ordinary clock dials on which are engraved or painted at intervals the extent of the equation for any day, these are not equation dials.

DIAL, FLAT ARCH. The earliest type of arched dial was less than semi-circular (Fig. 166). This came in about 1710-1715, later the full semi-circle was adopted.

DIAL FRAME. The wooden surround to a dial which is exposed when the door is opened.

DIAL, LUNAR. The mechanical indication of the phases and age of the moon was one of the earliest additions to the mechanical clock. We know that Giovanni Dondi (q.v.) had a very exact portrayal of the lunar motion in 1364; it is suspected that the First Strasburg Clock 1354 had a simple lunar dial

165. *Astrological dial on the Ptolemaic system, by Samuel Watson. London, c. 1685. (Clockmaker's Company)*

166. *Clock by Joseph Windmills, London, c. 1715 with early form of flat arch dial. (Mr James Oakes)* 167. *Bracket clock by Samuel Watson, London, c. 1695, with the two lower dials for securing the pendulum bob when carrying. The upper dials are for pendulum regulation and strike silent. (Messrs Garrads Ltd)*

168. *Rack and pinion pendulum regulation operated from a dial in front.* (*Mr H. Dimely*)

169. *Pendulum regulation by means of an eccentric cam.* (*Lord Harris*)

showing the phase and age of the moon during its $29\frac{1}{2}$ day lunation; there was probably also a black-and-white disc giving visual indication of the phases. Lunar dials were incorporated early in iron domestic clocks and since $29\frac{1}{2}$ is an awkward number to deal with, they usually had a disc with 59 teeth and a two-month period of revolution (Figs. 123 and 140).

DIAL, PENDULUM FIXING. In the early days of domestic pendulum clocks they were very expensive and were carried from room to room, hence the handles on them, which continued to be fitted until the latter part of the 18th century, when clocks were cheaper and there were more than one in the house. Usually a small hook was provided on the back plate (q.v.) into which the pendulum could be slipped (Fig. 183) while carrying the clock. In some of the more elaborate clocks of the last quarter of the 17th century, which had lenticular shaped bobs, (q.v.), there were, at the bottom corners of the dial, right and left, two quadrants the arbors of which passed through to the back plate, and had set on them two fingers in a narrow V which could be turned down to fit over the bob from either side and so prevent any motion whilst carrying the clock (Fig. 167).

DIAL, REGULATING. Pendulum bobs (q.v.) were at first small, round or pear-shaped bobs, hence the name. With the verge escapement (q.v.) they needed only to be very light and could be screwed up and down the pendulum rod for regulation. With the introduction of the anchor escapement (q.v.) and spring suspension for the pendulum, a flat lenticular bob was introduced. The position of this on the pendulum rod could not be varied by less than a 180° turn, which might well be too much, so it was necessary to introduce methods of changing the effective length of the pendulum rod. This was done by means of a rack and pinion (Fig. 168), or by a snail-shaped cam (Fig. 169), and an auxiliary dial (q.v.) was placed in the upper part of the main dial so that the adjustment could be made from the front (Fig. 167, top right).

DIAL, SKELETON. The usual practice in the latter half of the 17th century and the first half of the 18th was to cover the exposed portions of the dial plate with matting (q.v.). In some of the more expensive clocks the minute ring and hour numerals were cut out. Fig. 170 shows an early example of this by Joseph Knibb (q.v.), who was the most frequent user of this kind of dial. As will be seen, the matted area is about double that needed when a solid chapter ring (q.v.) was used, and this combined with the labour of fretting out the hour numerals, must have added considerably to the cost of the clock. Occasionally one finds skeleton dials by other English makers and sometimes on the Continent (Fig. 261), only here, as the dial plate is covered with velvet, there would be only the cost of fretting the numerals involved. Another very fine skeleton dial is seen in Fig. 325. Here it will be observed that the maker was apprenticed to Joseph Knibb.

DIAL, STRIKE/SILENT. When the rack and snail strike (q.v.), was invented in 1676 by Edward Barlow (q.v.) it provided that any time during any hour the clock would strike the right number of blows, as opposed to the locking plate (q.v.) system which, when an hour was once struck, could only strike the next succeeding hour at the next striking. With the rack and snail system clock owners could put the strike out of action by temporarily preventing the striking fly from turning and then

171. *A tidal dial on a clock by Samuel Watson, London, c. 1695.*

be sure that, when the strike action was restored, their clocks would strike the correct hour. (*See* subsidiary dial in Fig. 167.)

DIAL, TIDAL. England being a maritime nation, and the Thames being the chief highway of London, the times of the tides at the main ports of the country and at London Bridge became of great importance to the community in general. Hence clocks were made which indicated the time of high tide on any day of the year at a selected port. The tidal cycle coincides with the lunar cycle of $29\frac{1}{2}$ days, hence when the time of high tide at new moon at any port is established, the twice daily tides can be divided into the $29\frac{1}{2}$ day lunar dial. It is only of recent years that these tidal dials have been understood. In Fig. 171 is seen a dial by Samuel Watson of Coventry and London (q.v.). Encircling the central lunar dial (q.v.) is a dial marked I to XII twice over with an aperture cut at one of the III's. This clock dates from the late 1690's and there is strong circumstantial evidence that it once belonged to Sir Isaac Newton,[28] who in 1695 was appointed Warden of the Mint and four years later, Master, so that he would be living in London at that time. Now a few years previously, John Flamsteed, who was the first Astronomer Royal, had established that high tide at London Bridge at new moon was at 3 o'clock,[29] so we see that this dial was made to show the time of high tide at London Bridge. Fig. 282 shows another example of this type of dial made for a port where the time of high tide at new moon is 6 o'clock.

DIAL, TIDAL, UNIVERSAL. The standard Tidal Dial (q.v.) will register the time of high tide at a given port; since, however, the tidal cycle coincides with the lunar cycle one needs only a fixed ring with the $29\frac{1}{2}$ days of a lunation to be combined with an adjustable ring marked I-XII twice over to set the dial to register the time of high tide at any chosen port. The hour of

170. *Bracket clock by Joseph Knibb, London, c. 1680, with skeleton dial. (The late Mr W. J. Iden)*

high tide at new moon at that port is ascertained and is placed under 29½ in the lunar ring (Fig. 172). This clock stands on the stairs in the author's house and is set for the tides on the south coast, so that the family may know the state of the tide for bathing should they elect to go to the sea for a day. A very complex Universal Tidal Dial by Antide Janvier (q.v.) is seen in Fig. 304.

DIAL, UP AND DOWN. A dial found in very high-grade spring clocks to indicate the extent to which the spring has run down, and first used by Jost Burgi (q.v.) in about 1590 (Fig. 100). The idea of checking the run down of the spring is much older, small doors were cut in the sides of the cases of drum clocks (q.v.) and could be opened to see how far the fusee (q.v.) had turned (Fig. 24).

DOME. The removable super-structure found on the top of long case clocks (q.v.) with square dials. It is thought that the majority of these clocks in the period 1690-1730 were originally so equipped to follow the fashion for raising the overall height of clocks, which started with the adoption of cresting (q.v.). This fashion enabled the overall height to be increased without bringing the dial and the winding squares to a level too high for the average person. As the clocks descended through the ages these domes were often discarded, partly through being out of fashion and often through necessity when the clocks were brought into much lower rooms (Figs. 19 and 17).

DOMINICAL LETTER. The first seven days of January are given the letters A to G and that allotted to the first Sunday of the year is the Dominical Letter for the year. Were the first

172. *A universal tidal dial on a clock by William Tomlinson, London, c. 1730. The inner ring is a friction fit and the time of high tide at new moon for the port selected can be set under the 29½. (Author's collection)*

173. *Overall view of Giovanni Dondi's astronomical clock, Padua, 1364, with dials for mean time, rising and setting of the sun, Primum Mobile (Sidereal Time) upper centre, Venus right and Mars, left. (Science Museum, London)*

174. *Dondi's clock. Dial of Mercury, the annual calendar wheel and perpetual calendar for Easter.*

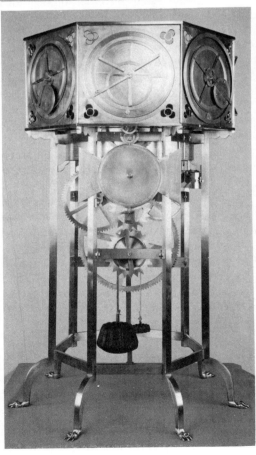

175. *Dondi's clock. Dial of the Moon.*

176. *Dondi's clock. Mean time dial and wings for the rising and the setting of the sun. Above the dial is the gearing for the conversion of mean to sidereal time.*

177. *Interior view of Dondi's clock showing the wheels driving the planetary dials off the annual calendar wheel. The moon dial is driven off the sidereal time dial by the rod seen. This is the earliest known example of skew gearing.*

Sunday 3rd January, the Dominical Letter would be C. As there are fifty-two weeks and one day in a year the Dominical Letter goes one day backward each year. In leap years the Dominical Letter goes up to 28th February and the next letter in succession is used for the remainder of the year, so that in leap years the Dominical Letter goes back two letters (Fig. 121).

DONDI, GIOVANNI (1318-1389). Son of Jacopo Dondi (q.v.). A professor of medicine, logic and astronomy at both Florence and Padua, and amongst the most famous horologists in the world. Dondi must have had some early acquaintance with horology since his father made a famous clock. In 1364 Giovanni Dondi completed a clock, of which he has left a very full description of the construction, supplemented by working drawings and details of the trains (q.v.).[30] It would seem that Dondi wrote a description on finishing the clock, and then re-wrote his description after he had made some alterations and additions. The first description has recently been published

178. *Memorial tablet to Jacopo Dondi in the wall of the Baptistry at Padua. (Acts of the Institute of Venice. Vol IIa. S viia. Pl. 1)*

under the title *Tractatus Astrarii*,[31] in this the latin text is reproduced facsimile and extended with copious notes in Italian. The second MS. *Opus Planetarium* exists in several copies, the oldest is in St Mark's Library in Venice; a very good copy, about eighty years later, is in the Bodleian Library, Oxford. Other copies are in the Eton College Library, the Ambrosia Library in Milan, and the Turin Library.[32]

Up to this time we have only knowledge of heavy turret clocks (q.v., Fig. 399), blacksmiths' work with simple going and striking movements. Dondi worked in brass and from his weight-driven clock he recorded the mean hour and minute, the times of the setting and rising of the sun, the conversion of mean time (q.v.) into sidereal time (q.v.), the temporal hours (q.v.), the day of the month and the month of the year, the fixed feasts of the Church, the length of daylight for each day, the dominical letter (q.v.), the solar and lunar cycles (q.v.), the annual movement of the sun and moon in the ecliptic (q.v.) and the annual movements of the five planets. From his clock the coming of the eclipses could be predicted. He also had a perpetual calendar for the movable feasts of the Church. He was two hundred years ahead of his time in the continuous recording of minutes, his is the first recorded conversion of mean to sidereal time, his provision for the slightly elliptical orbit of the moon was not repeated for four hundred years and his perpetual calendar for Easter for five hundred years. (*See* CALENDAR, PERPETUAL FOR EASTER.)

The original clock was thought to have been taken by King Charles V to Spain when he abdicated from the throne of the Holy Roman Empire in 1556. He retired to the Spanish monastery of San Juste and it has been assumed that Dondi's clock was destroyed when that monastery was fired by the French during the Peninsular wars. Later reports say that the clock so destroyed was an octagonal astronomical clock with a celestial sphere on top, whilst Dondi's clock was heptagonal and had no celestial sphere.[33] Paintings have since been found made after the abdication of Charles V showing the clock, which would indicate that it was then still in Italy. Having this full information about the construction of Dondi's clock, the author in 1958 conceived the idea of having the clock reproduced, and in 1961 this reproduction was completed. It is now in the Smithsonian Institution in Washington D.C. (Figs. 173, 174, 175, 176 and 177).[6]

DONDI, JACOPO (1293-1359). Jacopo Dondi was born in Padua and was appointed Municipal Physician to Choggia in 1313. He was recalled to Padua in 1342 and in 1344 made a clock which was placed in the Carrace Tower of Padua.[34] Of this clock we have no details; it was considered very exceptional and earned for its maker the title of del'Orologio (Of the Clock), a title borne by his descendants today. A memorial tablet was affixed to the walls of the Baptistry adjoining the façade of Padua Cathedral (Fig. 178). The latin inscription, which like most medieval latin inscriptions is somewhat obscure, has been translated for me by Dr R. Atkinson as follows 'I, Jacopus, was born in Padua and I give back to the Earth what it gave. Lo! a small urn hides away my ashes. I was well known to my native city as useful in my business. To me (belonged) the art of medicine and the knowledge of the heavens and the stars; thither I now proceed, freed from my bodily prison. Verily both my skills remain emblazoned in my books. Indeed gracious Reader, advised from afar from the top of a high tower how you may tell the time and the hours, though their number changes, recognise my invention, and also put up a silent prayer for peace and for forgiveness for me.'

We know that the early clocks had no dials and at first only struck one blow at each hour. By 1335 Galvano Fiamma wrote of the clock in Milan 'There is a wonderful clock, because there is there a very large clapper which strikes the bell twenty-four times according to the 24 hours of the day and night, and then at first hour of the night gives one sound, at the second two strokes and so distinguishes one hour from another, which is of the greatest use to men everywhere.'[35] So far there has been no mention of any visible recording of the time, only aural, and it seems to the author that the great step forward that earned for Jacopo the title of 'del'Orologio' may well have been the invention of the clock dial.

DOUBLE BASKET. *See* BASKET TOP, DOUBLE.

DOUBLE STRIKING CLOCKS. Over the years there have appeared clocks that repeat the hour at a short interval after it has first been struck. The interval is usually 2 minutes. An early example of this type of clock is seen in Fig. 179, an Augsburg clock (q.v.) of more or less typical design, but it will be noted that, whilst the ordinary Augsburg clock stands directly on the table, in this case the base of the clock is raised on lion feet and there is a bell showing. Having struck in the normal way by means of the ordinary striking train within the case, a separate striking train in the base is let off by means of a plunger. The clock is by Lucas Weydman of Crackow, 1648.

In the inventory of King Casimir of Poland, 1673, there appears an entry 'Item: Une horloge qui sonne les heures, les demies, les quarts, la répétition et marque les minutes'[146] Repetition here does not mean repeater as we understand it to-day, but a clock that strikes the hour twice. The clock in the Great Court of Trinity College, Cambridge, also strikes the hour twice.

DRUM CLOCK. The earliest form of portable clock (Figs. 11 and 31); the earliest watches also took the form of squat cylinders. Sometimes a loop is found brazed on to the body of the drum to enable a ribbon to be passed through to allow suspension from the neck. The example illustrated is of the mid-16th century (Fig. 180). The lid is pierced so that the hour can

179. *Clock by Lucas Weydman of Cracow, 1648, with double striking.* (*British Museum*)

180. *Drum clock, German, c. 1550. (Hessisches Landesmuseum, Kassel)*

181. *Bottom plate of Fig. 180.*

182. *Bracket clock by Claude du Chesne, London, c. 1725. One of a pair. The musical rolls are kept in a drawer in the base. (Rosenborg Castle, Copenhagen)*

be read without opening the case, also to facilitate the emission of sound. The hour is read off the long thin hand and the position of the sun in the ecliptic (q.v.) off the lower edge of the hand on the left marked 'Vero loco'; the other hand is marked 'Loco opposi'. The clock strikes the hour and the quarter on two bells, one nesting inside the other. The back plate (q.v.), seen in Fig. 181, is interesting, as it shows a fine example of a stackfreed (q.v.) and of hog's bristle regulation (q.v.). The bristle can be seen standing up from the lower arm of the C shaped holder, the other end of which carries a pointer registering against a scale; the small dial indicates the last quarter struck.

DuCHESNE, CLAUDE. Clockmakers' Company 1693-1730. A Huguenot who came from France about 1689; he made mostly musical clocks. The back plate (q.v.) of one of his clocks is seen in Fig. 199. The spiked musical rolls seen in the photograph are kept in a drawer in the bottom of the case and are changed by hand. A fine pair of musical three train clocks (q.v.) by him

are in the Rosenborg Castle in Copenhagen, one of which is illustrated in Fig. 182. Here again, the rolls are housed in the drawer under the clock. The clock and bracket are finely mounted with silver, unfortunately very tarnished when the photograph was taken. The subsidiary dials show, in the arch, the age and phase of the moon; whilst this has the common two lunation train of fifty-nine days, the ring is marked 1-59 for the double period instead of 1-29½ twice over. Top left is the dial for pendulum regulation (q.v.) and that on the right for strike/silent (q.v.). Those at the bottom of the dial are for the days of the week, left, and of the month, right.

DUTCH STRIKING. A form of dual striking where the hours are struck on a big bell and at the half hours the hour is repeated on a smaller, higher toned bell; this method of striking is only possible with a locking plate (q.v.). In Fig. 183 it will be noted that the locking plate (or count wheel) is notched in duplicate, so that the locking arm will allow a repetition of each number of blows. Dutch striking is not often found, and as it is not practical with the rack and snail striking (q.v.), it soon dropped out after that system became generally adopted towards the end of the 17th century. For an interesting variation of the usual form, *see* JOHN HILDERSON.

EAST, EDWARD (1602-1697). Until a few years ago the biographical details about Edward East were very uncertain. The fact that he lived to be ninety-five years old, combined with

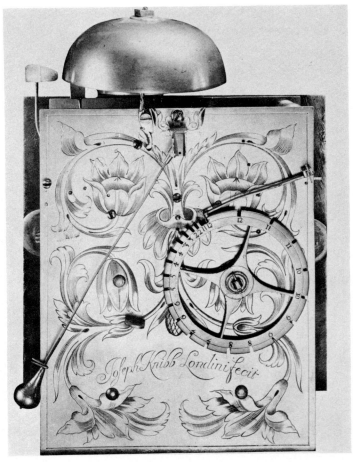

183. *Back plate of a clock by Joseph Knibb, London, showing doubly cut locking plate for Dutch striking. (Mr James Oakes)*

some faulty research work in the registers of the Society of Friends, led to the speculation that there may have been two clockmakers of this name, father and son. The author's researches have led to the discovery that he was born at Southill in Bedfordshire and that he was baptised there on 22nd August, 1602. Incidentally, Southill is only a few miles from Northill, where Thomas Tompion (q.v.) was born. On 27th March, 1618, at the age of 15½ years, East was apprenticed to Richard Rogers, Goldsmith, for a period of eight years and was made Free by Service on 8th February, 1627. On the formation of the Clockmakers' Company in 1631, Edward East was the junior member of the original Court of Assistants. He was Master in 1645 and in 1652.

His early work in watches bears witness to his training as a goldsmith, and his clocks are usually distinguished by their extreme simplicity in his early period (Fig. 184). A very fine long case clock (q.v.) and its dial are seen in Figs. 185 and 186, the engraving on this dial should be compared with Fig. 278. His later clocks took on some of the styling of the Restoration period (Fig. 1). He made the only known long case night clock and remained active in the Clockmakers' Company for many years; in 1671 when the Company was applying for a Grant of Arms, Edward East is recorded as being the only survivor of the original Court of Assistants. In 1692 Henry Jones (q.v.), a former apprentice of East, now Master of the Company, recorded that Mr East wished to donate £100 in his lifetime for the benefit of the poor, which gift was recorded in 1693.

He was Clockmaker to King Charles I, who used to give East watches as prizes for tennis played in the Mall. When Mr Herbert, Groom of the Bedchamber, failed to call the King an hour earlier than usual, he was presented with a gold alarm watch to make things easier for him in the future.[36] East held the position of Clockmaker to King Charles II; he is so described in an inscription on a clock dial he presented to Queens' College, Cambridge in 1661. This clock now stands in the President's Lodging of the College. Incidentally, his daughter, Anne Saunders, was bequeathed the inn 'The Swan with Two Necks' in London, on condition that she pay yearly £2. 10s. 0d. to the College, who report that they are still receiving an annual rent in respect of this site.

East appears to have moved to Hampton in Middlesex during the last years of his life. His will is dated 21st July, 1688 and was proved on 3rd February, 1696/7. In it he describes himself as Edward East, Watchmaker, Citizen and Goldsmith of London. (Note: In those days the word 'watch' was applied equally to a pocket watch or to the going train (q.v.) of a clock, which was known as the watch part.) (See also Fig. 62.)

EBONISE. To stain black in imitation of ebony. Pear wood was frequently used for this purpose, owing to the absence of grain.

ECLIPSE. If the orbits of the sun and moon were in the same plane there would be an eclipse of the sun and moon at each lunation; they are, however, inclined to each other at about 5°. The two points of their intersection are called the Nodes (q.v.). When the sun, the moon, the Earth and a node are in line an eclipse of the sun or the moon will take place, according to whether the moon is new or full. A partial eclipse takes place when the node is a few degrees off the straight line. Therefore,

184. *Bracket clock by Edward East, London, c. 1660 with early architectural case and overall matted dial. (The late Mr W. J. Iden)*

185. *Long case clock by Edward East, London, c. 1675, in walnut case. (Mr N. G. Terry)*

186. *Dial of East's clock. Note the early narrow seconds dial and the fine engraving.*

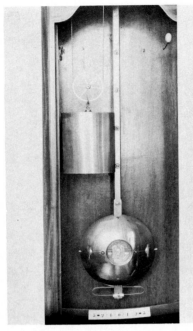

187. *Ellicott's compensated pendulum in a clock by Spencer and Perkins, London, c. 1785. (The late Mr H. N. Fry)*

188. *Long case clock by John Ellicott, London, c. 1750 with equation dial. (The late Mr W. J. Iden)*

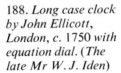

189. *Inverted bell clock by John Ellicott, London, c. 1740. He is generally credited with the invention of the brass bezel to the dial and the wooden surround. (The late Mr W. J. Iden)*

from clocks showing the motion of the Earth, moon and nodes around the sun the coming of an eclipse can be predicted (Fig. 171).

ECLIPTIC, THE. The sun's apparent orbit.

EIGHT-DAY CLOCK. Up to the middle of the 17th century it was very rare indeed to find any clock with a going period of more than 24 or 30 hours; indeed some early lantern clocks (q.v.) only go for 12 hours. With the coming of the pendulum (q.v.) makers began to produce clocks to go for a week or longer. In fact Ahasuerus Fromanteel (q.v.), whose nephew John was sent to Holland to learn the secret of the making of pendulum clocks as invented by Christaan Huygens (q.v.), and who brought the secret back with him in 1658, was in 1658 advertising clocks to go for a week, a month or a year with one winding up, as well as those that are wound every day.[37] At first clocks were made to go for seven days exactly; the author has such a clock by Edward East (q.v.) with only fourteen turns on the fusee (q.v. Fig. 62). Standard practice is for the fusee to make one turn every 12 hours. It soon became apparent that a clock with sixteen turns on the fusee, capable of going for eight days with one winding, was much more practical.

ELLICOTT, JOHN, F.R.S. (1706-1772). A maker of renown, and Clockmaker to King George III. He was elected to the Royal Society in 1738 and was later a member of the Council. He made high-grade clocks and watches, but he was also interested in astronomy and had his own observatory in Hackney. He invented a type of compensation pendulum (Fig. 187), in which a rod of brass and a rod of iron are coupled together. Fixed to the bottom of the iron component are two hinged levers on the outer ends of which rest the ends of two long screws which carry the bob in the zero position. The brass component rests on the upturned inner ends of the hinged levers so that when the brass expands it pushes the inner ends of the hinged levers down, thus raising the whole bob in compensation, a movement assisted by a spring held below the bob. With a fall in temperature the converse takes place. The pendulum was expensive to make and never widely adopted. A fine clock by Ellicott is seen in Fig. 188, this has a month movement, with a seconds hand in the arch and a 24 hour dial with minute hand revolving once in 2 hours. The effigy of the sun traverses the 'heavens' every 24 hours and the shutters rise and fall with the seasons, giving the readings for sunrise and sunset on the chapter ring. In the door of the case the long hand is an annual calendar hand, and the short hand shows the equation (q.v.), in the method adopted by Quare (q.v.).

A pleasing design of case introduced by Ellicott, and later copied by others, is seen in Fig. 189.

ENTABLATURE. The portion of the hood top (q.v.) of a clock between the top of the supporting columns, if any, and the top of the hood, excluding dome (q.v.) or cresting (q.v.), if any.

EPACT. The age of the moon on 1st January. It is necessary to know this when calculating the date of Easter Sunday.

EPAGNOMAL DAYS. Days inserted to bring the calendar into line with the solar year. The Egyptian year of twelve months of thirty days each was five days short of the solar year, as reckoned in those times, hence the five days were inserted after the twelfth month.

EQUATION CLOCK. A clock which registers mechanically the equation of time (q.v.). Many clocks have the difference of the equation, plus or minus, shown at short intervals by painting or engraving on the dial the appropriate number of minutes; these are not equation clocks. (*See* FROMANTEEL.)

EQUATION TABLE. Once the anchor escapement (q.v.) was established the improved timekeeping it brought with it drew to the attention of the ordinary clock owner the difference between his clock showing mean time and the sundial with which he was wont to compare it. The anchor escapement was at first only used in long case clocks (q.v.) with one seconds pendulums, for in bracket clocks, which were carried from room to room, the verge escapement (q.v.) was more practical as it did not need such careful levelling. In order to tell the clock owner by how much his clock, if going correctly, should differ from the sundial, tables showing the daily differences were pasted on the inside of long case clock doors (Fig. 190).
Note. Since this table bears two crowns it is supposed that it was issued during the reign of William III and Mary II. It will therefore be based on the old calendar and will be eleven days out in relation to the present calendar. Also the amounts of the equation vary very slightly with the centuries. This should be borne in mind by the meticulous reader who tries to reconcile it with the dates given under the heading EQUATION OF TIME.

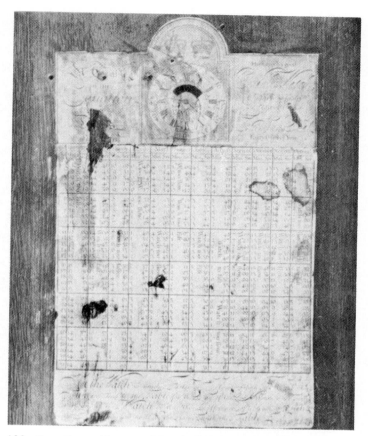

190. *Equation table pasted inside the door of a long case clock showing the daily difference between mean and solar time, c. 1695. Note the continued use of the word 'watch' to denote the going train of a clock.*

EQUATION OF TIME. With the advent of William Clement's anchor escapement (q.v.) (*circa* 1670) the clocks owned by the general public achieved a much greater degree of accuracy and this led to a general awareness (as opposed to specialised knowledge confined to astronomers) that the solar day does not accord with the mean day. This variation, which is due in part to the Earth's eccentric path around the sun and, in part, to the inclination of the Earth's axis to the equator, is irregular both in amount and direction, the two above-mentioned factors sometimes acting in concert and sometimes in opposition. On only four days of the year are solar and mean days to within a few seconds of being exactly 24 mean hours long; about 16th April, 14th June, 1st September and 25th December. In between these dates we get the following extremes, 11th February, 14 m. slow, 14th May, 4 m. fast, 26th July, 6 m. slow and 23rd November, 16 m. fast. It will be noted that there is no regularity about the intervals between these dates, nor do the differences build up or decrease regularly.

The method of recording their variations in a clock dial by means of a kidney-shaped cam was worked out by Christaan Huygens (q.v.) in 1695. In his last recorded letter, which was written on 4th March, 1695 to his brother Constantan, then secretary in London to King William III, he speaks of his newly invented clock, of which he was going to make a description and demonstration, and which he had adapted from an old clock with a 3 foot pendulum; this clock also showed the solar hour without need for equation tables.[38] A long case clock (q.v.)

192. *Details of the dial of Quare's clock.*

191. (*Left*) *Clock by Daniel Quare housing mean time with equation and sidereal time in the same case. c. 1710. (The Admiral President, Royal Naval College, Greenwich)*

193. (*Right*) *Back plate of Quare's dual clock showing the equation kidney.*

housing in one case both mean and sidereal movements, in addition to an equation dial in the arch is seen in Figs. 191, 192 and 193. The daily difference of so many minutes and seconds can be translated into so many degrees of arc on the circumference of the dial and the problem is therefore to produce a hand that will go forwards or backwards the necessary number of degrees day by day. This was achieved by making a kidney shaped cam turning once a year. When a pin at the end of an arm fixed to a wheel or rack bears against the edge of this kidney it will approach or recede from the centre of revolution and transmit a forward or backward motion to a hand mounted on the arbor of a toothed wheel engaging with the rack (Figs. 192 and 193). The kidney is revolved once a year by means of an endless

worm on the end of the rod, seen to the left, which is driven off the movement. On the right is the follower arm with the pin bearing against the kidney's edge, the other end of the arm being on the arbor of the wheel seen. Actually, only a segment of this wheel is ever in contact with the wheel carrying the equation hand, but a whole wheel is cut to provide a counterpoise. The equation dial is seen in Fig. 192, the upper half having graduations from 15 m. slow on the left, to 15 m. fast on the right. In fact, as will have been seen from the text, this symmetrical arrangement of the dial is not quite right as the limits are 14 m. and 16 m. The equation will refer to the mean time movement. The long hand is fixed to the kidney arbor and will rotate once a year to give the date. The example illustrated is by Daniel Quare (q.v.).

The earliest dials had two minute rings, the inner fixed and the outer moving. At first the movable ring had to be set by hand in advance and in accordance with the equation tables (Fig. 237). The outer ring had then to be displaced in relation to the fixed ring in the same way as the hand in the illustration is displaced against the fixed minute scale. Later equation clocks were made with the mean time hand and the equation hand concentrically fixed, but these require elaborate differential gearing that cannot be discussed here. A good view of an equation kidney is seen in Fig. 356.

EQUINOX. The days when daylight and night are of equal length are found at the Summer and Winter Solstices (q.v.), which occur when the sun crosses the equator in its ascending or descending path (the translation of the German term is the sun's turning point). The 1st point of Aries (q.v.), the vernal or spring equinox on 21st March, used to be in the constellation Aries (the Ram), but now, owing to precession (q.v.), it is in the constellation Pisces (the Fishes); similarly the autumn equinox has passed from the constellation Libra (the Balance) into Virgo (the Maiden).

ESCAPEMENT. That part of the clock mechanism that checks the driving force of a clock, i.e., the weight or spring, and prevents its uninterrupted action in running down the trains (q.v.). The various forms of escapement release the escape wheel at regular short intervals, thus allowing the driving force to operate, and then lock it again, and so the sequence continues.

ESCAPEMENT, ANCHOR. This escapement is now generally credited to William Clement (q.v.). It is called the anchor escapement because of the resemblance of the pallets to the flukes of an anchor (Fig. 141). It has recently been established that Clement was first employed as an anchorsmith,[20] which lends support to the claim now made on his behalf. When the escapement was first so known is not certain, but when it was first used in conjunction with the 39 inch one second pendulum the combination was called the 'Royal' pendulum, because it was so much superior to any verge escapement (q.v.) that, at the time, it was thought that finality had been reached.[39] Christaan Huygens (q.v.) proved in his *Horologium Oscillatorum* that to be isochronous (q.v.) a pendulum should not swing in an arc of a circle, but should follow a cycloid curve (*see* CYCLOIDAL CHEEKS), which is more 'U' shaped than the true circle (Fig. 194). The anchor escapement allows the pallets to clear the teeth of the escape wheel with an amplitude (q.v.) of 3° to 4°,

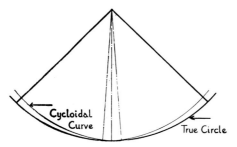

194. *Diagram showing how the anchor escapement limits the amplitude of the pendulum to an arc coincident with the cycloidal curve.*

195. *Robert Hooke's experiment to show how a long pendulum with a heavy bob, having a long period, could be kept in motion by a very small force. (Mr A. C. Aimer)*

thus confining the arc of swing to an area where the true and the cycloidal curves coincide, whereas the verge escapement required an amplitude of some 40°.

For centuries this escapement has been credited to Dr Robert Hooke (q.v.). No doubt between the years 1657, when the pendulum was invented, and 1670 when the anchor escapement was first made, there were many experimenting and searching, for it seems probable that the desire for a pendulum with a long period and a short arc was generally recognised. The claim for Dr Hooke was based on the fact that in 1669 he suspended a 14 foot pendulum with a heavy bob, beating two seconds, and kept it in motion by a pin fixed on the rim of a watch balance. (The amplitude of the pendulum, about ½°, was, of course, limited by the traverse of the pin on the rim of the balance and would have been the same whatever length of pendulum with whatever period was selected, since the pendulum rod and the balance were connected.) Here was a long pendulum with a small arc, BUT the pendulum was freely suspended and there was NO escapement, indeed the anchor escapement could not work with so small an arc. Certain horological authors, however, claimed that this experiment proved Dr Hooke's claim, so a Mr Aimer reproduced the experiment a few years ago. Fig. 195 shows the pin on the watch balance connected with the pendulum rod near the bob. The experiment merely showed that a long pendulum with a heavy bob, freely suspended, could be kept in motion by a very small force. However, although the experiment did not lead to the invention of the anchor escapement it was put to very good use a few years later (*See* THOMAS TOMPION). The anchor escapement is also known as the 'recoil escapement' as the pallets 'jar' when coming into contact with the escape wheel. This slight shuddering can clearly be seen in the seconds hands of the majority of long case clocks. Better quality clocks have the dead beat escapement (q.v.).

It may well be said that all subsequent clock escapements are but variants of the anchor escapement, which can be classed as an invention of equal importance, to horology, as that of the pendulum itself, hence the space devoted to it here and the

196. *Alexander Cumming's constant force escapement, 1766. (Mr H. Howard)* 197. *Pendulum suspension of Alexander Cumming's clock. Note the horns to receive the impulse from the weighted bars on the escapement.* 198. *Regulator by Brock, London, c. 1800. fitted with Bloxham's gravity escapement. (The late Mr H. N. Fry)*

199. *Details of Bloxham's escapement.*

necessity for destroying the false impression, given during the last two centuries by one author copying from another without research or verification, that Dr Hooke was the inventor. Dr Andrade in the Wilkins lecture on Hooke given before the Royal Society in 1949 stated that he 'could find no really satisfactory evidence for the attribution'.

For an early concept of the principle of the anchor escapement *see* VOLPAIA.

ESCAPEMENT, BLOXAMS. *See* ESCAPEMENT, CONSTANT FORCE.

ESCAPEMENT, CONSTANT FORCE. That the escapement should transmit a force of unvarying degree to the balance spring or pendulum is a standard always to be aimed at. The first efforts were made in connection with remontoires (q.v.) which, in the case of spring-driven clocks, wound up the spring at very short intervals (*See* BURGI). In a weight-driven clock the driving force of the weight is constant and so needs no remontoire. The final solution in achieving a regular impulse to the pendulum seems to have been the gravity escapement; this relieved the clock mechanism, which for a number of reasons could only transmit an impulse of varying force to the pendulum, of the direct impulsing and made it lift a small independent weight a slight distance, this was then allowed to fall from a fixed height on to the pendulum; thus gravity, which is constant, controls the force.

The earliest form of gravity escapement was introduced by Alexander Cumming (q.v.) in 1766. In Fig. 196 it will be seen

200. *Cross-beat escapement of Burgi's experimental clock No. 3, c. 1600. (Staat. Phys. Math. Salon, Dresden)* 201. *German clock with cross-beat escapement, c. 1600, with lunar train. (British Museum)* 202. *Movement of Fig. 201.*

that the pallet arbor has a weighted arm on either side of it; these strike alternately the two horns set across the top of the pendulum rod (Fig. 197), and since they always strike the horns from the same height, the force is constant. The only function of the crutch (q.v.) in this design is to unlock the pallets. It is often assumed that the true gravity escapement was invented by Lord Grimthorpe for Big Ben (q.v.), but the principle was already formulated by Bloxam about 1850. This is seen in Figs. 198 and 199. The spidery teeth of the escape wheel will push aside one side of the diamond-shaped frame and, as the wheel turns, that side of the frame will drop and its end will give an impulse to the pendulum; a similar action takes place on the other side. The amount of drop on these two sides is constant, being limited by the length of the escape wheel spokes. Grimthorpe's double three-legged gravity escapement, although more complicated, was, however, generally adopted.

ESCAPEMENT, CROSS BEAT. The knowledge of the cross beat escapement had been lost to the world until Professor Hans von Bertele of Vienna re-discovered it during his researches in Germany, Czechoslovakia and Austria in recent years. He unearthed a series of clocks, mainly anonymous, but of which the last bore the signature of Jost Burgi (q.v.), at the same time finding a solution for an expression that had considerably worried modern researchers. Writing in 1673, the great astronomer Hevelius refers to an escapement for which he implies the highest accuracy then attainable as *libramentum duplice*. The late G. H. Baillie, who was a very learned horo-

logical researcher, wrote regarding Hevelius' book *Machinae Coelestis, pars prima* 'There are references to a *libramentum duplice* arranged cross-wise as being an improvement on the ordinary *libramentum*. I do not know what this may mean unless it is another word for foliot and that two foliots were arranged at right angles.'[40] We now know that it was Burgi's escapement that Hevelius referred to and which von Bertele has called the 'cross beat'. Fig. 200 shows a later development than that shown under BURGI. The clock is not signed, but the circumstantial evidence is so strong that there can be no doubt of the authorship. Here two arms, geared together, each holding one pallet, are arranged to take into a vertical escape wheel having a large number of very finely cut teeth. This clock is typical of Burgi's later work. The cross beat was adopted by Burgi's pupils, but as the pendulum was invented within about half a century, it did not have a very long life.

Figs. 201 and 202 show another example of the cross beat, again anonymous, but very definitely lacking the refinement of Burgi's work, whereas all Burgi's clocks have concentrated on the accurate recording of the hours, minutes and seconds, this clock shows only $\frac{1}{4}$ hour sub-divisions, the position of the sun in the zodiac, the lunar phases, the day of the week and the day of the month.

ESCAPEMENT, DEAD BEAT. A modified form of anchor escapement (q.v.) invented by George Graham (q.v.) about 1715. In this type the pallets are set on an arc of a circle which has its centre in the escape pallet arbor and has a radius to the

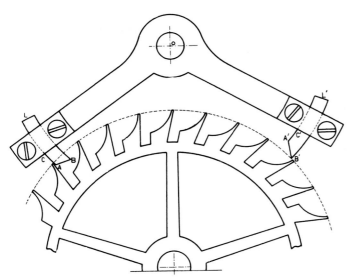

203. *Diagram of dead beat escapement.* (*Conservatoire des Arts et Métiers, Paris*)

centre of the pallets equal to that of the escape wheel; this eliminates the recoil. For 200 years this escapement held its own for the most accurate work in observatories, in spite of a host of other escapements (Fig. 203).

ESCAPEMENT, GALILEO'S. It is well known how, in about 1581, Galileo noticed that the period of oscillation of a swinging lamp in Pisa Cathedral was the same irrespective of amplitude (q.v.), thus establishing the principle of the iso-chronism (q.v.) of the pendulum. (This is not quite accurate, *see* CYCLOIDAL CHEEKS). Later, at a date difficult to determine accurately, but probably in the 1630's, Galileo devised a form of escapement coupled with a pendulum, and his son Vincenzio, who died in 1649, is reported to have made a clock with a pendulum. The list of the effects of Vincenzio's widow mentioned 'an iron clock, unfinished, with pendulum, the first invention of Galileo'.[41] Fig. 204 shows a working model of Galileo's escapement made in Florence in 1883 and now in the Science Museum, London, constructed from a drawing sent to Huygens and now in the Library of the University of Leyden (Fig. 205). The frequently reported fact that Vincenzio Galileo, in a delirium, destroyed the iron clock that he was building and which incorporated Galileo's escapement is shown to be in-correct as a result of the recent researches of Mr Silvio Bedini, who shows the error to be due to a mis-translation. The word-ing as revised reads 'But in the course of this unaccustomed labour he was overcome by acute fever, and he had to leave it (the clock) unfinished at the point where it is seen (in the sketch thereof) and on the twenty-second day of his illness, 16th May, 1649, all the most accurate clocks together with this most precious time measurer, *for* him went out of adjustment and stopped for ever.' That is, he died. Previously this passage had been translated '*by* him went out of adjustment' etc.[149]

In 1877 Signor E. Porcelotti of Florence made a clock with

204. *Model of Galileo's escapement.* (*Science Museum, London*)

205. *Drawing of Galileo's escapement sent to Huygens, 1660.* (*Leyden University*)

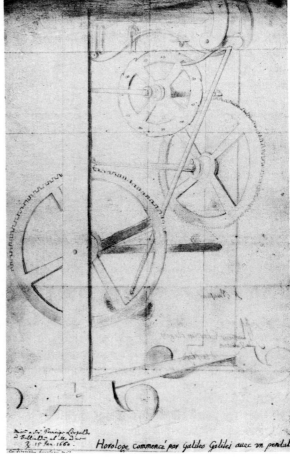

Horologe commencé par Galileo Galilei avec un pendule

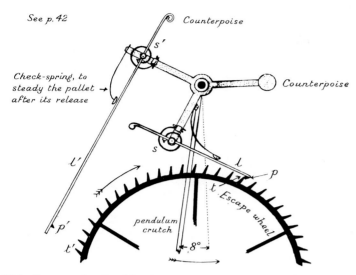

See p. 42

Counterpoise

Check-spring, to steady the pallet after its release →

Counterpoise

206. *Commander Gould's drawing of a grasshopper escapement.* (The Marine Chronometer. *Potter, London, 1923*)

Galileo's escapement, centre seconds hand and $\frac{1}{2}$ seconds beat, the seconds hand making 1 second advances, so that Galileo's escapement is, in fact, a Coup Perdu escapement (q.v.), a fact not previously recognised, since, as far as the author knows, none of the previous models of this escapement have been provided with a dial and seconds hand.

ESCAPEMENT, GRASSHOPPER. The invention of this escapement has, until now, been credited to John Harrison (q.v.), but is now believed to be the invention of his younger brother, James (q.v.). Fig. 206 shows a drawing made by the late Commander Gould and published by him in his *Marine Chronometer*.[42] His description is as follows. 'The pallets *p* and *p′* are mounted on levers kept at right angles to each other by the springs *s* and *s′*. The tooth *t* is holding the pallet *p* and the spring is tensioned. When the pendulum swings to the right, at the end of the swing the pallet *p′* meets *t′* causing a slight recoil

and freeing *p′*. The action is noiseless and practically frictionless. As used by the Harrisons it gave excellent results, but it is delicate and difficult to make and is no longer used.'

John Harrison used this escapement in his Nos. 1, 2 and 3, three instruments made by him in his search for the solution of the 'problem of the longitude' (*see* JOHN HARRISON). In these clocks the two pallets of the escapement were on separate arbors. An example of this type is seen in Fig. 207 on a clock by B. L. Vulliamy (q.v.), now on loan to the British Museum by H. M. the Queen.

ESCAPEMENT, LEVER, DETACHED. This is primarily a watch escapement, but as it is very generally employed in travelling clocks, known as carriage clocks (q.v.) it is illustrated here, very much enlarged (Figs. 208 and 209)[43]. In Fig. 208 the balance, not shown, has its centre at O″, A shows the escapement pallet about to disengage. The lever impelled by the balance will move in the direction of the arrow f′ and free the tooth D′ for escape, which has been resting against the jewel R. The angle X, called the *Draw*, assures the safety of the contact against shocks. In Fig. 209 the escapement is seen after an impulse and at the moment when it is about to be locked again, the impulse given by D′ on to the face of the pallet AB has been transmitted to the balance by the horn of the anchor F. The

207. *Grasshopper escapement in a clock by Vulliamy, c. 1810. (British Museum, By Gracious Permission of Her Majesty the Queen)*

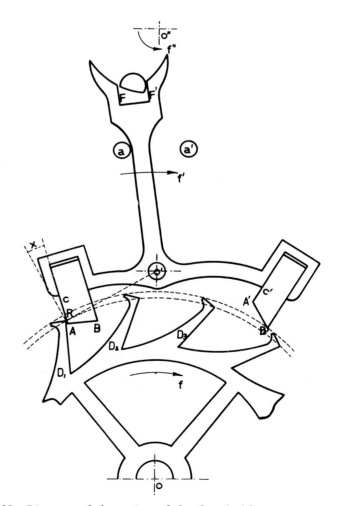

208. *Diagram of the action of the detached lever escapement. (Conservatoire des Arts et Métiers, Paris)*

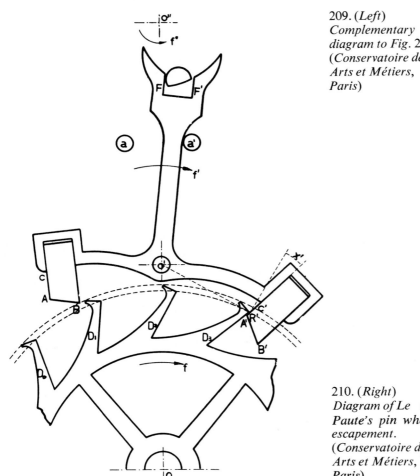

209. (*Left*) *Complementary diagram to Fig. 208.* (*Conservatoire des Arts et Métiers, Paris*)

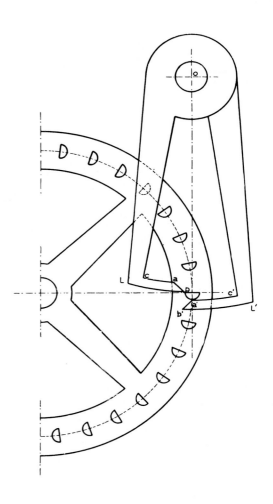

210. (*Right*) *Diagram of Le Paute's pin wheel escapement.* (*Conservatoire des Arts et Métiers, Paris*)

escape wheel has turned, the tooth D3 has come to rest against R' and the balance continues to oscillate freely in the direction of the arrow f; the sequence is then repeated in the contrary sense. The drawings are of a modern lever escapement; the

211. *Gut verge escapement in a clock by Tompion.* (*Institute of Civil Engineers*)

invention of this escapement has generally been attributed to Thomas Mudge (q.v.), but now a watch has been found by Julien Le Roy, of Paris (q.v.) with a type of lever escapement, and Le Roy died before the presumed date of Mudge's watch. There is, however, no evidence that Mudge had any knowledge of Le Roy's watch.[44]

ESCAPEMENT, PIN WHEEL. In which the arms of the 'anchor' embrace either side of a series of pins projecting horizontally from the escape wheel. It was invented by a Frenchman named Amant in the second quarter of the 18th century (Fig. 210), and improved by Jean André Leapaute in 1753. Another form of pin wheel escapement can be seen in Fig. 7.

ESCAPEMENT, RECOIL. *See* ESCAPEMENT, ANCHOR.

ESCAPEMENT, SILENT. The verge escapement (q.v.) is a noisy escapement, so when the fashion for night clocks (q.v.) came in naturally efforts were made to render them less noisy and several types of silent escapement were devised. In a grand sonnerie clock (q.v.) made by Thomas Tompion (q.v.) and given to Barbara Villiers, Duchess of Grafton, Tompion replaced the leading edge of the verge pallets with a small string of gut (Fig. 211). This clock was made just after the invention of the rack and snail strike (q.v.) and would be one of the first to have a strike silent arrangement enabling the strike to be shut off at night. The movement was taken out of the case by

B. L. Vulliamy and presented to the Society of Civil Engineers. The Duke of Grafton now has the case and the dial with a Vulliamy movement behind it. George Graham (q.v.) designed another type in which three triangularly set rollers are impulsed by two gut cords fixed on either side of a stirrup (Fig. 168). A third type is in a clock by Joseph Knibb (q.v.) in the author's collection. Here the leading edge of the verge pallets is formed by a weak spring adjusted by a depthing screw (Fig. 212). An Italian type where the reciprocal motion of the pendulum is converted into rotary motion is seen in Fig. 126.

ESCAPEMENT, SU SUNG'S. It is following a recognised pattern to find that the Chinese preceded Europe and the Arabs in mechanical clockwork. Dr Joseph Needham, F.R.S., the well-known researcher into early Chinese technology, assisted by Mr Wang Ling and Professor Derek Price, recently came across an early Chinese book of *circa* 1090 which gave a full description of a monumental astronomical clock constructed by one Su Sung which was in the Palace at Kai-Feng. This the authors have fully published[45] and from it the general description and Fig. 213 are taken, with permission. 'Su Sung's "clock" was, in fact, a great astronomical clock-tower more than 30 feet high, surmounted by a huge, bronze, power-driven armillary sphere for observation, and containing, in a chamber within, an automatically rotated celestial globe with which the observed places of the heavenly bodies could be compared. In the front of the tower was a pagoda structure with five storeys, each having a door through which manikins and jacks appeared ringing bells and gongs and holding tables to indicate the hours and other special times of the day and night. Inside the tower was the motive source, a great scoop-wheel using water and turning all the shafts working the various devices. The wheel was checked by an escapement consisting of a sort of weighbridge which prevented the fall of a scoop until full, and a triplever and parallel linkage system which arrested the forward motion of the wheel at a further point and allowed it to settle

213. *Pictorial reconstruction of Su Sung's clock, c. 1090. (Cambridge University Press, illustration from* Heavenly Clockwork, *by Needham, Ling and Price)*

back and bring the next scoop into position on the weighbridge. One must imagine this giant structure going off at full-cock every quarter of an hour with a great sound of creaking and splashing, clanging and ringing; it must have been impressive and we know that it was actually built and made to work for many years before being carried away into exile.' The most important fact in relation to western technology is that, although the clock was driven by water power, it provided for the alternate release and locking of a wheel, which propelled the time indicating features forward, step by step, or, in other words, it had an escapement. The Chinese description of this escapement and the illustrations of its component parts were somewhat difficult to understand and piece together. Mr J. H. Combridge tackled this question and Fig. 214 shows his solution. The numbers are as follows: 1. Wheel spoke, 2. Right-hand upper stop, 3. Scoop, 4. Water jet, 5. Scoop holder, 6. Checking fork, 7. Lower balance lever, 8. Lower balance weight, 9. Trip lever, 10. Long chain, 11. Upper balance lever, 12. Upper balance weight, 13. Short upper chain, 14. Left-hand upper stop. The description given here, with permission, is Mr Combridge's.

Fig. 214 shows the mechanism diagrammatically, but roughly to scale as reconstructed. At the beginning of a 24 second time-unit interval, the escape wheel is held stationary by the engagement of the top spoke 1 with the right-hand upper stop 2. An empty scoop 3 is held in the path of the water jet 4 by a scoop holder pivoted just below the horizontal diameter of the wheel. Soon after the water begins to enter the scoop, the scoop holder counter-balance weight 5 is overcome; the excess weight

212. *Silent verge escapement by Joseph Knibb. (Author's collection)*

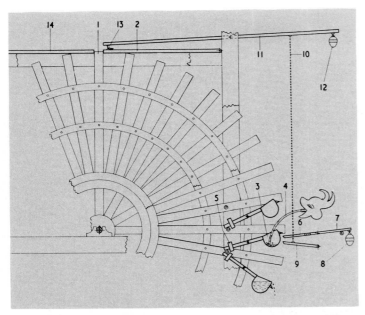

214. *Mr Combridge's drawing of Su Sung's escapement. (Horological Journal, February, 1962)*

of water is then supported by the engagement of a projecting lug on the scoop with the checking fork 6 at the end of the lower balance lever 7. When the excess weight of water is sufficient to overcome the lower balance weight 8, the lower balance lever suddenly tips up to release the scoop, and the scoop holder rotates about its pivot so that the lug engages with the trip lever 9.

A long vertical chain, 10, connects the trip lever 9 with the upper balance lever 11, passing freely between the prongs of the checking fork 6. The upper balance weight 12, at the right-hand end of the upper balance lever, is insufficient by itself to raise the left-hand end of the lever, but the added weight of the full scoop on the trip lever now sets both levers in motion. Momentum is gathered from the loaded scoop during the short swing of the levers, near the end of which the short upper chain 13 suddenly becomes tight and jerks the right-hand upper stop 2 out of engagement with the wheel spoke 1.

The wheel, which is carrying an unbalanced load of several previously filled scoops in its lower right-hand quadrant, now makes one quick step clockwise, while the trip lever 9, upper balance lever 11, and right hand upper stop 2, return to their normal positions ready to arrest the next wheel spoke. The left-hand upper stop 14 is lifted by the movement of this spoke and falls again to prevent recoil of the wheel after it has been stopped. The total time for a complete revolution, comprising thirty-six steps of the escapement wheel, is practically independent of irregularities in the scoops or their counterweights, or in the net available driving torque. It is almost exclusively dependent upon the adjustment of the lower balance weight 8 and the rate of water-flow, precautions being taken to maintain the constancy of these, which will not be gone into here.

The transmission system as described by Su Sung is shown diagrammatically in Fig. 215. The horizontal iron shaft of the escapement wheel drives the wooden vertical main shaft by means of a right-angled pinion and gearwheel drive 1 and 2; and the main shaft drives the vertical jackwork shaft by a pair of gear wheels 3 and 4. The armillary sphere and the celestial globe being driven from the upper ends of the vertical shafts by oblique gears 5 and 7, and 8 and 10, with intermediate pinions 6 and 9 respectively.[46]

Mr Combridge had made working models of the escapement which he has demonstrated at various times (Fig. 216).

(*Note.* Since the drawing for Fig. 214 was made further study has shown that in some details it should be amended.)

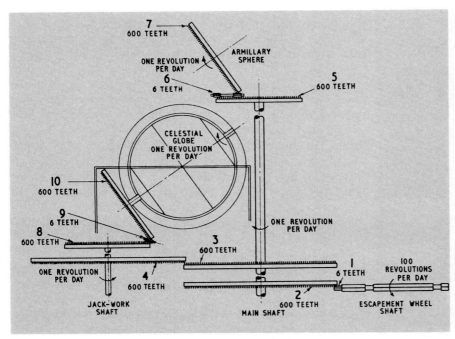

215. *Mr Combridge's drawing of the lay-out of Su Sung's clock. (Horological Journal, February 1962)* 216. *Mr Combridge's model of Su Sung's escapement.*

ESCAPEMENT, TIC-TAC. A type of anchor escapement (q.v.) embracing only two teeth; escapements of this nature only require a light bob, like a verge escapement (q.v.), (Fig. 217). Another form, between the true tic-tac and the true anchor is sometimes found, here 3/4 teeth are embraced instead of the usual 7/8. Fig. 218 shows the back plate of a clock with such an escapement. It will be noted that here also only a light bob is needed. In his early unnumbered series, Tompion occasionally made clocks with a tic-tac escapement; two, which are assigned the date of about 1675, are illustrated by Symonds in his *Thomas Tompion, His Life and Work*. The example illustrated in detail only embraces one tooth, but as will have been seen, the actual number of teeth embraced varies. (Whether Knibb knew of Tompion's work or not at this date, we cannot say).

ESCAPEMENT, VERGE. This is, excluding Su Sung's (q.v.), the oldest type of escapement known. Who first thought of fixing two pallets at right angles to each other on to an arbor surmounted by a cross bar and weights or a wheel, in order that, by oscillation, the pallets might alternately engage the teeth of a wheel and so stop the unhindered turning of that wheel caused by the descent of the driving weight, is quite unknown. There were probably several steps of which we have no record before the final invention, but once adopted the verge escapement held the field unchallenged for nearly 400 years, say from 1290 to 1660, and then side by side with other escapements until about 1830, a total life for the invention of some 540 years, clear evidence of its worth. Fig. 9 gives a good example of this escapement. Its name probably derives from

218. *Back plate of a clock by Samuel Watson, London, c. 1695, with tic-tac escapement embracing four teeth. (Author's collection)*

the latin *virga*, a wand or rod, from which we derive our word verger, 'the man who carries a wand of office'. Regulation was primarily by altering the amount of the driving weight, secondarily by altering the position of the small weights on the foliot cross arm and finally by altering the angle of impact of the pallets on the crown wheel to the extent that the play in the upper bearing of the pallet staff would allow; the gibbet arm from which the verge pallet suspension thread hangs is notched for this purpose.

ESCUTCHEON. A small metal plate, decorated or otherwise, surrounding a keyhole to protect the woodwork. Many examples are seen in different photographs. Fig. 170 shows an interesting variation sometimes used by Joseph Knibb (q.v.); the escutcheon is pivoted above the keyhole which it covers and has to be pushed aside in order to insert the key; the one on the other side of the door, for balance, is fixed.

217. *Tic-tac escapement in a clock by John Knibb, Oxon. c. 1680. (Dr C. F. C. Beeson)*

EXTRADOS. The concave side of an arch.

219. *Astronomical clock by Bernado Faccini, Venice, c.* 1725. (*Vatican Library*)   220. *View of the back plate and compensated pendulum of Faccini's clock.*

FACCINI, BERNARDO. A Venetian clockmaker who lived at the turn of the 17th and the beginning of the 18th century. A clock he made for Sophia, Duchess of Parma in about 1725 is seen in Figs. 219 and 220. The diamond-shaped pendulum suspension in Fig. 220 should be noted; it is made of a combination of steel and silver with a view to temperature compensation. It is interesting to note that the date of this clock is very near to that of the invention of the gridiron pendulum (q.v.) by Harrison and of the mercury pendulum by George Graham (q.v.) which took place in about the years 1720-1725. It is probable that these three men were working quite independently on the problem of metallic expansion and compensated pendulums.

In 1796 an engineer of the Royal Chamber, Nicola Anito, made a series of twenty-four drawings of the clock as he dismantled it, for the guidance of any who might follow him in cleaning or repairing it. These drawings show all details down to the smallest spring and screw.[6,16,47]

FACIO, de DUILLIER. A Swiss living in London, who, in 1704, in conjunction with a French clockmaker, Peter Debaufe, also living in London, invented a method of piercing rubies for use as bearings in watches. This greatly improved their timekeeping properties and was later applied to regulators (q.v.) and to escapement pallets. The method was kept a close secret for the best part of a century, during which time only English makers had the advantage.

FANZAGO, PIETRO. In 1583 he made the clock for the Law Courts in Clusone. This astronomical clock had five dials showing the hour, the day, the month, the positions of the sun and moon and the times of the rising of the sun. This is one of the very few 16th-century clocks to be still in commission.[16]

FERRACINA, BARTOLOMEO (1692-*circa* 1772). A hydraulic engineer and mechanic, he started making clocks in 1716. In 1748 he made the clock for the great Tower at Vicenza. In 1750 he was entrusted with the restoration of the clock in St Mark's Square in Venice.[16]

FINIAL. The decorative additions to a clock case, such as acorns, balls, spires, pineapples etc.

FIRE CLOCKS. Those which give a single audible warning by means of fire. A Chinese example of the 18th century is seen in Fig. 221. A bronze dragon has a hollowed out body in which is

221. *Chinese dragon fire clock. 18th century. (Chateau des Monts, Le Loche, Switzerland)* 222. *Mid-day cannon alarm, French. Mid-18th century. (Chateau des Monts, Le Loche, Switzerland)*

laid a slow burning fuse. The body is notched at hour intervals and a thread with weights on either end is hung across at the selected hour. When the fuse has burnt so far the thread is severed and the weights fall into a pan with a clatter. A second type, only useful to record midday, is seen in Fig. 222. This consists of a horizontal sun dial above which is placed a burning glass mounted on hinged arms for seasonal adjustment. When the sun passes the meridian its rays are focused on to the touch hole of a cannon and the charge is fired.

FIRE GILT. The surface to be gilded is painted with an amalgam of gold and mercury and heated in an oven. The mercury vaporises leaving a deposit of pure gold.

FLAGELLATION CLOCK. In the Renaissance period many fancy designs were adopted as the basis into which to introduce a clock movement. Religious subjects, birds and animals were most frequently chosen. The most common was the Crucifix (q.v.), but the Flagellation was relatively frequent. The hour is recorded on a band turning anti-clockwise and read off a pointer, presumably lost in the example illustrated (Fig. 223). The current hour is that showing to the front.

FLAMBEAU. A finial (q.v.) taking the form of a flaming urn (Fig. 2).

FOLIOT. The cross bar carrying an adjustable weight at either end fixed at right angles to the top of the verge escapement staff (q.v.) (Fig. 9). Until recently it was always considered that the foliot was the earliest form of controller, but the use by Giovanni Dondi (q.v.) of a balance in his astronomical clock of 1364 indicates that the two forms of control may have been used side by side from the earliest times.

FRANCHE COMTÉ CLOCK. *See* MOREZ CLOCK.

FRANKLIN CLOCK. The American philosopher, Benjamin Franklin, was born in Boston, Massachusetts, in 1706. At the age of twenty-four he came to London and worked as a printer, returning to America about two years later. He revisited London several times during the third quarter of the 18th century, when he formed a close friendship with the well-known astronomer, James Ferguson, F.R.S. Ferguson designed, it would seem as a diversion, many astronomical clocks, always seeking to simplify

the design. Few of these were ever constructed, but the bent of his friend may have inspired Franklin to try his hand at designing a simple clock, which he did in 1757 (Fig. 224). Ferguson in his *Select Mechanical Exercises*,[48] London, 1773, opens with a description of Franklin's clock; he says on p.3 'Several clocks have been made according to this ingenious plan of the

223. *Flagellation clock. Anonymous. Mid-17th century. German. (Professor Hans von Bertele)*

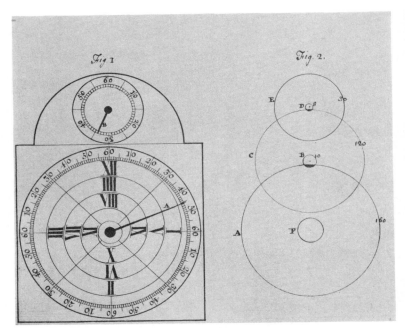

Doctor's and I can affirm that I have seen one of them, which measures time exceedingly well.'

These clocks would seem to have been made in different sizes as Ferguson, in his *Commonplace Book*, now in the Library of Edinburgh University says, 'If the diameter of the groove at the bottom of the pulley be 2 inches, the weight will descend about 38 inches in 24 hours.' On the other hand a footnote on p. 233 of *Henderson's Life of James Ferguson, F.R.S.*, London, 1870,

224. *James Ferguson's drawing of Franklin's clock with seconds dial. (Edinburgh University Library, illustration from* James Ferguson's Commonplace Book)

225. *Ferguson's simplified version of Franklin's clock. (Ilbert Collection, British Museum)*

226. *Movement of Ferguson's clock.*

reads 'We have in our possession a small Franklin Horologe, the dial plate is thick brass, 3 inches in diameter. . . . The works are of an extraordinary strong watch attached to the back of the dial. (Benj. Franklin LLD, 1757, is engraved on the back of the dial outside the watch works).'

In 1758 Ferguson modified the design for a clock to go for a week; he adds on p.11 of his *Select Exercises* that he considers a seconds dial unnecessary on these three-wheel clocks as the ordinary man has no use for them. A Franklin clock, without seconds dial is seen in Figs. 225 and 226, it is dated 1770.

FRENCH CLOCKS. To attempt to deal with this subject in a dictionary of this nature is like trying to put a gallon into a pint pot. In the early days of the Renaissance the French makers at Blois and in the surrounding area were renowned for their fine craftsmanship. Their styles were very akin to those of the makers of the period in Germany and Italy (*See* GOTHIC CLOCKS and FUSEE). In the reign of Louis XIII there was a tendency to simplify (Fig. 395), and there was adopted a style more nearly corresponding to the English of the period (*See* RELIGEUSE). With the development of Versailles and its elaborate decoration, a very highly decorated style developed, adorned with heavy ormolu figures and Boulle (q.v.) inlay, (Fig. 433). For some fifty years or so the hour numerals in French clocks were separately shaped, enamelled plaques (Fig. 227) and each minute was marked. French clocks were usually on a wall bracket or on a pedestal; there were some long case clocks (q.v.), but their cases were very elaborate to the English eye. A detailed view of the dial of Fig. 227 is seen in Fig. 228, it is by Mynuel of Paris. The pendulum bob takes the form of a radiant sun, in honour of the 'Roi Soleil', Louis XIV.

227. *French clock on a pedestal by Mynuel, Paris, c. 1720. Note the radiant sun pendulum bob. (Wallace Collection, London)*

228. *Dial of Mynuel's clock. Shaped enamel numerals and every minute marked.*

229. *French clock by Gaudron à Paris. The medallion bears the inscription 'Ludovicus Magnus, Francoru. Rex 1677'. The clock would appear to be later. (Wallace Collection, London)*

230. *Louis XV bracket type clock by Viger à Paris, c. 1770. (Wallace Collection, London)*

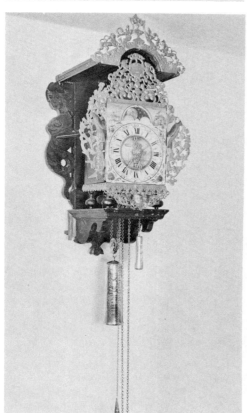

231. *Anonymous French cartel clock, c. 1780. (Wallace Collection, London)*

232. *Magnificent ormolu clock by Delunésy à Paris, c. 1785. See frontispiece caption. (Wallace Collection, London)*

233. *Typical Friesland clock (Stoeltjesklok). Note the mermaid decorations on the wall bracket. (Mr L. R. S. Monckton)*

234. *Side view of the Friesland clock showing the doubly cut count wheel.*

Later the enamel plaques have straight edges (Figs. 229,433), and still later, under Louis XV, we have dials consisting of twelve close-fitting enamel numerals radiating from a plain enamelled central circle, known as the 'Cadran à treize' (Dial of thirteen). The placing of the clock on a wall bracket or pedestal persisted, but towards the latter part of the reign of Louis XV the clock without a bracket or pedestal became more common (Figs. 229 and 230). In the reign of Louis XVI there were some very fine ormolu cases (Fig. 231) however, it is difficult to classify French clocks, since French individualism has its fullest sway in the clockmaker's art, and after the type on the bracket had gone out, there is not a collective trend. Some cases are really magnificent (Fig. 232), and although one may assume that a fine and expensive case will contain a good grade movement, one might say that the collector of French clocks collects clock cases rather than clocks.

The Directoire and Napoleonic Empire styles follow on at the turn of the 18th century, still elaborate, although not quite so much so; we have to await the coming of Janvier (q.v.) before we get restrained wooden cases. For those wishing to study more closely French clocks the best book is *La Pendule Française* by Tardy of Paris, undated. Originally published in four parts (with a fifth dealing with English clocks), Gothic to Louis III, Regency to Louis XV, Louis XVI, Directoire and Empire to modern times, it has recently been published in a second edition in two parts, Vol. 1 up to Louis XV, Vol. II Louis XVI to date.

FRET. A wood or metal piece pierced by a design with the object of facilitating the emission of sound. Also the decorative openwork panels found around three sides of lantern clocks (q.v.) (Figs. 332, 334).

FRIESLAND CLOCK. A very general Dutch type in the 18th century. Also known as Stoeltjesklok (Little Stool Clock), on account of the stool supporting them on their bracket. They have brass-cased cylindrical weights as opposed to the pear-shaped weights of the Zaandam clock (q.v.), painted dial and gilded cast lead fret decoration (q.v.) (Figs. 233 and 234) also Dutch striking (q.v.) as is shown by the dual cutting of the count wheel (q.v.). The wall bracket usually has a mermaid fret at each side. The verge escapement (q.v.) is vertical, as with a balance clock, and a horizontal projection from the verge enters a slot in the pendulum rod, which is suspended from the wall bracket. They are usually chain-driven and of 30 hour duration. The 'arched' decoration between the hour numerals on the dial is typical of nearly all Dutch clocks and watches.

FROMANTEEL FAMILY. A famous clockmaking family of Dutch extraction. The first was Ahasuerus, a blacksmith who made turret clocks and who joined the Clockmakers' Company on its foundation in 1632. There were two more named Ahasuerus, the first of these entered the Company in 1655 and the second in 1663. In 1663 a John Fromanteel was admitted; he had been apprenticed to Thomas Loomes in 1651, but was taken over by Ahasuerus Formantel (sic). His relationship to the Ahasuerus apprenticed in 1651 is not known. John, while still an apprentice of Ahasuerus, was sent to learn from Salomon Coster of the Hague, who was Huygens' (q.v.) clockmaker there, the art of making pendulum clocks, which he brought back to his Master in 1658. There exists a poor wreck

235. *Early equation clock by A. Fromanteel, London, c. 1680, for manual adjustment. (Lord Harris)* 236. *Long case clock by A. Fromanteel with polished dial plate. (Lord Harris)*

237. *Dial of Fromanteel's manually adjusted equation clock.*

238. *Detail of Fromanteel's polished dial plate.*

of a verge pendulum clock with the backplate engraved A. Fromanteel, London, fecit. 1658, which is, in all probability, the remains of the first pendulum clock to be made in England. Unfortunately the author, when shown this relic did not appreciate that the dealer was offering it for sale; he thought it too interesting a piece for anyone to part with, and so lost a great opportunity. How on to this horological 'trouser button' a horological 'pair of trousers' was attached is described in R. W. Symonds book *Masterpieces of Old English Furniture and Clocks* on p. 142. Thus equipped the 'button' sold recently for £850; it was sold for £25 in the mid 1930's. All work by any of the Fromanteels is of the highest grade. The bulk of that still existing is probably the output of the Ahasuerus of 1663; not many examples of John's work are known, but there is not much to differentiate between the output of any of them.

A most interesting A. Fromanteel clock, *circa* 1680, is seen in Figs. 235 and 237. It will be noted that the minute ring is displaced, that it has a ◇ instead of 60 and that the hour ring has a ◇ instead of XII. This minute ring is a friction fit and the holes every 10 minutes are for the insertion of a peg to move it. Equation Tables (q.v.) existed and the clock could be set to show the equation of time (q.v.) on any pre-determined day when it could be checked by the sundial. The minutes are divided into 10 second intervals and the ◇ in the minute ring would be set + or – in relation to the hour ◇ to the nearest 10

239. *Illumination to MS. c. 1450–60 showing, extreme right, a clock with fusee. (Royal Library, Brussels, MS. IV, III, Fol. 13v.)*

seconds; adjustment to the nearest second would be made by turning the seconds dial. The object of the dial above VI is not quite clear since the variation due to the equation is never more than 16 minutes; variations involving an hour do not occur. The hand is movable and fits over the winding square. This square turns once in 12 hours in an anti-clockwise direction with the gut drum, so this dial has to be engraved anti-clock-wise. Since the hand can be placed on the square in only one of four positions, in order that it may tally with the hour hand of the clock, this small ring can be moved to suit the hand. In Fig. 237 it is a little out, the clock shows 2.22 and the little hand 2.12. When the mechanical equation clock was invented about 1695, the first made in England by Tompion (q.v.), and now in Buckingham Palace, has a dual minute ring, the outer moving and the inner fixed just in the manner of Fromanteel's clock. Figs. 236 and 238 show a clock probably by the first Ahasuerus. The fine polished dial plate must have been a very expensive item in those days; there were no rolling mills, all plates were cast and then beaten out. The standard method of decoration, matting, as in the other clock, would hide any slight surface flaws, but these could not be hidden in a highly polished plate. At the turn of the century we find the firm of Fromanteel and Clarke (*See* also Fig. 266).

FUSEE. The spring as a motive force was introduced at an unknown date, somewhere in the first half, or middle, of the 15th century. It was speedily recognised that the loss of the spring's force as it unwound was such as to seriously impair the timekeeping properties of a clock. To counteract this an un-known inventor produced the conical-shaped drum, which has been called the fusee, a name derived, it is thought, from the latin *fusata*—a spindle filled with thread, a not inappropriate description. The earliest picture we have of a fusee is seen in Fig. 239. The date of the invention of the fusee has been steadily set back during the last ten years owing to the amount of research that has been taking place. Previously the drawings of Leonardo da Vinci, *circa* 1485-1490 were believed to be the earliest indication that we had of this invention, but recently there has come to light the example seen in Fig. 239, as a result of the researches of M. Henry Michel of Brussels. This MS. can be dated on various grounds around 1450-1460; on the table on the right is seen an octagonal clock movement, taken out of its case; a most rare artistic proceeding in those days when the outer decoration was all important. It would seem probable that the invention of the fusee was then quite new and in order to show it the clock had to be taken out of its case. The earliest surviving fusee is probably that in a clock dated 1525, by Jacob the Zech (miner, not Czech), owned by the Society of Antiquaries in London and often illustrated. There is a small drum clock (q.v.) with fusee in the Musée des Arts Decoratifs, in Paris, dated 1504, but the 0 is suspect. Fig. 240 shows another very nice early French fusee. The early form of the fusee was too sharply tapered but in the 17th century, when clockmaking was becoming more scientific, the curve of the fusee was much flattened out. Reverting to Fig. 239, for a pos-sible explanation of the 'contraption' right centre, *see* under CANONICAL STRIKING, and for the clock on the left under WISDOM CLOCK.

GALILEO. *See* PENDULUM

240. *Early French clock with fusee, c. 1545. (British Museum)*

241. *A Girondel clock, c. 1818. An American development of the Willard banjo design. (Mr Walter M. Roberts)*

GIRONDEL CLOCK. A development of the Banjo clock (q.v.), but which has lost the simple elegance of that design and which, in the example shown, suffers from 'over fussiness' (Fig. 241). There should be a spread eagle surmounting the whole and scroll arms to the dial case.

GLOBES, MECHANICAL. The great influence that as-

tronomy and astrology held over medieval people is reflected in the many astronomical clocks and other devices to show the celestial movements that were made in the Middle Ages in Europe. Here in England we did not develop any parallel activities until late in the 17th century. All the earliest of these clocks are on the Ptolemaic principle, many were devised to be hand operated and do not concern us here, but mechanically operated globes, with clock dials as well, were made. Fig. 242 shows a mechanical globe in the Rosenborg Castle in Copenhagen, made in 1572 by Josias Habrecht (q.v.), where the whole turns about a central Earth. The time is indicated on the dial, the hand of which is missing. The inscription immediately above it reads Die XII Stunden des Tages (The 12 hours of the day). The shaft from the clock turning the globe is seen protruding to the left. This is the masterpiece that Josias Habrecht brought with him to Strasburg when he and his elder brother, Isaac, sought the patronage of Dasypodius (q.v.) in the quest for the contract for the making of the second Strasburg clock in 1574. Josias was born in 1552 and, incredible as it may seem, was only nineteen when he made this piece in 1572. It is clearly dated and signed. It shows hours, minutes, days of the week with their ruling planets, strikes the hour and is adjustable for latitudes 51° to 55°. The globe makes a daily revolution and shows sidereal time (q.v.) in the dial on its arbor. Isaac, who was accompanied by Josias on the visit to Dasypodius, produced a planisphere of which we have no details.[49]

A mechanical globe by Jost Burgi (q.v.) is seen in Fig. 243, now in the Landesmuseum, Kassel, Germany. Mean time is shown by the dial on the quadrant on the left, sidereal time on the globe at the top and calendar indications through slots on the horizontal, (horizon) band. Another fine globe at Kassel is that by Jean Naze (1554-1581), the case work is by D. L.

242. *Mechanical globe on the Ptolemaic principle by Josias Habrecht, c. 1572. (Rosenborg Castle, Copenhagen)*

243. *Mechanical globe by Jost Burgi, 1575, Ptolemaic. (Hessiches Landesmuseum, Kassel)*

244. *Mechanical globe by Jean Naze, c. 1575. Ptolemaic (Hessiches Landesmuseum, Kassel)*

Cordelier (Fig. 244). In this case the orrery part in the base is independent of the globe, which has its own mechanism. Over the globe, at the end of wires, are the principal stars. At an angle of $23\frac{1}{2}°$ running from upper left to lower right is an equatorial circle on which are marked the 24 hours of the day; as the globe rotates local time for any country in the world can be read off this circle, which probably makes it the first universal clock (q.v.). On the right of the base is the lunar dial and that for the days of the week.

A fourth and most interesting example is seen in Fig. 245. It is an anonymous globe made in 1651 for the Bishop of Lubeck and is now in the Frederiksborg Museum in Denmark. It is the first made to show the Copernican system. Through the centre protrudes a small shaft carrying on its end a small gilt ball representing the sun; around this travels the globe in one year whilst turning once a day on its own axis. The disc below the Earth globe revolves once a lunation and carries the moon, a small ball on the end of the fretted stand. By means of an obliquely set wheel the stand carrying the moon rises and falls so that the moon is at the level of the ecliptic (q.v.). The Earth also is raised or lowered so that the sun is always at the right declination (q.v.). As this piece does not record the hour it is, strictly speaking, not a clock, but it is included here for its historical interest.[50]

GOLDEN NUMBER. *See* LUNAR CYCLE.

GOTHIC CLOCKS. A term given to iron domestic clocks from about 1450-1525. During the period a large number were made on the Continent, but there was no production in England. Virtually only turret clocks (q.v.) were made here until the last quarter of the 16th century when a few makers, largely of foreign origin, started to produce domestic clocks in brass.

245. *Copernican mechanical globe. Anonymous. Made for the Bishop of Lubeck*, 1651. (*Frederiksborg Museum, Denmark*)

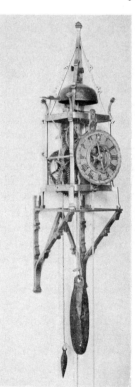

246. *Early Gothic vertical frame alarm clock, with shutters for telling day and night hours.* 15th century. (*Germanisches Museum, Nuremberg*)   247. *Gothic clock with 'restored' bell canopy, bracket and dial,* 1578. (*Private collection*)   248. *The original parts of Fig. 247.*

 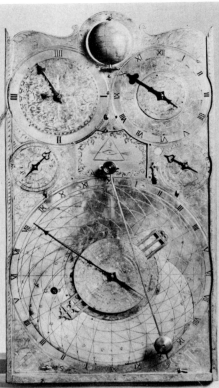 

249. *Gothic clock with alarm mechanism and hand-setting lever, c. 1460, German or Italian (Mr K. Kellenberger, Winterthur)*
250. *Late German Gothic clock with astronomical indications, 1592. (Deutches Museum, Munich)*
251. *Very finely decorated movement of Fig. 250.*

Since there was no home production all examples in collections have had to be imported from abroad, and where there is a demand the trade will usually find a way to meet the demand, consequently great care has to be exercised when considering the purchase of an iron wall clock, more so than in the case of other kinds. The earliest form had strip iron frames, usually horizontal (Fig. 9), but sometimes vertical (Figs. 246 and 8). Later they were always built within a framework of four corner pillars. Since there were none of English make we have no English nomenclature and we have to use translations of the German, where possible, otherwise we have to adopt the German terms. The four main pillars forming the structure are called 'Strebpfeilen' or buttress pillars, in these the moulded caps correspond to the changes in profile in a buttress as it rises higher. These should therefore have a functional positioning; in spurious cases they are often used indiscriminately.

France, Germany, Italy and Switzerland made these gothic clocks. Fig. 247 shows a clock by one of the famous Swiss family, Liechti (q.v.), dated 1578, as sold, and Fig. 248 shows how much of the clock and its bracket are original. This provides a good example of the indiscriminate use of the moulded cap; on the bracket and in the canopy there is no functional positioning. The bell canopy's function is to support the bell, but it will be seen that it does not do this. There is an alarm train, but no provision for this on the dial. Fig. 249 is a good example of an early gothic clock, dating about 1460, with going, striking and alarm trains. The verge for the last can be seen in the upper part of the frame at the side. Holes for setting the alarm release are pierced below each arabic numeral, they are most clearly seen at 5 and 11. Halfway down the side can be

seen the lever to lift the verge pallets out of contact with the escape wheel for setting the hands.

A very fine, but late, German example is seen in Figs. 250 and 251. This has a globe turning once a day, and records hours, quarters, day of the week with deity and the age and phase of the moon. It has been converted to pendulum. The large central dial shows the temporal hours (q.v.), as well as the astronomical hours. The triple grid hand will slide forwards and backwards with its point resting on one of the concentric circles as the seasons progress and indicate the hour by the intersection of the numbered curved line of hours and the circle of the season. Particular attention should be paid to the most delightful movement with the knight striking the hours and the man with a club striking the quarters. Here the moulded caps are correctly positioned, both in the lower and upper frame; note too how the bell canopy fulfils its proper function, and that the moulded caps tend to close and to form nearly closed O's as the period of production advances. The scrolling on the bell canopy is a feature of the later clocks. (*See* also Fig. 123).

GRAHAM, GEORGE, F.R.S. (?1673-1751). One of the most renowned clockmakers of the hey-day of English clockmaking; he was also a maker of astronomical instruments and on the Continent he is the more remembered in this connection. In Westmorland, where he was born at Fordingbridge, the name of Graham is quite common and the author's researches in the archives of the Society of Friends in recent years have revealed that George Graham has wrongly been considered to have been a Quaker. His father, in his latter years, was a Quaker, but died when George Graham was quite young and the son seems to have passed out of the Quaker influence. He was *not* apprenticed to Thomas Tompion (q.v.) as is so often erroneously stated, he was apprenticed to Henry Aske in 1688. He worked as a journeyman for Tompion, married his niece and was later taken into partnership, succeeding to Tompion's business. He was made Free of the Clockmakers' Company in 1695, Master in 1722 and was made F.R.S. in 1721.

Graham's work is always noted for its clear, simple and pleasing lines (Fig. 252). As inter-hour marks he frequently used lozenges (Fig. 94) supplanting the fleur-de-lis or derivations therefrom used by Tompion. Graham's invention of the dead beat escapement (q.v.) in 1715 and the mercury pendulum (q.v.) in 1726 were important steps in the improvement of timekeeping; both are still in use today. The dead beat escapement held the field for astronomical observation for nearly 200 years, and his cylinder escapement, for watches, for 100 years. These achievements, which are still employed in high grade clocks today, are emphasised, as Graham tends to be overshadowed by Tompion. Tompion was a genius with a facility for designing complicated pieces, he was also a workman of the highest quality; he raised the standard of *clockmaking* and placed England in the forefront, but Tompion's productions today are only collector's pieces, whereas Graham's contributions to *exact timekeeping* are still in daily use.

George Graham assisted John Harrison (q.v.) financially when he came to London in 1726 with his grid iron pendulum (q.v.) and his grasshopper escapement (q.v.), although the pendulum could be considered as a rival to Graham's own mercury pendulum, invented at about the same time. An iron quadrant made in 1725 by Graham for Greenwich was in use there until 1750, when it was replaced by a brass quadrant by Bird, a noted instrument maker who followed on after Graham. Graham's astronomical instruments had a much better finish than those of most of his competitors, no doubt a legacy from the worthy Tompion, hence they were much sought after on the Continent. He was the first to design an instrument to give visually the motions of the Earth and moon around the sun (Fig. 253); this was operated by a cranked handle. Later versions of this device incorporated the planets; they were called Orreries (q.v.).

Graham did not make many clocks, his chief output was of watches, of which he made some thousands. He died in 1751 and was buried in Westminster Abbey in the same grave as Tompion, which was opened to receive him; a mark of their close association. He has come down to posterity as 'Honest George Graham'. Could anyone wish for a better remembrance?

GRANDE SONNERIE. A system of striking whereby the four quarters of the hour are struck on one or two bells, striking one, two, three and four times, and after each quarter the hour is repeated on a different toned bell. Grande Sonnerie was rarely practised before the invention of rack and snail striking by Barlow in 1676 (q.v.). As explained under LOCKING PLATE (q.v.), once the hour had been struck, with a simple locking plate, the clock had to strike the next succeeding hour. With Dutch Striking (q.v.) the locking plate had to be doubly notched, but with Grande Sonnerie there had to be a separate train for the quarters and the locking plate had to be notched four times over. Figs. 254, 255 and 256 show a clock by Georg Mayr of Munich *circa* 1660. Top right is seen the quarter snail

252. *Exquisitely plain dial and case of a long case clock by George Graham.* (*The late G. C. Hirst*)

253. *Orrery by Tompion and Graham, London, c. 1710.* (*Museum for the History of Science, Oxford*)

254. (Left) Four sided clock by Johann Georg Mayr, Munich, 1660. (Bayerisches National Museum, Munich)

255. (Right) Back plate of Mayr's clock showing locking plate cut for Grande Sonnerie. (Bayerisches National Museum, Munich)

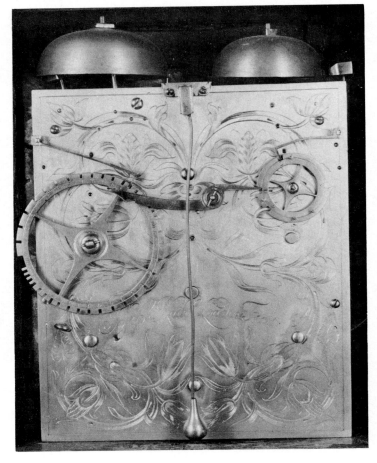

256. Back dial of Mayr's clock with indications of striking, minutes and original cross beat escapement.

257. Back plate of a clock by Joseph Knibb, London, with Grande Sonnerie striking for six hours, c. 1680. (Lord Harris)

and then, half concealed, the quadruple cut locking plate. In Fig. 256 top left is a dial recording, by a hand (missing), the last hour and quarter struck. From the dial below, marked I-XII twice for each hour, it can be seen that the clock could be switched to Dutch Striking. On the right is a dial showing how many minutes had expired in each hour. The clock was made with a cross-beat escapement (q.v.), the two arms with their floral counterpoises can be seen low centre, but seems to have been converted to pendulum as there is a crutch (q.v.) to be seen at the top. The two hands seen in Fig. 256 are to be read off a dial engraved on the glass of the door. As far as the author knows, no English maker achieved full Grande Sonnerie striking with a locking plate; the nearest is a clock by Joseph Knibb (q.v.), where the hours one to six were repeated every six hours (Fig. 257), and one had to use one's intelligence in deciding which quarter of the 24 hours was involved, as in Franklin's clock (q.v.). In this clock the quarter count wheel is on the right, when it has finished striking it releases the hour strike. Grande Sonnerie with rack and snail striking involved a quite complicated arrangement, seen in Fig. 258, in a clock by Graham (q.v.). On the Continent Grande Sonnerie is sometimes applied to clocks that strike one, two, three, four, at the quarters and only sound the hour after the last quarter.

GRANDFATHER CLOCK. *See* LONG CASE CLOCK.

GRANDMOTHER CLOCK. A long case clock (q.v.) not more than 6 feet 6 inches high. Fig. 259 shows the comparative

259. *A grandmother clock and a standard size clock, c. 1680–5. (Mr Ronald Lee)*

heights of a third quarter 17th-century grandmother clock by Joseph Knibb (q.v.) and a long case clock (q.v.) of the same period, in an early flowered marquetry case and having a central lunar dial. Scaling off from the length of the pendulum in the larger clock, the smaller would be about 6 feet high. Grandmother clocks are exceedingly rare and consequently much sought after.

GRAY, BENJAMIN (1676-1764). Gray was Clockmaker to George II, appointed in 1744. He did not enter the Clockmaker's Company and as he worked in St James's Street and Pall Mall, his place of business was outside the City of London, where the Clockmakers exercised a more strict control. His work is always of high quality, but very little survives; Fig. 260 shows a long case clock (q.v.) by him. He was one of the first, if not the first, to make a pedometer in England. In 1743 he formed a partnership with a young Swiss, François Justin Vulliamy, who in 1746 married Gray's only daughter. The

258. *Grande Sonnerie arrangement by George Graham. (The late Mr W. J. Iden)*

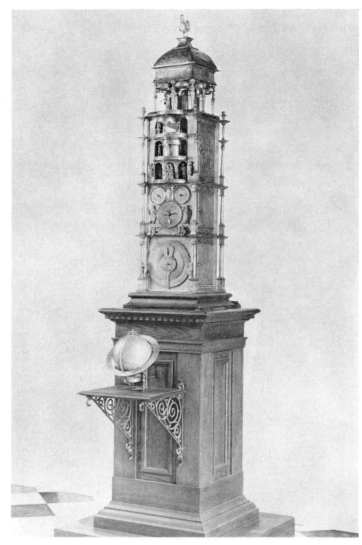

ment (q.v.) is hinged into the back of the case and swings forward for pendulum regulation, and in the earliest examples, for winding (Figs. 261 and 262). The Dutch fashion was to cover the dial plate with velvet; and not to-matt it as in a contemporary English clock. The chapter ring was frequently in skeleton form and there were no spandrels (q.v.). The decorative cartouche (q.v.), bearing the maker's name, is suspended from two rings and can be lifted to allow the insertion of a finger to start or stop the pendulum. As is natural in Holland at this time, these clocks are fitted with Huygens cycloidal cheeks (q.v.). The clocks are still single handed with indications only to the nearest half hour. As an example of conservatism, it will be noted that the distance pillars between the plates are in baluster form, which would be logical if the clock were a table clock with the bottom plate downwards, where they would have the appearance of supporting something. The same delay in bringing the decoration of the horizontal pillar to its logical position in the centre is to be found in English clockmaking.

HABRECHTS, THE. This family of clockmakers stemmed from Joachim Habrecht, who lived in Schaffhausen in the first

260. *Long case clock by Benjamin Gray, London, c. 1740.* 261. *Dutch clock (Haags Klokje) by Peter Visbach, Hague, c. 1700. (Deutches Museum, Munich)* 262. *Back plate of Visbach's clock showing the method of swinging out the movement hinged to the case.*

Royal Warrant granted in 1744 passed through the Vulliamy family (q.v.) to the third generation, ending in the death of Benjamin Louis Vulliamy in 1854.[51]

GREAT CIRCLE. A circle, the plane of which passes through the centre of the Earth and cuts the Earth into two equal parts.

GRIMTHORPE, LORD. *See* BIG BEN.

GUILLAUME, F. C. A French metallurgist who, in 1904, discovered the 36/64 nickel/iron alloy which he called Invar. This has the lowest coefficient of expansion of any known alloy, viz. 1×10^{-6}. This discovery solved the problem of a suitable alloy for pendulum rods in clocks of the highest precision.

HAAGS KLOKJE. A Dutch form of bracket clock that came into being soon after Huygens' (q.v.) invention of the pendulum. The front of the case, as a rule, does not open, but the move-

263. *Miniature reproduction of the Second Strasburg Clock by Isaac Habrecht, Strasburg, 1594. The globe may be a later addition. (Rosenborg Castle, Copenhagen)*

half of the 16th century. He made the Tower Clock of Soloturn in Switzerland in 1545. Of his many children Isaac I (1544-1620) and Josias (1552-?1575) were noted clockmakers. They came to Strasburg in 1573, having two years earlier entered into a contract with the City of Strasburg, in conjunction with Dasypodius (q.v.), for the construction of the new clock for the cathedral, which was completed in 1574 (q.v.). Up to this date they had been working on the clock in their home town of Schaffhausen. In 1571 both had brought examples of their work as a recommendation to Dasypodius, that of Josias being the mechanical globe described under that heading (Fig. 242). In all there were twelve clockmakers Habrecht in three generations.[52] Isaac I made two miniature copies of the big Strasburg clock, one of which is in the British Museum and one (Fig. 263) in the Rosenborg Castle in Copenhagen, signed and dated 1594. For a further example of a Habrecht clock *see* Fig. 294.

HAHN, PHILIP MATTHAEUS (1739-1790). Pastor Hahn of Echterdingen in Wurttemberg made several very fine astronomical clocks (q.v.) and also some watches. His main output was of astronomical clocks and a favourite layout was to have the clock proper in the centre and to extend the base on either side of the dial to support a terrestrial and a celestial globe respectively. Clocks with this layout are almost invariably by him or his son, Christoph Matthaeus Hahn, who made a few clocks after his father's design. A modification of this design is seen in Fig. 264. Hahn laid great stress on getting the exact

265. *Two hanging ball clocks by George Seydell, Coellin a.d. Spree, c. 1650. The clocks drive themselves by their own weight. (Hessiches Landesmuseum, Kassel)*

reproduction of the astronomical periods, and to this end he made his own calculating machines in order to work out the necessary gearing.[53] As was the case with the globe seen in Fig. 242, in this one of Hahn's the terrestrial globe on the left has the 24 hours of the day engraved on the equatorial band, so that from this the time of day can be ascertained for any part of the world, making it a *universal clock* (q.v.). Above the celestial globe, on the right, is a lunar orb which will revolve showing the phases.

HANGING BALL CLOCK. In the middle of the 17th century clocks of ball shape were developed, the driving force of which was provided by their own weight. To wind them they are supported and the suspension chain is wound up by a spring action. They then gradually descend the length of the chain. A fine example of about 1650 is seen in Fig. 265, signed George Seydell in Coellin a.d. Spree.

HANGING CLOCK. As the name denotes, a clock that hangs on the wall, also known as a wall clock. Scarcely known in England before 1600 when the English lantern clock (q.v.) began to be made, but made in large numbers on the Continent. (*See* GOTHIC CLOCKS, some of which did not have brackets, but hung directly on the wall.) Fig. 266 shows a fine example by Edward East (q.v.) *circa* 1665. Before the invention of the anchor escapement (q.v.) the amplitude (q.v.) of the pendulum with the verge escapement (q.v.) was such that any pendulum of more than ½ seconds beat, and about 10½ inches in length, was greater than could be kept within the case. This example has a

264. *Astronomical clock with terrestrial and celestial globes by Philip Matthaeus Hahn, Echterdingen, c. 1770. (Dr A. Sobek, Vienna)*

266. *Hanging clock by Edward East, London c. 1665.* (*Lord Harris*)

267. *Detail of the dial of James Harrison's clock.* (*Fig. 268*)

268. *Wooden long case clock with grasshopper escapement by James Harrison, Barrow,* 1728. (*Clockmaker's Company*)

short pendulum; the weights have not yet been enclosed in the case, but soon hereafter the long case clock (q.v.) appeared, albeit still with a short ½ seconds pendulum (Fig. 236). In the apron (q.v.) is a keyhole to lock the hood; to get at the winding holes the hood must be slid up (*see* HOOD) and the discs covering them pulled aside to bring into operation the maintaining power (q.v.). This clock also illustrates Acorn, Acanthus and Flambeau.

HARRISON, JAMES (1704-1766). A younger brother of John Harrison (q.v.) who lived at Barrow in Lincolnshire. Until recently he has not been credited with any particular

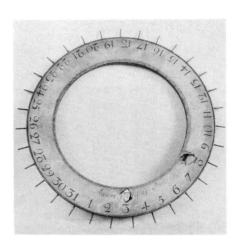

269. *Date ring with signature and date of James Harrison's clock.*

accomplishments beyond making some long case clocks (q.v.) with wooden movements, both he and John being carpenters. Recent researches, however, particularly the very painstaking work of Colonel Humphrey Quill, have revealed that, in all probability, it was James and not John who invented the gridiron pendulum (q.v.) and the grasshopper escapement (q.v.). The only known clock by James is in the Clockmakers' Museum in the Guildhall, London (Fig. 268). The table in the door is for the equation of time (q.v.). Fig. 267 shows the dial and signature in the arch, and Fig. 269 the calendar date ring, again signed James Harrison 3rd 1728 Barrow. Does this mean that this is the third clock that he made, or the third month of 1728? Fig. 270 shows the component parts, all the wheels and pinions being of wood, except the escape wheel. Fig. 271 shows his gridiron pendulum and Fig. 272 the pallets (q.v.) of the grasshopper escapement. This escapement requires an arc of 12½°, so to compensate for this wide amplitude Harrison introduced curved cheeks; the point has often been raised whether the Harrisons were aware of Huygens' cycloid theory (q.v.), published in 1673, and the conjecture has been made that, living in so remote a district, it was most unlikely. However, in a MS. dated 10.6.1730 John refers to a cycloid applied to a clock pendulum for use in a house. 'And first as to a clock to be fixed in a house . . . (for in ye adjusting a Clock whose Pendulum moves in a cycloid . . .)'.[54] As this MS. is only two years after the date of James' clock, it is a fair assumption that the Harrisons had knowledge of the cycloid at that time. It will be noted from Fig. 268 that the trunk of the clock has pockets on either side to allow for the extra wide amplitude. The case is not believed to have been the work of Harrison, but to have been adapted to his need. In Fig. 270 it will be noted that all the pivot bearings have been bushed with lignum vitae, a naturally oily wood. One guiding principle of the Harrisons was the elimination of friction and hence the necessity for using oil. The grasshopper escapement needs no oil and the wear on it is so light that the pallets are frequently made of lignum vitae. In this photograph are also seen the lantern pinions (q.v.) of which the 'bars' are wooden rollers mounted on brass pins, thus greatly reducing friction; the wooden locking plate fixed to the side of the wheel should also be noted. Writing in the *Mechanics Magazine* Vol. X, 2.8.1828 James Harrison's grandson writes, 'My grandfather, James Harrison, was the workman who made the two regulators (q.v.) for the timekeeping for ascertaining the longitude at sea; and the first of these machines or timekeepers was almost entirely made by him, the first being made in Barrow and the second in London.' The exact apportionment of credit between the two brothers is difficult to assess, but we have no wooden clocks with gridiron pendulums and grasshopper escapement bearing John Harrison's signature. At an unknown date James retired to Barrow on Humber and took up bell founding.

HARRISON, JOHN (1693-1776). The son of a carpenter, when about eighteen he began to make wooden long case

273. (*Above*) *John Harrison's No. 3 Timekeeper, 1757.* (*National Maritime Museum, Greenwich*)

270. *Component parts of James Harrison's clock.*
271. (*Right*) *Gridiron pendulum of James Harrison's clock.*
272. *Detail of the pallets of the grasshopper escapement. This is probably the only grasshopper escapement with original pallets.*

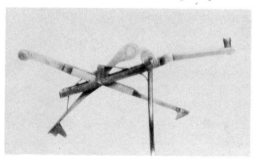

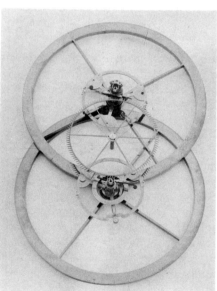

274. (*Right*) *The heavy balances and grasshopper escapement of Harrison's No. 3.* (*The Astronomer Royal*)

clocks (q.v.). The earliest known, dated 1715, is in the Science Museum, London, another, dated 1717, is in Nostell Priory, a few miles south-east of Wakefield in Yorkshire. A third is in the Clockmakers' Company Museum in the Guildhall, London. This is inscribed as being the first production of John Harrison 1715, but this is certainly incorrect, as the previous two movements referred to are just copies in wood of the standard long case clock brass movement of the day, whereas that in the Clockmakers' Company Museum embodies the roller pinions already referred to in James' clock (q.v.).

If we accord that the gridiron pendulum (q.v.) and the grass-

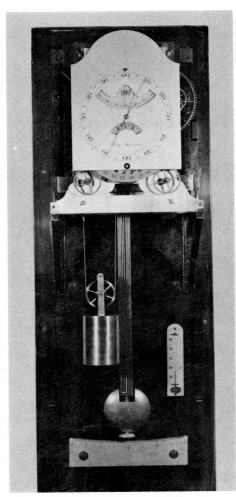

275. *John Harrison's astronomical clock* (*Royal Astronomical Society*)

276. *Movement of John Harrison's astronomical clock showing the roller pinions.*

hopper escapement (q.v.) were the inventions of James Harrison (q.v.) and also if James' grandson's claim that his grandfather made Harrison No. 1 and much of No. 2, we must accord to John much originality of thought in the production of his marine clocks Nos. 3 and 4, both of which are in the National Maritime Museum, Greenwich. No. 3 is illustrated here (Figs. 273 and 274). It has received much less publicity than the others and embodies many novel ideas. The arrangement of the grasshopper escapement has one pallet fixed to each of the huge circular balances (Fig. 274), the gridiron is abolished and a bimetallic strip is substituted;[57] in these matters he can have had no help from James. No. 3 was never tested at sea, it was abandoned in favour of No. 4, which is no longer a clock, but a large watch of completely different design, and as such is excluded from consideration here. It was with No. 4 that Harrison won the £20,000 prize (today worth about £100,000) for the making of a timepiece sufficiently accurate to enable longitude to be ascertained at sea.

Another clock that emphasises Harrison's ability as a designer and craftsman is seen in Figs. 275 and 276. This clock was with the Royal Astronomical Society in London, but is now at the Royal Greenwich Observatory, Herstmonceux, Sussex. It has a gridiron pendulum swinging between cycloidal cheeks (q.v.) and a grasshopper escapement which has an amplitude (q.v.) of $12\frac{1}{2}°$. The pendulum is not original; the late Commander R. T. Gould, to whom we owe the rescue of all Harrison's marine clocks from official neglect and oblivion, overhauled this clock, probably some time in the '30's. He found it fitted with a wooden pendulum, but being of the opinion that Harrison would certainly not have used an uncompensated pendulum, he had a gridiron pendulum made for it. As will be seen, frictionless rolls are used for the pinions, there is also a remontoire (q.v.) which acts every $7\frac{1}{2}$ minutes. The main arbor pivots do not rest in bearings, but on the intersection of the circumferences of two large overlapping wheels, another device to reduce friction.

HENLEIN, PETER (*circa* 1479-1542). For many years considered as the first to make a clock so small that it could be carried on the person (*see* DRUM CLOCK). The date 1510 has always been assigned to this; but the researches of Professor Morpurgo[55] have established that small clocks, 'that struck and that did not strike' were already carried on the person in 1488 in Italy (*see* under MANFREDI, BARTOLOMEO). Attached to the letter embodying this information were some Spanish verses, of which the following is a translation:

> For Signor Lodovico
> Although it does not strike
> Its work satisfies.

> For the Duke,
> The ingenuity of the work
> Makes this watch strike

> For Signor Galazzo.
> As long as this satisfies,
> My glory shall grow.

277. *Bracket clock by John Hilderson, London, c. 1665. (Authors' collection)*

278. *Dial of Hilderson's clock.*

Henlein undoubtedly made small watches in Nuremberg and popularised their use. His construction may well have been independent of the Italian craftsmen, but it must now be accepted that he was not the first to make a clock small enough to be carried on the person.

HILDERSON, JOHN. A very fine maker of whom very little is known. Baillie[13] merely gives London 1657. There is no record of him in the Clockmakers' Company List of Apprentices; it is probable that he was Free of some other Craft and so entered the Clockmakers' Company as a 'Brother'. His style is very akin to that of Edward East (q.v.) in the period shortly after the introduction of the pendulum in 1658. The only clocks by Hilderson known to the author are bracket clocks (q.v.) in plain architectural cases (Fig. 277). He may have used the same case maker as East, he certainly, on occasion, used

279 *Unique method of Dutch striking in Hilderson's clock.*

280. *Back plate of Hilderson's clock.*

286. *Dial of a clock designed for direct reading of the changing Nuremberg hours of daylight and darkness. (Germanisches Museum, Nuremberg)*

nected with the early transmission programmes and on 21st April, 1923, to encourage listeners to put their watches right, he counted out the seconds from 9.55 p.m. to 10 o'clock. Later he was instrumental in getting a connection made between Greenwich Observatory and the B.B.C., which was the beginning of the 'six pips' as we know it today. His *Electrical Timekeeping* has run into many editions.

HORLOGE DE SAPIENCE *See* WISDOM CLOCK.

HOUR CIRCLE. *See* CHAPTER RING.

HOURS:

Babylonian. The Babylonians adopted their astronomy from the Sumerians. (*See* ORIGIN OF THE CIRCLE). The Sumerians had a year of twelve lunar months and started their day at sunset, when the first crescent moon would appear. From Greek and Roman times the start of the Babylonian day has been given as sunrise, but some modern writers now contend that it did, in fact, agree with the Sumerian and start at sunset.[79] (*See* CAJETANO).

French. Sometimes so called in Italy to denote our usual 2 × 12 hours as against the old Italian hours (q.v.).

Great. A medieval continental expression referring to the systems that counted the hours 1-24.

Italian. The Italians reckoned 24 hours starting at sunset and kept this up, in spite of its inconveniences, until the 19th century.

Japanese. (*See* JAPANESE CLOCKS).

Mean. The 24 hours of the day of 60 minutes each. Only four times in the year is the mean day of the same length as the solar day. (*See* EQUATION OF TIME).

Nuremberg. In the Nuremberg district and regions round about, the hours were counted as so many of daylight and of darkness, varying from 16 hours of daylight at midsummer to the con-

verse at midwinter. Public notices stated when one should take an hour off one and add it to the other. Clocks were often made with shutters that could be slid one over the other, changing the number of daylight hours (Fig. 246). Fig. 286 shows another variation of the Nuremberg dial. There are eight concentric rings, the outside marked 1-16 and 1-8 and the innermost 1-8 and 1-16. The cranked arm is marked 8-16, the numbers on this arm being complementary to those on the dial, to make up the 24 hours in each case.

Planetary. As explained under ASTROLOGICAL DIALS (q.v.), the five planets and the sun and the moon were supposed to govern the lives of men, hour by hour.

Sidereal. Each sidereal hour is 1/24th of a sidereal day. There is no variation in the length of a sidereal day as there is in that of the solar day. (*See* SIDEREAL DAY).

Small. A central European expression for the 2 × 12 hours, as opposed to 1 × 24. (*See* HOURS, *Great*).

Temporal. The division of the day and night into twelve equal parts, each varying with the seasons. They were in monastic use until the coming into general use of the mechanical clock *circa* 1300.

HUYGENS, CHRISTAAN, F.R.S. (1629-1695). A renowned physicist, the range of whose interests in Holland and France may be equated with those of Dr Robert Hooke (q.v.) in this country. The Société Hollandaise des Sciences published over many years the *Ouevres Complètes de Christaan Huygens* which runs into twenty-two thick volumes, from which may be deduced the range of his interests. His experiments with clocks and pendulums are to be found in Vols. XVII and XVIII.

In horology Huygens' name is chiefly connected with the pendulum (q.v.). He never claimed to have invented it, and there is no doubt that pendulums existed before that designed by Huygens, but it was he who investigated and demonstrated its theory. Besides the vertical pendulum he made experiments with conical pendulums (q.v.) in 1658. Together with Alexander Bruce (later Earl of Kinkardine) he constructed two pendulum clocks, one made in England and one in Holland, that were tried at sea in a voyage to Portugal in 1663. They were of two sizes, the larger performed fairly well, but the smaller frequently stopped.[58] A second trial was made in a voyage in 1664 to New Amsterdam in the West Indies and then to West Africa. The expedition was running short of water and the logs of the various ships showed the distance from Fuego in the Cape Verde Islands as 80, 100 and 120 leagues. Calculated from the clock the distance was 30 leagues, and indeed the island was reached in two days. The correctness of the identification of the landfall was later queried. Huygens continued his experiments for a marine clock and his best known experimental type, made in 1671 or 1672, is shown in Fig. 287 and 288. It is a spring-driven clock with a triangular cord pendulum swinging between cycloidal cheeks (q.v.) that are not visible in the illustration; but the clock was not successful.

Huygens devised a new way of grinding and polishing lenses in connection with his work on improving telescopes, and he also did much work on the wave theory of light. He was interested in astronomy and had a clock in use in the Paris Observatory in 1666 with a seconds pendulum for the observation of the eclipse of the sun on 2nd July of that year. Two more were made for him in 1670/1, probably by Isaac Thuret (q.v.). These were

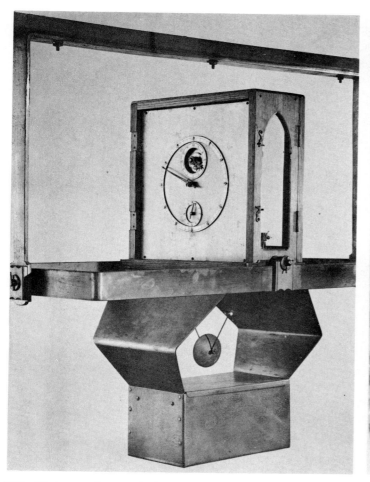

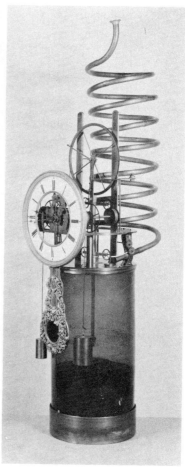

287. *Christaan Huygens' clock with which he essayed to 'find the Longitude'.* (*Museum for the History of Science, Leyden*)   288.
Movement of Huygens' clock.   289. *Pasquale Andervalt's Trieste hydrogen clock, c 1835.* (*Clockmakers' Company*)

for use in observation and were taken by Jean Picard to Denmark, one has a seconds pendulum and the other a ½ seconds pendulum. That with the seconds pendulum went so accurately 'that during two months it kept mean time exactly, not varying a second.' This clock, no doubt, had cycloidal cheeks. A clock made for Huygens by Isaac Thuret is in the Museum for the History of Science in Leyden (Figs. 431 and 432). Huygens also devised a method of maintaining power (q.v.) for weight driven clocks. In 1685 he designed a planispherium (q.v.) which was made for him by J. van Ceulen (q.v.) and is also in the Leyden Museum. (*See* BALANCE SPRING).

HYDROGEN CLOCK. Pasquale Andervalt (1806-1881) devised and made several clocks from about 1835 onwards which were driven by the evolution of hydrogen generated by dropping zinc pellets into sulphuric acid (Fig. 289). The pellets are placed in the spiral tube and allowed to drop into the ruby glass acid container at controlled intervals. The gas pressure forces up the rod, seen partly in the container, which carries the large wheel, round which runs the cord carrying the remontoire (q.v.) weight. The two tall flats behind act as a guide to the wheel. There are examples in the Clockmakers' Museum, London and in the Vienna Clock Museum.

IMSER, PHILIP. Philip Imser is believed to have been born in Strasburg and was later resident in Tuebingen, where he was Professor of Mathematics and Astronomy. In 1554 the Pala-

tinate Elector Ottheinrich of Neuberg on the Danube was in negotiation with him that he should make 'a new astronomical work that should aim at showing by means of wheelwork the true course of all the planets and all other trains (q.v.) and movements.' He was promised 700 florins and an additional 100 florins if the clock went well for a year. Imser replied that 'he had already the general plan so well in his head that he should not fail in the least detail.'[59] But Imser had undertaken more than he bargained for. He got into difficulties with the original plans and then extended them at a heavy cost to himself. At last, in 1556, he delivered a mere framework of the finished article and demanded 1,600 florins. Ottheinrich refused to depart from the original contract and told him 'to get on with it' although Imser said that his brain would not stand any further strain. At the end of 1557 he delivered the finished clock, but declared that the planetary trains were not correct, but that this was the fault of the assistant who had been allotted to him. Pathetically he begged the Elector to take the clock as it was and to let him rest his weary brain. After several more trials, early in 1558, in the presence of various astronomers it was found that the astronomical trains were still incorrect. Imser refused to touch the clock again. Ottheinrich, now bedridden, lost patience, sent the clock and clockmaker away and demanded back the money already paid if the clock were not delivered in perfect condition. Poor Imser must have succeeded as Ottheinrich, in his will, leaves the 'Astronomical Work that

290. *Front view of Philip Imser's clock, Tuebingen 1555. (Technical Museum, Vienna)*

291. *Back view of Imser's clock showing the planetary movements.*

Dr Imser shall have made for us to the Library'. The subsequent history of the clock is not known until it came in a derelict condition from the Austrian Imperial House to the Technical Museum in Vienna, where it now is.

In the main dial (Fig. 290) Imser uses seven hollow arbors on one shaft, a unique achievement at that time. The hands carry

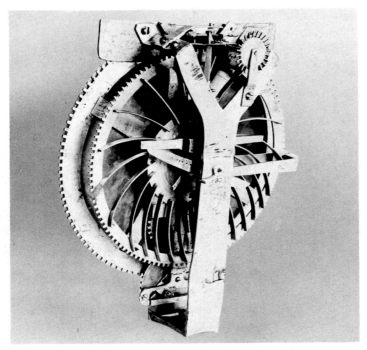

292. *Arrangement for showing the temporal hours in Imser's clock.*

the sun, the moon, the moon's age and phase, the five planets and the nodes (q.v.). In Fig. 291 the motions of the five planets are shown, that of Mercury being in the middle; this dial also has the date 1555. A side dial has an annual calendar with the indication of the fixed saints' days and shutters to show the hours of daylight and darkness. In the cupola above, the lower tier doors open at the quarters to show the four ages of man and above, at the hours, Christ comes forward in blessing. The whole is surmounted by a celestial globe that turns once in 24 hours. The clock is made to record temporal hours (q.v.) and the method for providing for their varying length is seen in Fig. 292. Around the gallery (Fig. 290) a female figure proceeds marking the minutes. One can well understand how the working out of all these various details, all for the first time combined in one clock, nearly drove poor Imser mad. Compare with Baldewin's Clock, 1561 (Figs. 59, 60 and 61).

INCENSE CLOCKS. Fire and incense clocks are first recorded in the Chinese literature of the 6th century A.D., and were as much in use as water clocks (q.v.) and sundials until the coming of the mechanical clock. They made their appearance in Japan somewhat later. In their simplest form they were the incense or joss-stick; later came the spiral, both forms having hourly markings. Finally came the Incense Seal, a continuous train of burning incense marked off into specified periods. The Chinese hour was equal to two western hours and their unit, the *K'o*, was equal to one quarter of an hour, (actually 14 minutes 24 seconds). Later the term *K'o* was applied to a clock or timepiece.

In 1073 A.D. the Hundred Graduations Incense Seal was invented for the telling of the times of sunrise and sunset, as in

293. *Chinese Incense clock.* (*Science Museum, London*)

summer and autumn there was frequently not enough water to run the water clocks and in the winter they froze up. The Hundred Graduations Incense Seal consisted of a circular plate divided radially into twelve equal compartments arranged in pairs, each of which was divided by low maze-like partitions of similar design. The incense would be inserted and packed tight between these maze-like partitions; it would then be lit at the centre of the circle, at the first half of one pair of divisions, and would burn outwards to the circumference, then return to the centre of the other half of the division, thence passing to the first half of the next pair and so on. Another form was known as the Five Night Incense Seal. This was circular in shape and was divided radially into five sections. These were sub-divided concentrically into broken maze-like partitions, each designed to burn for a specified number of *K'o*, according to the length of night in the season. Their size varied from about 3·3 inches diameter, with a burning length of $31\frac{1}{2}$ inches, for a night of 60 *K'o* at the winter solstice (q.v.) to 2·3 inches diameter, with a burning length of $19\frac{1}{2}$ inches for 40 *K'o* at the summer solstice.

The use of Incense Seals has continued up to the present day in China. These are now generally made of metal and consist of five parts, a base, a rectangular or circular wall, a tray for the ash bed, a perforated grid pattern and a perforated cover (Fig. 293). A little tamper and shovel (not shown) are supplied. When the grid of the pattern has been filled with incense and smoothed off, the grid is removed and small bamboo pegs marked with hour signs inserted. Once the incense is lit the perforated cover is placed in position to protect the whole from draughts.

Those interested are referred to Bedini's *The Scent of Time*, American Philosophical Society, Philadelphia, 1963, on which these notes are based.

INCLINED PLANE CLOCK. A clock in which the motive force is provided by the weight of the clock itself acting against the resistance of the train (q.v.). These were mostly made in the 17th century, one by Habrecht (q.v.), probably Isaac I, is seen in Fig. 294, its date is around 1600. The clock reaches the bottom of the slope every Saturday and is lifted up and placed again at the top.

INDICTION. A period in Roman Law of fifteen years, starting on 1st September, used in ecclesiastical contracts for the reckoning of interest payments. (*See* CALENDAR, PERPETUAL FOR EASTER.)

INGRAHAM, ELIAS. A pioneer in the American clock-making industry. Trained as a joiner, he started making clock cases in Bristol, Connecticut in 1828. Bristol was already an established centre of the American wooden clock industry and Ingraham had no difficulty in finding work. In 1831, in partner-

294. *Inclined plane clock by Isaac Habrecht, Strasburg, c. 1600.* (*Herzog Anton Ulrich Museum, Brunswick*)

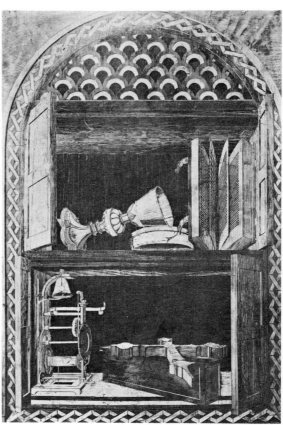

295. *Sharp Gothic clock by Brewster and Ingraham, c. 1845. (Smithsonian Institution, Washington, D.C.)*

296. *Italian intarsia panel, 15th century. Compare clock with Fig. 10. (Victoria and Albert Museum, London)*

297. *Steeple clock with eight-day wagon spring movement by Birge and Fuller, Bristol, Connecticut, 1835. (Smithsonian Institution, Washington, D.C.)*

ship with W. G. Bartholomew, he started making his own clock cases, mirrors, chains, etc. He suffered in the depression of 1837, but in 1841 he started the firm of Ray and Ingraham producing complete 30 hour and eight-day clocks. That was the beginning of the firm that still operates today under the name of The E. Ingraham Company, under the direction of lineal descendants of Elias Ingraham. During the wars the Ingraham Company turned its activities to anti-aircraft fuses and other war supplies.

Ingraham introduced the 'Sharp Gothic' clock, an example by Brewster and Ingraham is seen in Fig. 295.[60] This is a very popular model in the States and is much sought after.

INLAY. A form of decoration where the design is laid into a base. (*See* INTARSIA and MARQUETRY.)

INTARSIA. The earliest form of inlay where grooves were cut out of the wood or metal base and the inlay material fitted into them. In Fig. 296 the little clock should be compared with the little alarm clock in Fig. 10.

INTRADOS. The convex side of an arch.

INVAR. *See* GUILLAUME, F. C.

ISOCHRONOS. Occupying equal periods of time.

IVES, JOSEPH. The young economy of the United States in the early years of the 19th century did not embrace rolling mills capable of producing homogenous spring steel, consequently all clocks were weight driven up to about 1840-1850. The exception that proves the rule is the wagon-spring clock invented in 1825 by Joseph Ives of Brooklyn, New York. A laminated spring, analogous to a cart spring, was firmly fixed to the base of the clock case and tensioned by drawing up its two ends

298. *The functioning of a wagon spring movement.* (*Smithsonian Institution, Washington, D.C.*

299. *A French clock by Lagvile à Chaalons, c. 1680, with the wagon spring principle.* (*Chateau des Monts, Le Loche, Switzerland*)

by cords connected with the winding drums. Not many examples are now to be found of this ingenious arrangement (Figs. 297 and 298). An earlier anticipation of this principle of a vertical pull from a horizontal spring is seen in Fig. 299, which is a French clock by Lagvile à Chaalons (*circa* 1680).

JACKS. Automata employed to strike the hours and the quarters. They take various forms, often men in armour (Fig. 300), men and women, animals, etc. The name is believed to be a shortened form of Jacquemart, which, in turn, probably derives from Jacques and marteau (hammer). The jacks, a man and a woman, at Dijon are amongst the oldest; they were brought from Courtrai by Philip the Bold in 1382 after the siege of that city. Another pair are those of the clock in St Mark's Square in Venice of 1499. Based on a calculation given in a pamphlet describing the clock, written in 1960, these jacks have struck 27,027,100 blows! One strikes the hour and the other repeats it after two minutes.

JANVIER, ANTIDE (1751-1835). The son of a peasant who later turned to horology. He inherited his father's horological instinct and received his first horological education from Abbé Tournier at the age of thirteen. When only fifteen he set himself to make a clock to show 'the effect of the annual movement of the sun, together with its daily motion and the revolution of the Earth on its axis, to show at the same time sidereal, mean and true time, the length of the days, the rising and the setting of the sun for any horizon and finally to show the mean motion of the moon in longitude and latitude, that of its nodes, its phases, southing, rising and setting and ecliptical conjunctions'. A year or so later he presented this clock to the Académie des Sciences et Belles Lettres at Besançon, where it still is. In 1784 he was appointed Clockmaker to King Louis XVI and in 1789 he was paid 24,000 francs for an astronomical clock that showed

Uranus. This brought him into world renown.

In 1791 he made another clock for Royal approval; this showed the time at any part of France by means of a map (Figs. 301 and 302). At that time mean time had not been established for the whole country, and each large centre had its own local time. The dial by the famous enameller, Coteau, is probably the first to show France by départements, it also carries the lines of latitude and longitude. Above the sun's effigy is a jumping hour figure and above that is a seconds dial. The outer ring is the minute dial revolving once in three minutes and is read off the bottom of the Paris meridian. For local times 4 minutes have to be added to Parisian time for each degree of longitude that

300. *A pair of jacks clad in armour, 15th century. The gongs are modern.* (*The late Mr R. P. Howgrave-Graham*)

115

301. *Universal time clock for France by Antide Janvier, Paris, 1791. (Malmaison Museum, near Paris)* 302. *Detail of the dial of Janvier's clock.*

places are east of Paris and subtracted for places west of Paris. Janvier's demonstration of the clock to the Queen was unfortunate. He overlooked the fact that the Royal family had only recently been brought back to Paris from Metz, whence they had fled and when he chose a town for which he wished to ascertain local time, he unfortunately chose Metz; the Queen immediately left with her children and 2 hours later Janvier was told that the Queen had no interest in the clock.[61]

In 1789 Janvier constructed a universal tidal dial which not only showed the approximate time of high tide at the chief ports of Europe, but provided corrections that could be applied to any selected port (Figs. 303 and 304). The lower dial, the hand of which revolves once a week, shows the hour to the nearest $\frac{1}{2}$ hour, only the hours VI, XII, XVIII and XXIV for each day are marked. In the centre is a hand turning once a year giving the month and a third hand turning once a month, giving the date. Finally, in the centre is a lunar dial giving the moon's phases and age. Incidentally the disc has a correct depiction of the moon's surface, there is no 'Man in the Moon'. The upper dial centre turns once in $14\frac{3}{4}$ days and indicates the time of the tides twice daily at all the places enumerated on the dial. But as these times are only approximate, there is provision for an adjustment which can be made to take care of local conditions, known as 'the Establishment of the Port'. The long hand of the upper dial indicates the full hour and the shorter hand the number of minutes to be added or subtracted. The movement is produced by a shaped cam, rack and wheel

similar to that used in an equation clock (q.v.).

A third unique clock by Janvier is seen in Figs. 305 and 306. It is an equation clock, and is based on the law of equal areas, that is that although the angular rate of the radius vector (q.v.) of an ellipse varies the areas contained are uniform. It had been demonstrated that when an ellipse is nearly circular, as is the orbit of the Earth around the sun, the radius vector around the second focus of the ellipse makes very nearly a uniform sweep. Janvier sought to reconstruct the true motion resulting from the eccentricity of the Earth's orbit and the obliquity of the Earth's axis, the two factors that make up the equation of time (q.v.). In Fig. 306 the oblique wheel is inclined on its axis at the maximum obliquity that takes place at the solstices (q.v.). This wheel has a pin that travels in the curved strip seen at the top of the clock which is fixed parallel to the axis of the vertical wheel of which the edge is seen against the front plate. The arbor of this wheel is fixed eccentrically to that of the oblique wheel to the extent of twice the eccentricity of the orbit. Both wheels are identical and turn once a year and their hands will show mean and solar time respectively. Janvier's work is always marked with a dignified restraint and he rarely made a clock that did not embody one or more astronomical features. In general, his case designs followed the style of the time, plain, but with rich details.

JAPANESE CLOCKS. In Japan until 1873 a medieval system of timekeeping was used. They used the temporal

303. *Universal tidal dial clock by Antide Janvier, Paris 1789. (Conservatoire des Arts et Métiers, Paris)*
304. *Tidal dial of Janvier's clock. (Conservatoire des Arts et Métiers, Paris)*

305. *Janvier's simplified equation clock. (Diette, Paris)*

306. *View showing lunar train and equation movement of Janvier's clock.*

307. *Japanese lantern clock with two foliots for day and night hours.* (*Science Museum, London*)

308. *Japanese lantern clock on a pedestal.* (*Science Museum, London*)

309. *Japanese spring-driven clock with adjustable openings for the hours.* (*Science Museum, London*)

divisions, that is they reckoned six equal periods from dusk to dawn and six equal periods from dawn to dusk, but the length of these periods, of course, varied with the seasons, so that the Japanese hour was an unequal period of two to four mean hours. At mid-summer a day hour was $2\frac{1}{3}$ longer than a night hour. At mid-winter they reckoned equal periods of day and night, so that an appreciable amount of dawn and dusk must have been taken into the day to arrive at this result.

Clocks were not generally found in homes, except a few in the houses of the very rich, as they were too expensive; the clocks were mainly in the temples, where they served the populace. 1-3 strokes on the temple bells were reserved for temple use, so that, for the populace, the temple bells sounded 4-9. Nine seems to have had some particular significance as it is used to denote midday and midnight. When a clock was made to strike the half hours, one was struck after the odd hours and two were struck after the even hours; the sequence on a clock striking half hours would then be 6, 2, 5, 1, 4, 2, 9, 1, 8, 2, 7, 1.

Clocks had to be adjusted every few days in the earliest times; when the dual escapement, described below, was adopted, they were adjusted every fourteen days, to keep pace with the change in the seasons. The hour numerals were associated with the Chinese signs of the zodiac, which were: Rat (winter solstice) (q.v.), Bull, Tiger, Hare (Vernal equinox) (q.v.), Dragon, Serpent, Horse (summer solstice), Goat, Ape, Cock (autumn equinox), Dog, Bear. These signs were delineated on the clock dials as well as the hour numeral as each hour was known by its zodiacal sign, which appears to have been regarded in an astrological sense, like the planetary hours in Europe (q.v.)[139].

There were three main types of clock in Japan, lantern, bracket and pillar. Early lantern clocks were weight driven with foliot balance (q.v.) and verge escapement (q.v.). They had a single hand revolving once in 24 hours, alternatively a fixed hand and a revolving dial plate, marked with twelve divisions for the 24 hours. Owing to the continual change in the length of the days due to the change of season, they would require very frequent adjustment of the weights on the foliot. In order to overcome this, clocks were made with two escapements and two foliots (Fig. 307), at the sixth and twelfth Japanese hours the striking train, after it had struck, switched the movement over from one escapement to the other. The divisions on the dial could be regular and equal, since the change of escapement regulated the speed at which the hand traversed each division. This particular clock is of iron. As Japanese houses do not have solid walls, lantern clocks were usually set on pedestals. In Fig. 308 we have another lantern clock on a pedestal, this time with a single foliot. The frequent adjustment needed by the earliest type with only one foliot is here avoided by the utilisation of sliding panels in the hours divisions, so that their length can be varied, causing the hand to take more or less mean time to pass from one to the next. This clock has a bob pendulum (q.v.). Fig. 309 shows a spring-driven bracket clock with the hour divisions arranged for long summer days. The two pins indicate midday and midnight, the positions of which are fixed, the size of the other hour divisions can be adjusted according to the season.

The pillar clock was very popular, it was cheap and could hang on the timber framing of a Japanese room. As this type has only one foliot or balance, the adjustment for the varying hours is made on the trunk of the clock. Fig. 310 is of a type where the indicator descends with the weight and is moved transversely across the bar on to the line of the current month, it will be noted that the intervals between the cutting of the vertical line on the left by the wavy lines are nearly equal, that is midwinter with equal length of day and night; on the right we have these intervals lengthening all the way down, towards midsummer. In the second type (Fig. 311) the hour plates can be adjusted up and down in the groove. The scale of tenths on the left would assist in placing the plates so many tenths of an hour longer or shorter than the midwinter hours. This clock has a bob pendulum.[140]

The reader may have noticed that no mention has been made of any long case clock; for a nation which habitually sat on the floor, these would be unsuitable.

JEWELLING. *See* FACIO.

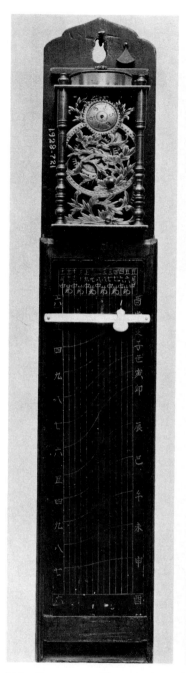
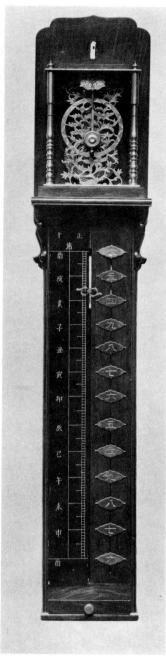

310. *Japanese Pillar clock with cursor on a transverse bar.* (*Science Museum, London*) 311. *Japanese Pillar clock with adjustable hour indication.* (*Science Museum, London*)

JONES, HENRY (*circa* 1640-1695). An apprentice of Edward East (q.v.) who became a famous maker in his own right. He was master of the Clockmakers' Company in 1691, during which year he and Edward East both gave £100 for the benefit of the poor. His style was much influenced by that of his master, East. Where he first worked is not known, his clocks are signed 'Henry Jones, Londini', but his later work is signed 'Henry Jones in yᵉ Temple'. His shop is believed to have been situated on the left just inside the gateway to the Inner Temple from the Strand. He made few long case clocks, one is seen in Fig. 312. The circular banding (q.v.) in the door and the base of this clock is most unusual. A night clock by him, the only one

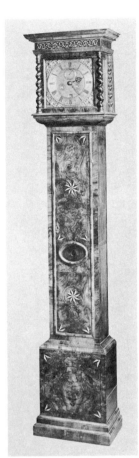

312. *Long case clock by Henry Jones, London, c. 1675. (Mr James Oakes)*

313. *Night clock with strike by Henry Jones, London, c. 1680. (The late Mr Percy Webster)*

314. *Outer covers of a magnificent book clock by Hans Kiening, Fuessen, Bavaria, c. 1580. (Ashmolean Museum, Oxford)*

known to the author, is seen in Fig. 313. Charles II gave a clock by Jones to Mrs June Lane, in recognition of her services at the battle of Worcester.[62]

Jones died in 1695—two years before his master, who lived to be ninety-five—and is buried in St Dunstans in the West; there is a memorial to him on the north side of the chancel.

JULIAN DAY. A method of reckoning time used by astronomers to avoid the complications arising from months and years of unequal length. The days are numbered consecutively, starting from the 'Julian Era' 1st January, 4713 B.C., 1963 is Julian year 6676 and 1st January of that year is Julian Day 2,438,032. The Julian day starts at noon.

JUMP CLOCKS. A fine craftsman, Richard Thomas Jump was apprenticed to B. L. Vulliamy (q.v.) in 1825 and took over his business when he died. Jump made many fine clocks in the Breguet (q.v.) style. When Jump's successor died in the 1930's; the business was closed down, the late C. A. Ilbert obtained permission to look through the waste papers and found many of Vulliamy's ledgers, which are now in the Ilbert Library in the British Horological Institute.

KARNACK CLOCK. *See* WATER CLOCK.

KIENING, HANS (2nd half 16th century). Kiening is only known to us by the few examples of his work that have survived, and they are magnificent. Figs. 314, 315 and 316 show three views of a portable clock in book form (*circa* 1580). Its beauty needs no emphasis; the outer side of the lid has a perpetual calendar, to be adjusted by hand, on the under side of the cover there is a collapsible sundial with different rings

315. *Inside covers of Hans Kiening's book clock.*

316. *Movement of Hans Kiening's book clock.*

for different latitudes from 30° to 46°N and below this is a dial for the age and phases of the moon and an astrological dial (q.v.). On the clock dial proper there is a scale for measuring temporal hours (q.v.) with a hole for the insertion of the gnomon. Below is a dial marked 2 × XII and 1-24 for the Italian hours (q.v.), together with a central dial for setting the alarm. On the bottom plate, on the left, is the hour striking train actuated by a lever from the going train with an internally cut count wheel the numerals of which do not seem to coincide with the spaced notches. Top left of this count wheel is a spring to stop the strike, there is no quarter strike. On the right we have the main movement with stackfreed principal (q.v.) regu-

317. *Another book clock by Hans Kiening.*

318. *Bottom plate of Fig. 317.*

lation and Kiening's own fine adjustment device for altering the period of contact between the pallets (q.v.) and the crown wheel. How this operates will be better seen when the second example by Kiening is described. The small dial, top left, records the extent to which this fine adjustment has been applied.

Another clock by Kiening, less elaborate, but showing more clearly his method of regulation is seen in Figs. 317, 318 and 319. The dial has two hands, one recording civil time, 2 × I-XII, and the other astronomical or Italian hours (q.v.) marked 1-24 in arabic numerals. These hours are always in arabic numerals, why we do not know, but possibly because our knowledge of astronomy came to us via the Moorish savants. The shutters in the centre indicate the length of day and night and, incidentally, the times of the rising and setting of the sun. The purpose of the small dials marked 1-13 is to record the extent that the fine regulator has been applied. Fig. 318 shows the bottom plate, the tooth wheel under the pierced cock engages

319. *Hans Kiening's special regulation device.*

with a pinion, which in turn engages with a rack on the end of a cranked lever connected with the curved arm which forms the upper pivot bearing of the verge spindle (Fig. 319).

In the Kunsthistorisches Museum, in Vienna, there is a fine weight-driven mantel clock by Kiening, some 3 feet 8 inches high, dated 1578 in one of the earliest wooden cases known, beautifully painted in tempera.[6]

KNIBB, JOHN (1650-1722). A younger brother of the better known Joseph Knibb (q.v.) to whom he was apprenticed in Oxford in 1664. He was made a Freeman of Oxford in 1672 and later became very prominent in the civic life of the City, being appointed Bailiff in 1686 and again from 1690-1696; he was elected Mayor in 1697 and again in 1710. He was very active in his trade, employing ten apprentices at one time or another between 1673 and 1722, and made all sorts of clocks, lantern, 30 hour, wall clocks, long case, etc. and many of his productions survive. He is thought to have worked largely with his brother Joseph. That he co-operated with others is seen from a clock now in the Victoria and Albert Museum, London, which, although bearing his name on a cartouche (q.v.), has underneath the name of Samuel Aldworth, his first apprentice. The workmanship of this clock is poor and not worthy of the name of Knibb. Fig. 320 shows a fine long case clock (q.v.) by John Knibb and Fig. 321 a bracket clock that has a tic-tac escapement (q.v.). The clock in Fig. 320 is signed John Knibb, Hanslope, a village in Buckinghamshire to which Joseph retired; this would seem to indicate that John took over Joseph's business when he died in 1711; perhaps only for a short while, as the illustration shows the only known example with this signature.[21]

KNIBB, JOSEPH (1640-1711). A celebrated maker of the last half of the 17th century and elder brother of John (q.v.)

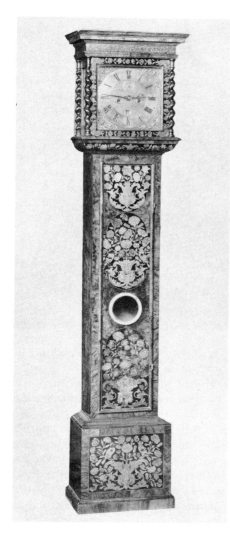

320. *Floral marquetry long case clock by John Knibb, Hanslope. c. 1712. (Dr C. F. C. Beeson)*

321. *Bracket clock by John Knibb, Oxford, c. 1670. (Dr C. F. C. Beeson)*

322. *Bracket clock with Roman strike by Joseph Knibb, London, c. 1685. (The late Mr W. J. Iden)*

323. *(Right) Fine dial of long case clock by Joseph Knibb, London, c. 1680.*

who was apprenticed to him in 1664. His establishment of himself as a clockmaker in Oxford was opposed by those already Free of that city and he traded for some years outside the city limits. In 1667 he applied for the Freedom, but this was opposed. Knibb then entered the trading ranks of Oxford by becoming a privileged tradesman in the employ of the University. He was eventually accepted as a Freeman in 1668. He did not remain long in Oxford after this, as in 1670 he was made Free of the London Clockmakers; in London he lived in Sergents Inn, Fleet Street. Why he left Oxford so soon after winning his fight for freedom is not known. Beeson in his *Clockmaking in Oxfordshire* suggests that he came to London to take over his cousin Samuel's (q.v.) business. Many fine clocks by Joseph are known, bracket, long case (q.v.), and night clocks (q.v.). Knibb introduced into England what is known as 'Roman Striking', utilising one bell for the I's and another for the V's. This results in a saving in the power needed for the striking train. Blows up to III are struck on the smaller bell and the V's on the larger. Clocks with Roman Striking have IV and not IIII on their dials (Fig. 322 and 323). The latter is an example of a superb long case dial.

Beeson records that a turret clock with anchor escapement (q.v.) in Wadham College, Oxford, which is not signed or dated, can with certainty be attributed to Joseph Knibb. The records for the maintenance of the clock date from 1670, one year earlier than the date on William Clement's clock now in

324. *Long case clock with skeleton dial by Peter Knibb, London, c. 1675. (British Museum)*

325. *Detail of the dial of Peter Knibb's clock. (British Museum)*

326. *Bracket clock by Samuel Knibb, London, c. 1665. (Clockmaker's Company)*

327. *Dial of Samuel Knibb's clock.*

the Science Museum. This does not necessarily mean that Knibb preceded Clement in the making of the anchor escapement.[21] (*See* WILLIAM CLEMENT.)

KNIBB, PETER (1651-?). Apprenticed to Joseph Knibb (q.v.), Oxford, 31st July, 1668 for seven years. He went to London with Joseph Knibb as a journeyman, and was made Free of the Clockmakers' Company 5th November, 1677. He left London in 1679. A clock by him is seen in Figs. 324 and 325.[21] This clock is very reminiscent of Joseph Knibb's work, except that the nicely chamfered hour hand is a little heavier than is usual with Joseph; there is nothing to differentiate between the two makers and one wonders if it were not made in Joseph's workshops and sold by Peter after he had established himself on his own account.

KNIBB, SAMUEL (1626-?1670). Samuel was a cousin of

Joseph and John Knibb (q.v.). Nothing is known regarding his apprenticeship. He started as a clockmaker in Newport Pagnell, Buckinghamshire, and became a member of the Clockmakers' Company by Redemption in 1663. A fine bracket clock by him is in the Guildhall Library, London (Figs. 326, 327 and 328). This clock is fully illustrated as it is one of the very few known to be by him that have come to the knowledge of the author. As will be seen this is a very fine clock, the dial especially so; it is by the same engraver who engraved the dial of the Hilderson clock (Fig. 278) and the East clock (Fig. 28). As Knibb entered into partnership with an instrument maker, Henry Sutton, when he came to London, it is possible that he devoted most of his time to that line.[21]

A fine example of a 17th century calculating machine is seen in Fig. 329. This is signed 'Henricus Sutton et Samuel Knibb,

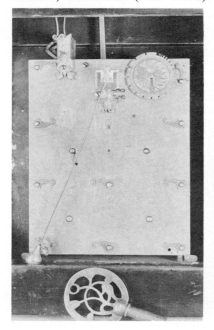

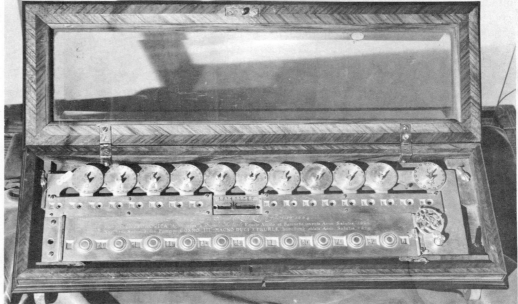

328. *Back plate of Samuel Knibb's clock.* 329. *Henry Sutton and Samuel Knibb's calculating machine. (Museum for the History of Science, Florence)*

330. *Long case lacquer clock by William Webster, London, c. 1735. Dial about 1750. (Rosenborg Castle, Copenhagen)*

331. *(Below) Mahogany lancet clock by Hawkins, Southampton, c. 1790. (The late Mr Percy Webster)*

332. *(Above) English lantern clock by William Selwood, London, c. 1620. Note copper sheathed driving weight. (Author's collection)*

Londini, fecerunt 1664'. The next line of the inscription is somewhat puzzling as it seems to indicate a date of invention 2 years after the machine was in fact made. It reads 'Machina Arithimetica a Samuele Morlando, Equite Aurato et Baronetto inventa Anno Salutis 1666.' The third line of the inscription indicates that it was offered to Cosmo III, Grand Duke of Tuscany in 1679, which accounts for its present situation in the Museum for the History of Science, Florence.

KREUZBLUMEN. A German term used to describe the finials (q.v.) on gothic clocks (q.v.). The earlier forms are single (Fig. 249), later they are more elaborate or double (Fig. 248). The literal translation is 'Cross Flowers', but as we, here in England, had no production of any domestic clocks during the period in which gothic clocks were made, we have no English equivalent to this and many other German terms.

LACQUER. A term used to denote coloured and sometimes opaque varnishes applied to wooden clock cases, which varnishes are based on the resin-lac. Originating in China, with the sap of the *Rhus Vernicifera*, it has been copied in Japan. Layers of lacquer of different colour are applied and then cut to expose the desired colour in the right position in the design. Fig. 330 shows a fine lacquer clock *circa* 1750. Early cases were sent

out to China to be decorated and often some years elapsed before their return; we can, therefore, find a difference in style between case and dial in these clocks. In the west, lacquering usually means covering the metallic surface of an article with a colourless varnish to prevent tarnishing.

LANCET CLOCK. A type popular at the end of the 18th century having a pointed top (Fig. 331). Here the carrying handles, usually on the top of earlier clocks, have been removed to the side as decoration and for occasional use. Clocks at this period were sufficiently cheap for there to be several in a household, so that the necessity for carrying them from room to room was no longer present.

LANTERN CLOCK. A name applied to the typically English style of wall clock developed from the beginning of the 17th century to the first quarter of the 18th century, and even later in country districts. Frequently referred to, erroneously, as 'Cromwellian Clocks', since they were in use at least half a century before Cromwell came to power. The name lantern clock is believed to have been inspired by the shape of ships' lanterns of the period. In the Rosenborg Castle in Copenhagen there is a silver ship's lantern taken by King Christian IV on his journey to the North Cape in the late 16th century; this, in

125

333. *Wing lantern clock by Thomas Wheeler, London, c. 1675. (Author's collection)*

shape, is not unlike the lantern clock design. Fig. 332 shows an early London made clock by William Selwood (*circa* 1620). It was made before the invention of the pendulum (q.v.) and has a balance which is hidden by the frets (q.v.). In these clocks the rate of going was controlled by the amount of the driving weight and this clock is the only one known to the author to have its original going train weight, a copper sheathed lead weight with room at the top for loose lead pellets to be added or removed, as desired. There was no necessity to provide for adjustment of weight in the striking train. The general design follows that of the gothic clock (q.v.) with a square pillar frame, going train in front, striking train behind and a bell carried in a canopy (q.v.). The frets above the clock in front and on the sides are of the early heraldic type.

Fig. 333 shows a later development which was really only a passing fad lasting about twenty years, in the latter half of the 17th century. After the pendulum was invented the greatly improved timekeeping caused practically all lantern clocks to be converted to pendulum; quite a simple operation really, the pendulum hanging down behind. (On the Continent the pendulum was often hung in front of the dial and known as a 'Cow's tail'). In the wing lantern the pendulum was cut from a thin brass sheet in the form of an anchor which was suspended between the two trains, the flukes of the anchor showing alternately in the wings on either side; the maker of this clock is Thomas Wheeler, 'neare the french Church' (London) date about 1675-1680. In this clock the frets are of the later 'dolphin' type.

Genuine English lantern clocks are always weight driven and

have only one hand. There are many modern reproductions to be found in the shops today, spring driven and with two hands. Fig. 334 shows a late continental (Italian) development of the lantern clock, a piece signed and dated 'Jo. Baptae de Alberto, Brixiae, 1685'. The outer hand tells the hour and the lower dial the quarter and minute, the centre of the upper dial is for setting the alarm. There are touch knobs for telling the time in the dark. In the triangular slot below, the day of the week appears. (*See also* 30 HOUR CLOCKS.)

LANTERN, DOOR. A small glass window let into the trunk door of a long case clock (q.v.) to allow the motion of the 1 seconds pendulum bob to be seen (Fig. 320). In clocks with a 1¼ seconds pendulum this lantern should be in the base, the front of which should be hinged to allow access to the bob. (*See* Fig. 283.)

LANTERN PINION. A hollow pinion as opposed to the solid leaf pinion. It is formed by fixing a series of small rods between two solid circular end plates. The Salisbury Clock (q.v.) shows two good examples.

334. *Italian lantern clock by J. B. de Alberto, Brindisi, 1685. (Clockmakers' Company)*

LANTERN, WING. *See* LANTERN CLOCKS.

LATCHED PLATES. Where the pillars between the plates, riveted into the front plate, are secured to the back plate by swivelling catches instead of pins passing through their protruding ends. (*See* Fig. 328.)

LENGTH OF DAY AND NIGHT. From the earliest times clocks were made that showed the length of the day, day by day and conversely the length of the night. At first, especially in the Nuremberg district (*See* NUREMBERG HOURS), by means of sliding shutters and later by a rising and falling shutter worked by an oval cam to indicate the times of sunrise and sunset throughout the year (Fig. 71). In Fig. 335 the two are given side by side in hours in a somewhat peculiar manner; in the outer ring are the days of the month at five days' intervals, next come two circles in which the outer and inner numerals always add up to twelve. The outer ring is for civil time, that is for the day starting at sunrise and ending at sunset. The two outer figures denote hours and the middle one, minutes. For sunrise add the minutes to the hour on the left, for sunset subtract the minutes from the hour on the right. The inner circle deals with the astronomical day which begins with dawn, that is when the sun in rising is 18° below the horizon and in setting has sunk 18° below the horizon. During the midsummer days the sun never gets as far as 18° below the horizon, so that, astronomically speaking, there is continual daylight during the period marked No Real Night. Within these two circles is a ring for the equation (q.v.) showing how much a clock should be fast or slow on a sundial on any given day.

The clock dates from about 1730-1735, but nothing is known of Daniel Man, its maker. Upper left is a tidal dial for London Bridge with an aperture for phases of the moon. The dial is not quite correctly set, the III should be opposite the 0, so possibly it is a universal tidal dial (q.v.). It is a three-train clock with a strike/silent dial (q.v.) upper right, and is an early example of a centre seconds hand. The clock is in an old established shop in St James's Street, it was probably delivered to that shop when first made.

LE ROY. A famous family of French clockmakers whose descendants are still in business and are Clockmakers to the Observatory in Paris. The first, Julien, 1686-1759, was appointed Clockmaker to Louis XV in 1739. Many fine examples of his work exist; according to Baillie he introduced the horizontal layout for turret clocks (q.v.). Many people have thought that this originated with Grimthorpe's 'Big Ben' (q.v.). Le Roy's high standard of workmanship did much to raise French clockmaking from the low level to which it had fallen.

His son, Pierre, was still more famous, he succeeded his father as Clockmaker to the King and is considered one of the greatest of French clockmakers. He concentrated on the problem of the 'Longitude' and shortly after John Harrison's success (q.v.), he produced a chronometer which he presented to the King in 1766. This is outside the scope of this book, it may, however, be mentioned that in trials at sea it had a performance about equal to Harrison's No. 4, although it was never subjected to the rigorous tests that Harrison's had to undergo.

LIECHTI FAMILY. A famous family of Swiss clockmakers that started with Laurenz I, born about 1480 and proceeded

335. *Dial of astronomical clock by Daniel Man, London, c. 1730.* (*Messrs Locke & Co.*)

through twelve generations to Jacob Ulrich, who died in 1857, although there is not much work surviving from the later generations.

Laurenz I was commissioned in 1514 to build the astronomical clock (q.v.) with automata (q.v.) for the Church of Our Lady in Munich, so we assume that he was then in his thirties; he died in 1545. The first productions of this family by Laurenz I and his son Laurenz II (d. 1598), were turret clocks (q.v.). Erhardt, the second son (d. 1591), started making domestic gothic clocks (q.v.). Many of the turret clocks are still working, the last made by Laurenz I in 1545 was for the town of Solothurn and is still there today. It would seem that he died before it was finished because it was completed by Joachim Habrecht of Schaffhausen (q.v.).

An example of Erhardt Liechti's work is seen in Fig. 248. His domestic clocks are all well made, but vary in the richness of their decoration. All Liechti clocks are signed and dated, a commendable trait rarely found in others, and one that would take a lot of uncertainty out of the study of antiquarian

336. *Movement of musical clock by Thomas Lister, Halifax*, 1785. (*Mr C. A. H. Glossop*)

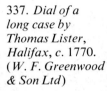

337. *Dial of a long case by Thomas Lister, Halifax, c. 1770.* (*W. F. Greenwood & Son Ltd*)

horology. In the turret clocks these inscriptions are cut with a cold chisel, but in the domestic clocks they are very lightly punched, usually on the lower cross bar of the frame, where they can easily be obscured if the frame be rusty or dirty. In some of the more elaborate the signature and date also appear painted on the dial. The makers' initials appear between the date figures, e.g., 15 E*L 84 for Erhard. Other known signatures are Andreas d. 1621 A*L, Ulrich-Andraeus d. 1627 UA*L, Andraeus II d.1663 A*L, Tobias d. 1673 T*L. Sometimes the upper cross bars of gothic clocks have a scrollwork lightly punched in. The work of the later members of the family is not so often found, nor do they continue the exact dating and signatures.[66]

LISTER, THOMAS (Halifax 1745-1814). He was a maker of repute during the last half of the 18th century. He made many astronomical (q.v.) and musical clocks. (Fig. 336). According to Britten he made a clock for the church at Illingworth, in 1802, with a 30 foot pendulum beating 3 seconds. (*Note.* A search in the Gazetteer has failed to establish a parish of Illingworth, however, let us accept that he made the clock.) The dial of a clock by Lister (Fig. 337) has an annual calendar dial showing the month and the day, the principal saints, a table for the equation (q.v.), the times of sunrise and sunset and the signs of the zodiac divided into degrees.

LOCKING PLATE. A disc in the edge of which are cut notches at increasing distances. At each blow of the hammer of the clock an arm is raised which falls either on to the circumference of the disc or into a notch. As long as it falls on to the circumference the clock can continue to strike, when it falls into a notch it stops the striking and the arm is then locked until raised by the warn (q.v.) for the next strike. The distance between notches is so calculated to allow the clock to strike one

to twelve in succession. This is for simple hour striking, for half-hour striking the notches are made wider to allow one blow after the finish of the hour. For Dutch Striking (q.v.) the spaced notches are duplicated (*see* Fig. 280), and for Grande Sonnerie (q.v.) quadruplicated (*see* Fig. 255). The inventor of the locking plate is not known, but as early as 1335 Galvano Fiamma writes of a clock in Milan that struck twenty-four blows according to the 24 hours of the day and night, one for the first hour, two for the second and so on. Renaissance clocks with locking plates for both 12- and 24-hour striking are not uncommon.

LONG CASE. The technical term for a 'Grandfather Clock.'

LUNAR CYCLE. The interval between two successive new moons is called the synodic period or lunation. The average length of this is 29·53 days. The sidereal period of the moon, that is the period for the moon to make a complete circuit of its orbit in respect to the stars is 27·3217 days.

In the year 433 B.C. the Greek astronomer, Meton, discovered that the number of days in nineteen years was an almost exact multiple of the number of days in a lunation. With a year of $365\frac{1}{4}$ days:

nineteen years equals 6939·75 days
235 lunations equals 6939·689 days

a difference of less than 2 hours. So that if full or new moon be on any given day, in nineteen years' time it will fall on that same day of the month. The Greeks considered this so wonderful that they ordered the dates of these 235 lunations to be cut in stone and the number of each year of the cycle to be gilded. Hence we have the alternate name of the Metonic Cycle and the numbers of the nineteen years of the cycle are known as 'Golden Numbers'.

338. *Fine Sèvres porcelain lyre clock by Kinable, Paris, c.* 1790. (*Victoria and Albert Museum, London*)

339. *American lyre clock, c.* 1845. (*Mr Walter M. Roberts*)

340. *A* 12-*hour Maltese clock, c.* 1820.

LYRE CLOCK. This style of clock, in which the pendulum bob forms the body of the lyre and the rods of the gridiron pendulum (q.v.), real or false, represent the strings of the instrument, came into being in France about 1785 in the reign of Louis XVI. The name of Kinable, a Parisian maker, is associated with their introduction (Fig. 338). The movement of the clock is contained in the base, the stand is made of Sèvres porcelain, ormolu mounted, decorated with brilliants. The dial is by the famous French enameller Coteau and indicates the hour, the minute, the month and the day. Clocks of this type were imported into America after the Revolution in France and gave rise to a style that became popular, although much less complicated than the French original (Fig. 339). A development of the American lyre clock was the replacement of the bracket of Fig. 339 with a box-like base, as seen in Fig. 70. This was then known as the banjo-lyre.[67]

MACHICOLATED. Some early balance wheels were decorated with crenellations and this type of decoration was also sometimes applied to early clock dials. (*See* Figs. 10 and 123).

MAINTAINING POWER. A subsidiary driving force brought into play whilst the main driving force, weight or spring, is ineffective during the action of winding. For weight driven clocks Christaan Huygens (q.v.) introduced an endless cord with a subsidiary weight which exerted power on the train of the clock whilst the weight proper was being drawn up. John Harrison's (q.v.) maintaining power within the cord drum of a clock is also still in use.

MALTESE CLOCKS. In the early years of the 19th century in the village of Siggiewi, about four miles from Mdina, in Malta, a certain Kalcidoniju Pisani started making clocks, later others in the village and also in the village of Zebbug made clocks, all of which were of very simple construction, weight driven with anchor escapement (q.v.), with a limited weight drop and only 12 hours going period. The first clock had only one hand as in Fig. 340, but later models had two hands and indicated minutes. A grandson of Kalcidoniju Pisani is still in the business.

MANFREDI, BARTOLOMEO. The son of Giovanni dell' Orologio (Dondi), he was a mathematician and astronomer, and was trained in the workshops of his father. On 26th November, 1462, he wrote a letter to the Marquis Lodovico Gonzaga which mentioned clocks so small that they could be carried on the person. This is, without doubt, the earliest

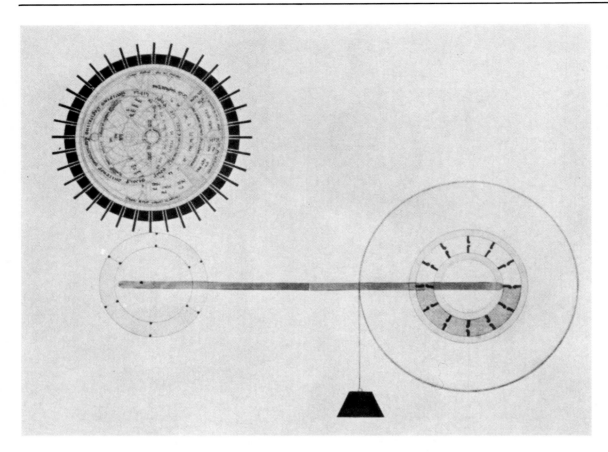

341. *Mercury clock with drum having perforated segments. The dial can record temporal hours. (Libros del Saber Astronomica. Manuel Rico y Sinoba)*

mention of the existence of this type of clock, and precedes by fifty years the mention of the work of Henlein (q.v.) and the 'Nuremberg egg'.[16]

MARQUETRY. A form of inlay, usually of complicated design, where sheets of veneer of different coloured woods are laid upon each other and cut to the same design. The different coloured designs are then fitted into each other and glued on to a base, usually oak in England and walnut in France. Marquetry cases were most popular during the period 1675-1730. The earliest forms were mostly with birds and flowers (Fig. 320). Sometimes coloured bone or ivory was used as well (Fig. 366), but later the designs became more conventional. The date of the introduction of marquetry into this country is uncertain. Very few clock cases in parquetry (q.v.), an earlier variant, survive and the author knows of no example that may be said to have been a beginner's effort; all are fully competent productions. The flower and bird designs of the early examples suggest Dutch influence, but there is no proof of this.

MASK. The representation of a human or animal head, usually in grotesque form, used as a decoration. In the latter, the lion head is most usual.

MATTING. In the latter half of the 17th century, with the coming of the classical period in English clockmaking, a fashion was introduced of 'matting' the base plate of the dial in those portions which were exposed. This very fine granulation of the surface, which has a most pleasing effect, is now a lost art. (*See* Fig. 62). It will be seen in most of the illustrations of clocks between 1660 and 1730.

Although matting may be considered an expensive method to adopt, it was probably much easier to attain than a flawless polished surface in those days before rolling mills.

MAZZOLENI, GUISEPPE. In 1551 he was the successful candidate for the contract for the restoration of the clock in St Mark's Square, Venice.[16]

MERCURY CLOCK. In the latter half of the 13th century the Court of King Alfonso X of Castille—Alfonso the Wise—was the centre of learning for Western European scientific knowledge. The Hispano-Moorish culture was based on the knowledge of the Arabs, especially in astronomy and mathematics. That the Arabs of the Middle East should be better versed than the Europeans in the west is not surprising when one considers that, apart from China, the origins of the science of astronomy lay with the Sumerians, later known as the Chaldeans and Babylonians (q.v.). The *Almagest*, the famous treatise on astronomy written by the Greek astronomer, Ptolemy, which also contained a catalogue of the stellar positions by him, was translated into latin by an unknown Sicilian about 1160; it was followed by a translation of the Arabic text by Gerard of Cremona in 1175.[68] These translations led to much activity in Spain and, under the patronage of the King, a new set of astronomical tables was drawn up at Toledo by fifty astronomers and named the Alfonsine Tables in his honour.[69] In 1276-1277 a series of volumes, the *Libros del Saber de Astronomica*, were published. These were reprinted under the aegis of the Spanish government in 1866.[70]

How far these were original findings and how far copied from earlier writings it is impossible to tell, but of the various time measuring devices, water clocks (q.v.), candle clocks, oil clocks (q.v.) we find nothing novel. The only one of interest is the mercury clock which works on the same principle as was adopted for the water clocks made in the 17th century. It is assumed that, had a mechanical clock with escapement existed

342. *A monstrance clock in unusual square form. German, 1605. (Mr K. Kellenberger, Winterthur)*

343. *Rear view of the monstrance clock.*

at the time of publication of this book, it would have been mentioned. Fig. 341 shows a sectional view of this 13th-century clock, consisting of a drum round which a rope carrying a weight is coiled, around the axle of this drum is an inner compartment divided into twelve divisions, the dividing walls being pierced. As the weight tends to pull the drum round in an anti-clockwise direction, the mercury, seeking its own level, as in the illustration, tends to turn the drum clockwise and the difference of these two forces can be controlled to allow a complete revolution of the drum in four hours. The line across the drawing indicates that on the same arbor is the six pin pinion on the left, of which the pins engage with the thirty-six oak teeth surrounding the dial of the astrolabe, thus the pinion of six pins is turned by the drum six times a day, causing one revolution of the astrolabe in 24 hours. The dial, which is designed for a latitude of 40°, that of Toledo, is divided into the temporal hours (q.v.). From the drawing it is not possible to say whether the base dial rotates once a day and the ecliptic (q.v.) makes a daily advance in relation to it so that it completes the circuit in a year, or whether the dial is fixed and the ecliptic circle makes an annual revolution before it. At any rate we have here a mechanical contrivance for recording temporal hours, which, being those in monastic use, were the more important at that time.

METAL BASKET. *See* BASKET.

METONIC CYCLE. *See* LUNAR CYCLE.

MICROMETER ADJUSTMENT. A method of pendulum regulation whereby the securing terminal to the pendulum suspension is fitted with a graduated ring so that fractions of a turn, or thread distance, can be measured (*See* Fig. 237). The method is used with spring-suspended pendulums as opposed to the facetted bob (q.v.) sometimes used with fixed-suspension pendulums.

MONSTRANCE. A name given to a type of Continental clock made somewhat in the form of a monstrance, which in the Roman Catholic church is used for holding the Holy wafers. Made mostly by the Augsburg makers in South Germany. Figs. 342 and 343 show two views of a rare monstrance clock inasmuch as it is square in shape instead of the usual circular form. This clock bears the maker's mark, [PB] of Augsburg. It is of gilt brass with silver ornamentation and a silver and enamel dial. It shows on the front the astrolabe, planispherium, sidereal time (q.v.), the position of the sun in the zodiac (q.v.), age and phases of the moon and its position in the zodiac, the nodes (q.v.), and has a ring showing the latitude of the moon. At the back there is an annual calendar dial with the fixed saints days for all the year, months, dates, and dominical letter (q.v.). In the small turret is a dial indicating the last hour struck which can be set for either 12 or 24 hour striking. On each of the four sides are auxiliary dials indicating mean time, day of the week and its corresponding deity, the sun's annual course in the ecliptic (q.v.), the times of sunrise and sunset and the lengths of day and night. There is also a dial for setting the alarm. The whole turns about on its ebony base.

MONTH CLOCK. A clock that will run four weeks with one winding. This involves an additional train (q.v.) necessitating a heavier weight or stronger spring. With the interposition of the extra train it winds anti-clockwise. The usual period is thirty-two days, that is four times an eight-day clock.

344. *Dial of a Morez clock with 1¼ seconds pendulum, 1820. (Messrs Camerer Cuss)*   345. *Movement of the Morez clock.*
346. *Back view of the Morez clock.*

MONUMENTAL CLOCKS. Those clocks whose size warrants the description. (*See* ATKINSON, SCHWILGUÉ and VERITÉ.)

MOREZ CLOCK. A type of clock which with its strip pillar framework recalls the gothic clock (q.v.). These clocks were first made towards the end of the 18th century in the village of

Morez in the Morbier district of the Franche Comté in the Jura mountains, near the Swiss frontier. Hence they are also known as Morbier clocks and Franche Comté clocks, their production continued, almost without modification, until the early part of the present century. Their peculiarities are that they have an inverted verge escapement (q.v.) with a seconds pendulum, or longer, which operates with a cranked fork which considerably reduces the amplitude (q.v.); and that they have a dual striking action; the hour is repeated two minutes later. This dual striking was not an innovation with these clocks, the principle had been in use for centuries. (Figs. 344, 345 and 346.) The dual rack is vertical instead of in the usual horizontal position and has a rod that falls by gravity on to the snail. From Fig. 347 it will be seen that the action is complicated, too much so for detailed discussion here. The drawing is introduced to show the vertical position of the rack.[71]

MOVEMENT. The technical name for the 'works' of a clock. It is sub-divided into trains (q.v.).

MUDGE, THOMAS (1715-1794). A very famous maker who was apprenticed to George Graham (q.v.) and for whom he worked, setting up on his own after Graham's death in 1751. He took William Dutton, who was also an apprentice of Graham, into partnership in 1755. One of his most famous inventions was the lever escapement (q.v.), which is the forerunner of the lever escapements to be found in almost all the watches and in most of the small travelling clocks of today. A watch hall marked 1770 was made for Queen Charlotte, wife of George III. Mudge made mainly watches; some long case clocks by Mudge and Dutton survive, they are all of good workmanship. In clocks Mudge's chief productions were his two clocks ca.1767, with lever escapement, which showed the moon's

347. *Diagram of the striking action of the Morez clock.*

348. *Bracket clock with exceptionally accurate lunar train by Thomas Mudge, London, 1777. (Watchmaker and Jeweller)* 349. *Back view of Mudge's clock showing the balance arbor supported on two intersecting segments. (Watchmaker and Jeweller)*

350. *'Musk apple' clock by Jacques de la Garde, Blois, 1552. (National Maritime Museum, Greenwich)*
351. *Movement of de la Garde's clock.*

352. *French Mysterious clock, c. 1880. (Science Museum, London)*   353. *Mysterious clock by McNab, Perth, c. 1850. (British Museum)*

orbit and took into account its eccentricity; he was the first maker to do this since Giovanni Dondi made his famous clock in 1364 (q.v.). One of Mudge's two clocks is in the Ilbert Collection, now in the British Museum (Figs. 348 and 349). Mudge also made a very fine marine chronometer which was given an award by the Board of Longitude after trial at sea; but it was too delicate and expensive for general adoption.

MUSK APPLE. In the days of the Renaissance (q.v.) it was the custom of the nobility to carry globe-shaped and pierced pomanders filled with sweet-smelling herbs, to counteract less agreeable odours; these were known as musk apples. Some early watches were made to be worn on a chain or ribbon and were globe-shaped with a dial on the underside. These are now exceedingly rare (Figs. 350 and 351).

MYSTERIOUS CLOCK. A type in which the means of maintaining motion is not obvious. There are several different kinds. One illustrated in Fig. 352 is a French type popular in the third quarter of the 19th century. The bronze figure is mounted on a rotatable base which has a scarcely perceptible motion, and which is connected with the escapement. Another type is shown in Fig. 353. Here a small movement is concealed within the larger end of the 'dumb-bell' and a small auxiliary weight is suspended from the centre, which provides that the centre of gravity of the whole is always below the centre of revolution.

NEWSAM, BARTHOLOMEW. Appointed to the reversion of the office of Clockmaker to Queen Elizabeth I in

1572 in succession to Nicholas Orseau or Urseau, who is believed to have been the son of Nicholas Orseau, Clockmaker to Edward VI and maker of the Hampton Court Clock. In 1590 he was appointed Clockmaker to the Queen; he had previously been Clock Keeper.[27] Newsam is one of the few makers working in London in the 16th century of whom some pieces survive; there is a very fine table clock by him in the British Museum. He died in 1593.

NIGHT CLOCKS. The desire to know the time in periods of darkness did not arise solely from the need to know the time during the hours passed in the bedroom. In the 17th century clocks were very expensive things and were only possessed by the wealthy, who, even then, would probably only have one in the house. Their rooms were large and illumination very poor and local, the recesses of the rooms were almost in darkness once the lamps or candles had been lit, so that to tell the time, except at the instant of striking, one had to go up to the clock with a light. This was one of the reasons for the introduction of Dutch Striking (q.v.) and Grande Sonnerie striking (q.v.). This probably accounts for some night clocks also having striking trains. (*See* Fig. 313).

The fashion arose of having dials pierced so that the light of a lamp placed behind could shine through the orifices. This fashion seems to have originated in Italy where night clocks are more often found than in this country. In Italy they have almost invariably 30-hour movements, whereas in England those known have eight-day movements. Edward East (q.v.)

made a well-known long case night clock, the only one known to the author. This has a seconds pendulum and anchor escapement (q.v.). Joseph Knibb (q.v.) made a few eight-day bracket night clocks (Fig. 354). The painted disc revolves once in two hours and carries subsidiary discs, one pierced with the even numbers showing, and one with the odd hours placed at 180° from the former. Fixed to the front plate is a small arm which carries each subsidiary disc forward one numeral as it passes. Thus when 6 disappears at the side of the dial on the right, 7 will appear on the left. In the arch each tooth represents a minute, small holes being pierced every five minutes; the slots represent the 1st, 2nd and 3rd quarters. Fixed inside the solid oak door at the back is a small bracket on which a lamp with a concave reflector behind the wick is placed, the chimney allows the heat from the lamp to escape. The escapement is verge (q.v.) and somewhat noisy for the bedroom. The author has a very similar night clock by Joseph Knibb in which the verge escapement has been silenced by fixing a weak flat spring under the leading edge of the pallets to take the recoil. This can be adjusted by a depthing screw and the result is almost noiseless operation. Complete silence was achieved by Campani (q.v.), but at the expense of accurate time-keeping.

A more simple type was a plain pierced revolving dial standing on a foot and shielded from a light placed behind, except for a section of 45° at the top, allowing a space of three hours to be read. A small night light was placed on a shelf

355. *Front view of Eardley Norton's astronomical clock made for George III in 1765. (By Gracious Permission of Her Majesty the Queen)*

behind the open sector, there was no cover to the light. (*See* also PROJECTION CLOCK and TREFFLER).

NODES, THE. The orbits of the sun and moon are inclined to each other at about 5°; were they both in the same plane eclipses of the sun and moon would take place every lunation. The points where these two orbits intersect are known as the ascending and descending nodes. Only when the sun, the Earth, the moon and a node are in line can an eclipse take place. If the node is within about $4\frac{1}{2}°$ on either side of this line, we get a decreasing total eclipse of the moon and a partial eclipse if the node is within 10° of the line. For the sun there is greater latitude, an eclipse, total or partial, will take place if the sun is within $15\frac{1}{2}°$ of the line through the nodes.

The ancients considered that the eclipse was caused by a dragon swallowing the eclipsed body, and the nodes were referred to as the dragon's head and tail. In all Renaissance clocks and in many continental ones of later date the nodal hand takes the form of a dragon. (*See* Figs. 116 and 423).

NORTON, EARDLEY (Working *circa* 1760, d. 1794). A maker of repute of complicated clocks and watches who was in the Clockmakers' Company from 1770 to 1794. One of his most famous pieces is a clock made in 1765 for King George III

354. *Night clock by Joseph Knibb, London, c. 1680. (Mr P.G. Dawson)*

sixteen bells.[73] The main dial has the astronomical 24 hours, the hand encircling the solar effigy in a ring rises on the left above the horizon plate forming the lower half of the circular opening in the dial, which plate rises and falls with the seasons. At sunset it will pass below the horizon on the right. The slender hand tells the minute and that with the solar effigy, the solar time or equation (q.v.). The small dial in the centre is for telling local mean time at the various places named thereon, a line being drawn from the place selected to the hour ring. In the upper portion of the dial is a segment showing the day and month which are read off a pointer at the top. This revolves once a year in connection with the equation kidney for the equation of time (q.v.), which kidney is very clearly seen in Fig. 356. Below are the winding holes for the three trains. On the opposite side are the lunar and tidal dials (Fig. 356). In the arch is the half-white half-black globe of the moon. In the main dial the outer ring is of $2 \times XII$ hours with, outside, the $29\frac{1}{2}$ days of a lunation. In the centre is a dial with various places around the coasts of England and Scotland marked on it; beneath this is Ferguson's oval tidal dial which shows the state of the tide at any of the places named by the degree to which the black edging shows at that place (foreshortened in the photograph). (*See* also Fig. 378.) On the side are, on the left a dial showing the orbits of the Earth and the five planets and their respective positions in the zodiac (q.v.) (Fig. 357) and on the opposite side, revolving anti-clockwise, an annual calendar is read off a fixed pointer (Fig. 358). Above is a segment showing

356. Back view of Eardley Norton's clock showing lunar and tidal trains. (By Gracious Permission of Her Majesty the Queen)

357. Planetary dial at the side of Eardley Norton's clock. (By Gracious Permission of Her Majesty the Queen)

358. Calendar dial at the side of Eardley Norton's clock. (By Gracious Permission of Her Majesty the Queen)

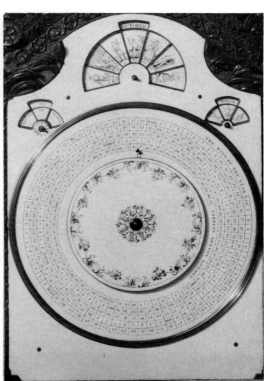

and now in Buckingham Palace. It is an elaborate clock with four dials, housed in a mahogany case with silver mounts. The clock cost £1,042 and the case, which was made by the King's cabinet maker, John Bradburn, cost £35 15s. (Fig. 355).[72] The clock is three train, astronomical and repeating. It chimes on eight bells at the quarters and plays a tune every three hours on

six of the months of the year with agricultural emblems, to the left, pendulum regulation and to the right, the day of the week with the daily planetary gods. James Ferguson, the famous astronomer of the middle of the 18th century, collaborated with Norton in the designing of the astronomical gears, and the oval disc for showing the state of the tide is his invention.

NUTATION. The polar axis does not revolve in a fixed position, but describes a small circle known as precession (q.v.). Imposed on this is a wavy movement (compared sometimes to the wobbling of a dying top), which is known as nutation and which was first discovered by the third Astronomer Royal, Bradley. He made his first observations in 1729, but waited for approximately 18½ years, the period of the revolution of the moon's nodes (q.v.), before making public his findings in 1748. The effect of nutation was not detectable in a clock until the coming of Shortt's free-pendulum clock (q.v.) in 1920.

OGEE. A moulding in which a convex curve continues in a concave form.

OIL CLOCK. This, like the candle clock (q.v.), is based on the regular rate of combustion of a commodity and like the candle, unless completely protected from draughts, could vary much in its time recording, so the oil clock is dependent on the constant regulation of its wick. Fig. 359 shows a German oil clock of the 18th century. In Fig. 360, a Japanese oil clock of the mid-18th century, the rat (the Japanese symbol for midnight) is filled with oil from a tube in the support which is connected with a cup fitted with a strainer. As soon as the access of air is prevented by the oil level, equilibrium is

 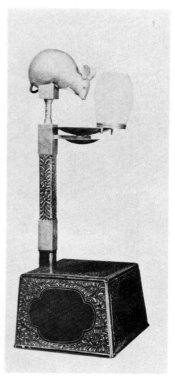

359. *A German oil clock, 18th century. (Science Museum, London)*

360. *Japanese oil clock, mid-18th century. (Chateau des Monts, Le Loche, Switzerland)*

361. *General view of the front of Jens Olsen's clock, Copenhagen, 1956. (Mr Otto Mortensen, Copenhagen)*

reached. A wick is laid in the oil cup; when the oil level has fallen sufficiently to admit air again, a fresh supply of oil is furnished, the cycle continuing as long as the oil supply lasts. The clock was used for timing night watches, vigils and prayers.

OLSEN, JENS (1872-1945). Olsen was born at Ribe, Denmark, the son of a weaver. He was apprenticed to a blacksmith and became proficient in instrument making. Later he went through Europe as a travelling journeyman, working in Germany, Switzerland and France, and visiting London before he returned to Denmark. Like Schwilgué (q.v.) it was through hearing as a child about a clock that could not be made to go that made him set his mind on being a clockmaker; it was

362. *General view of the back of Olsen's clock.*

363. *Front view of the perpetual calendar of Olsen's clock.*

364. *Back view of the perpetual calendar of Olsen's clock.*

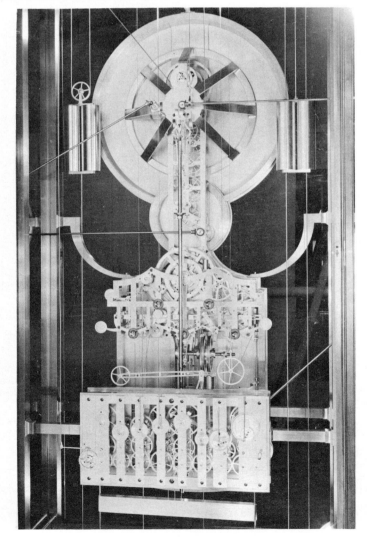

after a visit to Strasburg that he decided to make a clock on similar, but improved, lines. This was in 1901, but although in the intervening years he made his designs and calculations and had them checked at the Royal Observatory in Copenhagen, it was not until he was nearly seventy years old that he was able to start work on his masterpiece; then he was short of funds until 1943, when a public subscription was raised. He died in 1945 after an operation and before the completion of his clock, which was undertaken by his capable assistant, Otto Mortensen, who has published a most detailed and fully illustrated account of the clock.[74] Olsen had that very rare combination of mathematical theory and mechanical ability.

The clock seen in Figs. 361 and 362 is in three sections. In the centre is the mean time dial and below it the dial for sidereal time. Below this is the main calendar, which like that of Dondi, 1364 (q.v.) and Schwilgué, 1842 (q.v.) provides for the automatic registration of the movable feasts of the Church. On the left the dials show true solar time, the equation of time (q.v.) and local time, below this (left) the local time for anywhere in the world and (right) the times of sunrise and sunset. Below all these dials is a Gregorian Calendar (q.v.). On the right the upper dial shows the stars that rise and set as well as the circumpolar stars, taking into account precession (q.v.). Below are the planetary dials, on the left the heliocentric and on the right the geocentric motions of the sun and moon. Below these is the Julian Calendar (q.v.).

In calculating the astronomical trains Olsen may have achieved greater accuracy than his predecessors, but his is only an improvement on systems already well known; it is in his equation and perpetual calendar work that he introduces quite novel features.

In the very short notice that it is possible to give in this book it is proposed to confine comment on the general layout to that already given and to devote some time to the innovations in the perpetual calendar for Easter (q.v.), this being only the fourth made in the whole history of horology—Dondi, 1364, Schwilgué, 1842, Ungerer in the Messina clock on the lines of Schwilgué, 1933, and now Olsen, 1945. This calendar system is placed below the sidereal dial and has two dials, left for dominical letter (q.v.) and right for epact (q.v.). Below these are three more dials showing the solar cycle, the indiction and the lunar cycle (q.v.). Then come twelve strips, one for each month and each engraved 1-31 (Figs. 363 and 364). The days not required in short months are covered. Beside these fixed strips with the days of the month are movable strips showing the days of the week and the names of the movable feasts of the Church. A further strip carries the dates of the phases of the moon. At the last day of each year all these strips fall to their lowest position; as there is a certain amount of weight involved, the falling slides are connected with a plunger which descends into a cylinder which has only a small hole at the bottom, thus acting as a brake. The position of the strips is determined by the phases of the moon, since the chief indication is to be Easter Sunday. The clock sets the phase for the vernal full moon and from that all the other lunar dates fall into line. Details cannot be given here, but those interested are recommended to read Mortensen's profusely illustrated book.[74]

ORGAN CLOCK. A clock in which bells or gongs and hammers are replaced by pipes and bellows. There is record of a famous clock with an organ being made in London in the 1590's by one Thomas Dallam, a Lancashire man and an organ builder by trade, who lived in London. In 1599 he set sail with a famous organ embodying a clock, which was to be a present from Queen Elizabeth I to the Sultan Mahomet III of Turkey. Dallam described his journey and adventures (which included a peep into the Sultan's harem, which could have cost him his life) in a diary now in the British Museum.[75] His full adventures have also appeared in book form.[76]

ORMOLU. An alloy of copper and zinc, used largely in France, for the decoration of clocks. It is always gilded.

ORRERY. A mechanical device for portraying the relative motions of the sun, moon and the Earth, with sometimes the addition of the planets; operated either by hand or by clockwork. The first known is that made in about 1710 by George

365. *Orrery made in 1716 for Charles 4th Earl of Cork and Orrery by John Rowley, London.*

Graham (q.v.) and having the signatures of Tompion (q.v.) and Graham (Fig. 253). John Rowley of London is reported to have seen this machine and to have made a similar one in 1716 (Fig. 365), which came into the possession of Charles, Fourth Earl of Orrery. At the suggestion of Sir Richard Steele, the famous essayist, the instrument was called an Orrery in honour of its owner. (*See* under RAINGO CLOCK.) Rowley's Orrery was restored in 1937 by the late Commander Gould and was fully reported at the time.[77] It is now in the Maritime Museum, Greenwich.

OYSTER VENEER. A form of decoration achieved by cutting across the grain of branches. (Figs. 366 and 440).

PALLETS. That part of the escapement (q.v.) which, through the escape wheel teeth, imparts the impulse to the pendulum or balance.

PALLETS, GUT. A type invented by Thomas Tompion (q.v.) where the leading edge of the pallet in the verge escapement (q.v.) is formed by a small piece of gut. This gives a perfectly silent escapement (Fig. 211). It has often been said that this escapement was invented by B. L. Vulliamy (q.v.), but the fact is that Vulliamy took the fine Tompion Grande Sonnerie (q.v.) movement, which belonged to the Duke of Grafton, out of its case and substituted a movement of his own behind Tompion's dial. The Tompion movement he presented to the Institution of Civil Engineers, where it still is.

PARCEL GILT. A form of decoration where only part of the surface is gilded, in order to achieve a desired effect.

PARQUETRY. A form of veneer decoration that preceded marquetry (q.v.), where the individual pieces are cut with straight edges; diamonds, squares, rectangles, rhomboids, etc., and arranged to form a pattern.

PEDESTAL CLOCK. A clock placed on a pillar or pedestal so that it can be viewed from all round. A very fine example is seen in Figs. 367 and 368. This was made about 1590 and is of fine fire gilt brass (q.v.), it has three main trains with ting-tang quarters. The clock proper is surmounted by a gothic tower housing the bells and terminating in a turret with cannon, the whole surmounted by a conical roof. The decorations are partly of beaten brass and gilt and partly engraved. Below the main dial is a separate dial registering the quarters and at the back is a separate dial registering the last hour struck, up to twelve. The dials are silver with coloured enamel decoration. The trains are, going train with balance, hour striking, quarter striking and spring-driven alarm. The first three are weight driven, the weights in their gilt brass casings run down in separate compartments in the ebony veneered pedestal; these and the winding key are original. The alarm is spring driven. This is an outstanding example of late Renaissance craftsmanship from Augsburg.

PEDIMENT. Strictly speaking this is the triangular top to an architectural case (*see* Fig. 326), but is more loosely applied to that portion above the cornice in a clock case, irrespective of design.

366. *Long case month clock by Philip Cordery, London, c. 1685,* with oyster veneer. (*Biggs of Maidenhead*)

367. *A pedestal clock, Augsburg. Anonymous, c. 1590. The weights and key are original.* (*Mr K. Kellenberger, Winterthur*)

368. *Close up view of the back of the pedestal clock.*

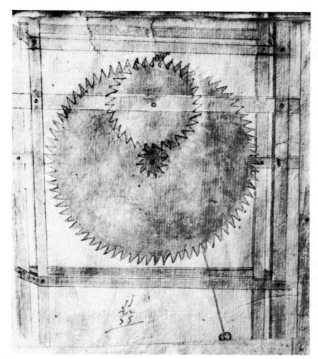 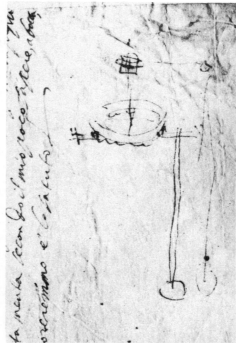 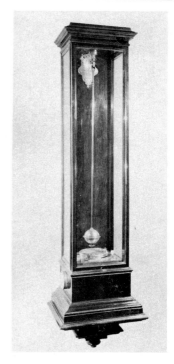

369. *Anonymous concept of a pendulum and tic-tac escapement, early 17th century, Italian. (La Clessidra, Rome. Illustration from L'Orologio e il Pendolo, Morpurgo, pp. 2, 4, 29)* 370. *Anonymous drawing of verge escapement and pendulum. Italian. (La Clessidra, Rome. Illustration from L'Orologio e il Pendolo, Morpurgo, pp. 2, 4, 29)* 371. *Clock with conical pendulum by Redier, Paris, c. 1859. (Conservatoire des Arts et Métiers, Paris).*

PEDIMENT, BROKEN. A pediment where the upper outline is broken. (*See* Fig. 28).

PENDULUM. A weight attached to a rod (or cord) which swings under the influence of gravity. Galileo (q.v.) discovered the principle and his escapement (q.v.) which functioned with a pendulum is seen in Fig. 204. There would seem little doubt that a clock was made with a pendulum by his son, Vincenzio, and also possibly one by Philip Treffler (q.v.). The practical application and its theoretical proof were introduced by Christaan Huygens (q.v.) in 1657 and 1673, although there are a few examples of clocks with pendulums before that date. (*See* CAMERINI.) Professor Morpurgo has illustrated several drawings for escapements with pendulums[80] which ante-date 1657, but whether they were actually constructed is difficult to say. Two of these are illustrated in Figs. 369 and 370. (*See* also VOLPAIA).

The length of the pendulum rod from the point of suspension to the centre of oscillation (not quite the same as the centre of gravity) determines the period or 'beat'. The amplitude (q.v.) and the weight of the bob do not affect the beat. (As regards amplitude *see* CYCLOIDAL CHEEKS).

PENDULUM APERTURE. A curved slot in the dial of a clock with a verge movement (q.v.) through which is seen a small swinging disc on an arm attached to the pallet arbor. (*See* BOB, FALSE.) This enables the clock to be stopped or set going again without tilting it or turning it around. The term is also applied to the window in the door of a long case clock (q.v.). (*See* LANTERN).

PENDULUM BOB. The weight set on the end of the pendulum rod. The earliest bobs were globular or pear-shaped and were used when the pendulum rod was fixed to the pallet arbor.

(*See* Fig. 280). With the coming of spring suspension a heavier type of bob was necessary. As a larger round or pear-shaped bob meant increasing the depth of the case, a flat lenticular bob was introduced (Fig. 147), which gave the necessary weight without calling for any extra depth of the case in those examples where the clock was encased. A pendulum bob can take any shape provided it has the necessary weight. In wing lantern clocks (q.v.) the bob takes the form of a thin brass sheet cut in the shape of an anchor.

PENDULUM, COMPOUND. A pendulum pivoted at the centre with adjustable weights above and below. Long periods can be achieved by this method with quite short pendulums.

PENDULUM, CONICAL. A pendulum that has a circular instead of a lateral motion and which should work, roughly, on the principle of the governor as used in engineering where, when the force increases, the governor balls spread out, lessening the effect of gravity, and slowing down the rate of revolution.

The Minutes of the Royal Society contain the reports of several experiments by Dr Robert Hooke (q.v.) with conical pendulums, which he termed inclined pendulums, in 1666/7, and many students of horology have confused these with experiments for the anchor escapement (q.v.).

The restoring effect of gravity decreases with the angle of inclination until at 90° it is nil and the construction ceases to be a pendulum becoming a bar balance. Whilst a pendulum controls the driving force of a clock, be it weight or spring driven, once the restoring force of gravity is lost, the rate of vibration of the foliot or balance is controlled by the weight or strength of the spring. Huygens (q.v.) did a good deal of research into the conical pendulum at the end of the 17th century, and in the

372. *Two double bob pendulums.*

373. *Early example of mercury pendulum by George Graham, London, c. 1727.*

18th and 19th centuries several attempts were made to produce clocks which should have had an uninterrupted recording of time with conical pendulums, but unpredictable difficulties arose which exceeded the limits of correction and the attempts were abandoned. A clock with conical pendulum is seen in Fig. 371.

PENDULUM, DIAL. Some French clocks were made towards the end of the 18th century in the shape of a lyre and in certain cases the movement of the clock itself and its dial constituted the pendulum bob. (*See* LYRE CLOCK).

PENDULUM, DOUBLE BOB. Towards the end of the 18th century a device was adopted for placing two lenticular bobs on one pendulum rod. Rough adjustment was achieved by moving the smaller bob and the final adjustment was by a rating nut (q.v.) under the lower, heavier bob (Fig. 372).

PENDULUM, ELLICOTTS. *See* ELLICOTT, JOHN.

PENDULUM, FALSE. *See* BOB, FALSE.

PENDULUM, FREE. The ideal pendulum is one that swings free from any interference from the movement of the clock. In the verge, anchor, dead beat and other escapements (q.v.) one pallet (q.v.) is always in contact with the escape wheel and the pendulum is never free. The first free-pendulum clock was made in 1898 by R. J. Rudd of Croydon (q.v.), but it was never a commercial success. An immense step forward was made in the free-pendulum clock invented by W. H. Shortt in 1920 (q.v.).

PENDULUM, GRIDIRON. James Harrison, or James and his brother, John (q.v.), conjointly in the 1720's experimented with various metals to ascertain their degrees of expansion under heat. They used rods of steel, iron, Sheffield, Birmingham

and Holland brass and hung them outside their house, where they were subjected to the maximum differences of temperature available.[81] They found that the brass to steel ratio was about 3:2, so that if they took a steel rod 9 feet long and a brass rod 6 feet long and united their lower ends there would remain a constant difference between the upper ends of 3 feet. Since these were, however, impractical dimensions, they cut the rods into 3 feet lengths and laid the rods side by side, adding four more on the other side to balance (*See* Figs. 30 and 271). This type of pendulum is still used today in high-class clocks and regulators (q.v.).

PENDULUM, HORIZONTAL. This is a misnomer, for to be a pendulum at all there must be the restoring force of gravity, which is nil when the pendulum is truly horizontal. The term is applied to a pendulum which is *nearly* horizontal, and which thus has a very small gravitational resorting force; it has a very long period. (*See also* PENDULUM, CONICAL).

PENDULUM, MERCURY. In the early 1720's George Graham was experimenting with the differential expansion of metals, steel and brass *inter alia*, as were the Harrisons (q.v.). He abandoned these experiments however, in favour of mercury, whose change of volume with change of temperature is very marked. His pendulum had a bob in the form of a glass jar partially filled, after experiment, with a definite amount of mercury. When the temperature rose or fell the level of the mercury also rose or fell, offsetting the change in the length of the pendulum rod, thus keeping the centre of oscillation constant (Fig. 373). The mercury pendulum is still used today in high-grade clocks.

PENDULUM, SIMPLE. A theoretical conception of a mass suspended by a weightless cord or rod.

PENDULUM, TORSION. A pendulum that twists on its suspension spring instead of flexing it laterally. At the bottom it carries a large circular bob, or balls at the end of four arms as the bob. Used in 400-day clocks and in the Atmos clock (q.v.). The torsion pendulum requires much less force than the ordinary pendulum. (*See also* TORSION CLOCK).

PENDULUM, 1¼ SECONDS BEAT. The greatly improved timekeeping resulting from William Clement's anchor escapement (q.v.) and its adoption with a 39 inch 1 seconds pendulum, led clockmakers to believe that still greater accuracy would be obtained by increasing the length of the pendulum and some long case clocks (q.v.) were made in the last quarter of the 17th century with 5 foot pendulums beating 1¼ seconds (Fig. 283). In this case the base of the case should be hinged and contain the lantern for the pendulum bob (q.v.) and the seconds ring should be marked with four divisions every five seconds. Original 1¼ seconds pendulum clocks are very rare; it is, however, an easy matter to change the escape wheel and to fit a 5 foot pendulum and so pretend that a genuine 1¼ seconds clock is available; the above points should be watched. The additional accuracy was not established and the long pendulum soon died out. Nowadays it is only found in some turret clocks (q.v.).

PENDULUM, 2 SECONDS BEAT. As mentioned under 1¼ seconds pendulum, clockmakers of the latter part of the 17th century were seeking for greater accuracy than was given with the 39 inch 1 seconds pendulum and the anchor escapement

374. *A picture clock with seaside scene by C. H. Rivère, Paris, 1846. (Messrs Camerer Cuss)*
375. *Long case clock by Christopher Pinchbeck, London, c. 1730*

(q.v.) and experiments were made with pendulums of 14 feet beating 2 seconds. (*See* THOMAS TOMPION.) These long pendulums are today only used in turret clocks (q.v.), where a stiff rod can give the necessary rigidity. Big Ben (q.v.) has a 2 seconds pendulum (1854). It is claimed that B. L. Vulliamy (q.v.) introduced the 2 seconds pendulum for turret clocks with that on the Horse Guards made in 1817.

A well-known example is the pendulum in Rye Church which has a beat of approximately $2\frac{1}{4}$ seconds. It is probable that the pendulum length was adapted to the beat of the foliot when the clock was converted, instead of modifying the movement to take a 1 seconds pendulum; this clock is the oldest clock to be continuously in use since it was made. A list of clocks with very long pendulums by the Rev. A. J. Nixseaman is given in the Horological Journal for January 1957.

PERIGEE. The perigee of a celestial body is when it is at the nearest point in its orbit to the Earth.

PICTURE CLOCK. A fashion arose in the latter part of the 18th century of painting a scene, either a village with a clock or a town scene, and of putting a watch movement in the church tower. Mostly these had to be wound every day and the picture was hinged in the frame to allow it to swing forward for winding. Fig. 374 shows a more elaborate example; it is an eight-day movement and the figures in the foreground are actuated. The monk in the tower nods his head, the guitar player plays his guitar and beats time with his foot, the flag flutters and the

ships in the foreground rise and fall with the swell, those in the background pass and repass, the fountain runs and the girl in the centre mends the nets.

PILLAR CLOCK. *See* PEDESTAL CLOCK.

PILLARS. The distance pieces between the top and bottom plates in a horizontal or table clock and between the front and back plates (q.v.) of a vertical clock. In the horizontal clock the pillars often took a baluster form with the bulging part resting on the bottom plate, a natural position. With the coming of the pendulum and the introduction of the vertical mantel clock we find tradition causing the continuance of the use of baluster pillars with the bulging part against the back plate, which corresponds to the bottom plate in a horizontal clock, quite an unnatural rendering (Fig. 52). It was some twenty years or more before the horizontal pillars were made with the centrally placed boss for decoration. (*See* Fig. 15).

PINCHBECK, CHRISTOPHER. A celebrated maker whose name is probably chiefly remembered by the alloy of four parts copper and three parts zinc, the colour of which closely resembles gold, which he invented and which is called after his name. The composition of this alloy was a jealously guarded secret between the father and son (q.v.). He described himself as a maker of astronomical (q.v.) and musical clocks and is known to have made clocks for Louis XIV and other European royalties. A fine long case clock (q.v.) by him *circa* 1730 is seen

376. *Dial of Pinchbeck's clock.*

in Figs. 375 and 376. Beyond the ordinary hours, minutes and seconds the dial shows in the arch the age and phases of the moon together with the times of high tide at various ports around the English coast. The subsidiary dial on the right shows the position of the moon in the zodiac (q.v.) and on the left the sun's position in the zodiac and the southing of 24 principal stars (q.v.). The lower dials show, on the left, the month with its sign of the zodiac and the day of the week, and its planetary deity on the right. The decoration of the dial is unusual in that it is of beaten brass sheet and gilt.

PINCHBECK, CHRISTOPHER JNR (1710-1783). Christopher Junior was the eldest son of Christopher (q.v.). He was appointed Clockmaker to King George III and it was through him, in virtue of his office, that Eardley Norton (q.v.) received his order for the astronomical clock (q.v.) he made for the King in 1765. In 1768 the clock seen in Figs. 377, 378, 379 and 380, was made by Christopher Pinchbeck Jnr, to the designs of the King and his architect, Sir William Chambers. There does not seem to be any record of the price.[82] A Mr Merigeot and a Mr Monk, both of the Clockmakers' Company, were associated with the clock, presumably with the astronomical work.

The clock stands on a circular base veneered with tortoise-shell and is richly decorated with ormolu fluted Corinthian columns (q.v.), with a fire gilt (q.v.) and pierced gallery surrounding the dome on top. Horologically the clock is much a replica of that supplied three years earlier by Eardley Norton, as will be seen by comparing the dials of the two clocks. In the

377. *Front view of astronomical clock made by Christopher Pinchbeck Jnr, London, in 1768 for King George III. (By Gracious Permission of Her Majesty the Queen)*

378. *Back view of Christopher Pinchbeck's clock.*

379. Planetary side dial of Pinchbeck's clock. (By Gracious Permission of Her Majesty the Queen)

380. Calendar and celestial dial of Pinchbeck's clock. (By Gracious Permission of Her Majesty the Queen)

main dial the seconds hand has been added, otherwise the rising and the setting of the sun, its passage across the meridian and the equation of time (q.v.) are the same. The lunar dial at the back has a similar revolving globe on top and Ferguson's oval tidal dial, which, in Fig. 378 can be fully seen instead of being foreshortened as in Fig. 356. This indicates the hour on the 24 hour astronomical basis, high tide being shown by the gilt hand reaching to the age of the moon circle and low tide by the small steel pointer at various places named on the small central dial as the black disc revolves below it. There are two extra auxiliary dials, that on the left is for covering the winding holes, to exclude dust, and that on the right is a pendulum fixing dial (q.v.). The side dials are slightly different, the positions of the setting and day of the week dials are reversed and the month dial shows the zodiacal sign instead of the agricultural figure. The daily calendar for the year is replaced by a monthly calendar and the central dial shows the northern sky. The planetary dial is almost identical and a bi-metallic thermometer is introduced into the arch.

PINEAPPLE. A type of decorative architectural finial (q.v.) adopted for clock cases from the Restoration period (Fig. 381). Rarely, if ever, found on long case clocks (q.v.).

PLANETARY CLOCK. A clock in which the hours of the day are coupled with the planetary sign which is supposed to rule each hour of the day and night. (*See* Fig. 132). Also a

clock in which the motions of the various planets are recorded. (*See* Figs. 392 and 163).

PLANISPHERE. A clock in which the motions of the various celestial bodies are projected on to a plane surface. An early one designed by Christaan Huygens (q.v.) in 1682 and made for him by J. van Ceulen of the Hague (q.v.), now in the Museum for the History of Science, Leyden, is seen in Figs. 382 and 383. At the top is a semi-circular opening marked with the minutes

381. A bracket clock by Francis Dowell, London, c. 1770, with pineapple finials. (The late Mr Percy Webster)

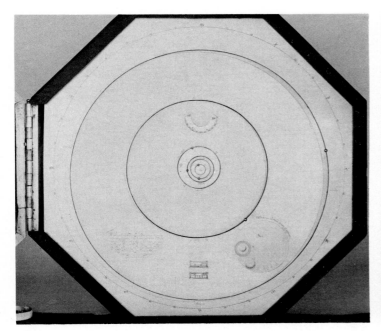
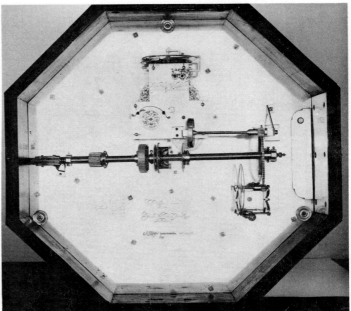

382. *Front view of Huygens' planispherium made by J. Van Ceulen, The Hague, 1682. (Museum for the History of Science, Leyden)*
383. *Back view of Huygens' planispherium.*

and behind this a dial revolves once in 2 hours in which are two holes, through which show in the one the odd hours and in the other, the even. As this revolves, the hour numerals change; in the illustration VIII will be disappearing on the right and IX entering from the left. The sun is in the centre of the main dial and around it are, first, the inferior planets, that is those between the sun and the Earth, Mercury and Venus, then comes the Earth followed by the superior planets, Mars, Jupiter and Saturn. The eccentricity of their orbits is indicated by a thin line. Lower right is a scale representation of the relative sizes of the sun and the planets. In the slots at the bottom are, upper, the days of the month, and lower the degrees divided into hundreds. Encircling all is the ecliptic (q.v.). Fig. 383 shows the back plate (q.v.) on which is inscribed that A. J. Reyer restored the planispherium with his own hands in 1786. (*See* also BALANCE SPRING.)

PLINTH. Another name for the base of a long case clock (q.v.). Sometimes confined to the skirting of the base.

POMEGRANATES. A stylised representation of this fruit found in some Continental iron clocks. (*See* Fig. 123). The pomegranates are the ball-shaped decorations surmounting the pillars on each side of the dial.

PORTICO TOP. *See* PEDIMENT.

PRECESSION OF THE EQUINOXES, OR SIMPLY **PRECESSION.** The axis of the Earth does not turn exactly on itself, but its end moves in a circle, rather like the cone described by the top of a top when slowing down. The pole of the terrestrial axis takes 26,000 years to complete this circle, which has the effect of imparting a retrograde motion to the Vernal Equinox (q.v.) and which, as a result, is now in the constellation Pisces instead of being at the 1st Point of Aries (q.v.). The motion is 50·2 seconds of arc a year. Newton first

explained the cause of the phenomenon, although its existence was known to the ancients.

PRIMUM MOBILE. The ancients in their observations noted that besides the fixed stars there were seven stars that wandered, i.e., the planets, the sun and the moon being included in the seven. The fixed stars were only fixed in their relative positions, while they continued in an unceasing motion in one direction, which they called the Firmament. They noticed that the sun and moon followed the same motion, so they attributed this also to the planets. There were, however, differences between the apparent motions of the fixed stars and the planets; the ancients then thought that beyond the Firmament and all the stars there was another sphere, which they called the Primum Mobile, because it was a law unto itself. (*See* Fig. 132). This sphere, having the swiftest motion of all, carried with it all the orbits, stars and spheres and influenced them. Two immovable points were accepted, about which the whole sphere of the Primum Mobile turned and which they called the poles of the world, one in the north they called after Arctus or Ursa, which is near it, and the other in the south, they called Antarctus, because it is diametrically opposed to the north.

PROJECTION CLOCKS. About the 1930's much advertisement was made for clocks, which, when a light was switched on, projected the dial of the clock on to the ceiling. This idea was already current in the early 18th century (Fig. 384), although its adoption might have been more general in the 20th century. However, the convenience of knowing the time at night, without having to sound a repeater, and perhaps wake up an angry spouse, continued and three early-19th century night clocks (q.v.) are seen in Fig. 385, two of which are projection clocks.

PRUNK UHR. A German term for a very elaborate clock. Usually the clock dial is the most insignificant part of the

384. *Early 18th-century projection clock.*

385. *(Left and Right) Two early 19th-century projection clocks. (Ilbert Collection, British Museum)*

whole, which may be an elaborate silversmiths' production and perhaps set with semi-precious stones (Fig. 386). To English eyes these clocks seem hideously overloaded. The nearest we get in England are the ornate silver dressing-table sets of the Restoration period In the author's opinion these clocks are 'A great deal of Prunk and very little Uhr'.

QUARE, DANIEL (1647-1724). A maker of great repute who was a rival to Thomas Tompion (q.v.). We must admit, however, that whilst Tompion never put out anything that was not absolutely of the highest order, some of the work which bears Quare's name is not up to the standard of his finest work, which can rank alongside the best of his time.

As a strict Quaker, Quare could not take the oath, and this prevented him from being appointed Clockmaker to the King; nevertheless he was received at the Palace and was free of the back-stairs. He had connections with many of the nobility and Sarah, Duchess of Marlborough was at his daughter's wedding to Silvanus Bevan in 1715. The Prince and Princess of Wales were invited, but because of an Act of Parliament which forbade their attendance at a ceremony in a non-conformist building, they were unable to attend. A letter from Rebecca Osgood, daughter of Salem Osgood, written nearly two months afterwards, describes the wedding. 'As to yᵉ wedding I don't know, but yᵉ hast had an account of it before this, but I will give yᵉ the best account I am capable of, being of yᵉ invited gest. Yᵉ Prince and Princess and most of yᵉ quality was invited, and thay gave them some hopes of honouring them with there company till yᵉ night before, and then they sent word yᵗ they could not come, nor none of yᵉ quality which had places, because of yᵉ Actt which obliges them to go into no meeting—but thare was severl of yᵉ quality yᵗ had no places, yᵉ Dutchess of Marlbourow was thare, and yᵉ Lord Finch, yᵉ Lady Cartwrite,

386. *Baroque 'Prunk Uhr' with chimes and automata by Caspar Hoffman, Augsburg, c. 1690. (Hessisches Landesmuseum, Munich)*

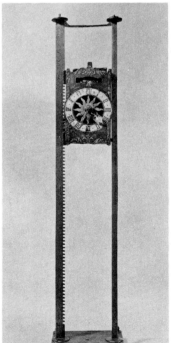

yᵉ Venetian Ambascior and his lady, and a lady that is governess to yᵉ young Princesses, hous name I have forgot, and severl other persons of distinction. Thay desiered yᵗ yᵉ meeting might be put of till one of yᵉ clock, which was don.

'Accordingly from thence we went to Skiner's Hall whare we dined thay gave a very splendid dinner as could be and yᵉ quality was mightily pleased both with yᵉ ceremony of yᵉ marriage and thare entertainment as to yᵉ young cuple thay came of very well. Yᵉ bridegroom spoke very hansomly and yᵉ bride better then could be expected before so great an ascembly. I had yᵉ honour to wate on them home at night.'[83]

Quare was a 'Great Clockmaker' when admitted as a Brother to the Clockmakers' Company in 1671, that is to say he served his apprenticeship and was made Free of some other Company before he joined the Clockmakers; probably the Blacksmiths' Company. In 1708 he was Master of the Clockmakers' Company. A very fine year equation clock (q.v.) by Quare is seen in Fig. 387, now in the Ilbert Collection in the British Museum. The author remembers the late Courtnay Ilbert telling him of the acquisition of this clock. He was in Brussels in a clockmaker and jeweller's shop and inquired if they knew of any old clocks for sale. They told him an address where they wound clocks, where there was one, but it was rather large. Ilbert went off to the address, acquired the clock for £100 and had it packed and shipped to London.

Quare was successful in an adjudication by King James II for a Patent for a repeating watch, his rival being the Rev. Edward Barlow (q.v.), the inventor of the rack and snail striking device (q.v.), which made repeating possible. Quare's watch repeated the hour and quarter at one push of the button, whereas Barlow's needed a push for the hour and another for the quarter. Quare is intimately connected with the production of the first mechanical equation clocks (q.v.). Until recently the claim of Joseph Williamson (q.v.) to have made all equation movements produced in England up to about 1720 had not been challenged, but the author's researches show that Tompion (q.v.) was making equation clocks as early as Quare, for whom Williamson then worked. It is now generally accepted that neither Quare nor Tompion invented the equation kidney, but that both got the idea from Christaan Huygens (q.v.). (See EQUATION OF TIME). All Quare's equation clocks have the equation kidney and its wheel and rack separate from the movement of the clock proper and connected with it by a rod and endless worm. It will be noted in the illustration that the equation dial, with its movement behind it, appears in the top of the door; it is, in effect, connected with the clock movement in the manner described. We see then that it would be quite possible for Williamson to have made the equation movements and for Quare to have made the clock proper. Quare also invented a portable barometer and many fine examples from his workshops exist.

QUATREFOIL. A Gothic window with four cusps instead of the usual three (Trefoil).

QUOINS. The imitation of the stone corner pieces used in masonry. This form of decoration of the base of a long case clock (q.v.), in the author's experience, is confined to Lancashire towards the end of the 18th century. Perhaps one particular case maker was working for several clockmakers in that county. Fig. 388 shows a clock by Archibald Coates of Wigan. (See also BARKER, WILLIAM).

387. *Year long case clock by Daniel Quare, London, c. 1710. Note that the equation dial in the trunk is separate from the clock proper.* (*Ilbert Collection, British Museum*)

388. *Long case clock by Archibald Coates, Wigan, c. 1760 with 'Quoins' decorating the base.*

389. *German rack clock, late 17th century.* (*Bayerisches National Museum, Munich*)

RACK CLOCK. A clock which uses its own weight as the driving force, its rate of fall being checked by the resistance of the movement (q.v.) to its descent of the rack. A supposedly early example is seen in Fig. 389. Possibly we have here a later adaptation of a clock of the Gothic type and period, as in the middle of the 17th century a clock of this type would not have had hour and minute hands. Rack clocks were popular in France towards the end of the 18th century and many types are found in Japan. (*See* JAPANESE CLOCKS).

RACK AND SNAIL STRIKE. A system invented by the Rev. Edward Barlow in 1676. The hour hand arbor carries a disc the circumference of which is divided into twelve equal segments, and on the surface of this disc are inscribed twelve equidistant concentric circles. The disc is then cut away down to each circle in sequence, thus forming a series of steps. Since there are twelve divisions on a 12-hour wheel it follows that it will take 1 hour for the disc to pass from one step to the next. Fixed to the front plate of the clock is a bent lever having a pin on the end of the shorter arm and a rack on the other end. Just before the strike the rack falls to the left and the pin on the lower arm comes in contact with the snail and places the rack in such a position that a number of teeth can be gathered by the gathering pallet (missing in the photo) corresponding to the depth of the step of the snail. After the correct number of teeth have been gathered—one for each hour blow struck—the system locks. It will be realised that since it takes 1 hour to pass from one step to the next, in a repeating clock

390. *Barlow's rack and snail striking movement, c.* 1680.

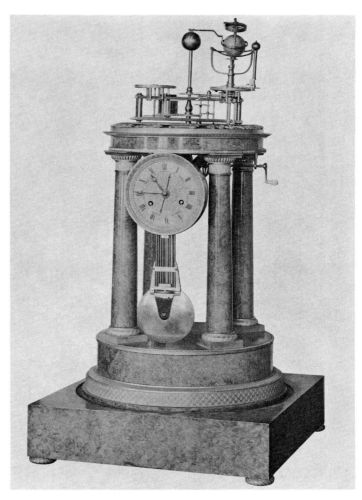

391. *Astronomical clock by Raingo, Paris* 1824. *Now in Windsor Castle.* (*By Gracious Permission of Her Majesty the Queen*)

the same hour will be struck throughout the journey from one step to the next (Fig. 390).

RADELOFF. A pupil of Jost Burgi (q.v.) who adopted Burgi's cross-beat escapement (q.v.) and who introduced the falling ball drive having a constant torque (q.v.). (*See* BALL DRIVE).

RADIUS VECTOR. Kepler's second Law is: The radius vector joining the sun to the planet, sweeps out equal areas in equal times.

RAINGO CLOCKS. The Parisian firm of Raingo made the usual range of domestic clocks. (The author's parents had a clock as a wedding present in 1886, signed 'Raingo, Paris'). All Raingo clocks were of good quality, the name is, however, used to denote a series of very fine clocks with orrery (q.v.) attachments on top. The latest information is that the Raingo who made these clocks fled to Belgium for political reasons when a young man, and that he remained there for many years, if not for the rest of his life.[84] He, or his successors in the firm, would seem to have been in France in 1823 as Raingo was Clockmaker to the Duc de Chartres. Figs. 391 and 392 show two typical Raingo clocks. Colonel Quill made a special study of Raingo clocks[85] and lists nine examples known, of which two have since disappeared, to this list must be added what is perhaps the finest of them all, made about 1810 and recently found

392. *Detail of the orrery of a Raingo clock, now in the Soane Museum, London.*

by Dr Bertele in Belgium and signed 'Raingo à Gand.'[84] The example (Fig. 391) is in Windsor Castle and the close-up view of the orrery is from the example in the Soane Museum, London. Of those in public collections we list Conservatoire des Arts et Métiers, Paris, Glasgow Art Gallery, Palais du Cinquentenaire in Brussels and the Royal Collection in Madrid. All are very much on the same lines, the cases being of beautifully mottled amboyna wood. A curious combination with such a scientific production as this is the provision of a musical box in the base of some examples. The Windsor Castle clock was purchased by George IV in 1824 for 300 guineas. Besides the hour and the minute hands on the main dial, the third hand indicates the day of the week with one end and the planetary deity with the other. These clocks have three motive springs, those for the clock and striking trains need winding every week, but that for the orrery, which can be seen in the upper part in Fig. 392, above the XII, only needs to be wound once in four years.

This illustration shows an enlarged view of the orrery (q.v.). Outside are the representations of the signs of the zodiac with the next ring dividing each section into 30° and within that the names and days of the month. The dial is read off the pointer over the dial at the end of the platform carrying the astronomical mechanism. The large dial in front is a four-year dial, three years being marked Commune (ordinary) and the fourth Bissextile (q.v.) (Leap Year). The hand in the photograph is nearly on to Bissextile, which is an indication that the astronomical train has to be re-wound. Of the celestial indications, the sun is in the centre and the Earth revolves around it once a year, turning on its axis once a day. The curved arm,

and another not seen, indicate those parts of the globe where it is sunrise and sunset. The large dial below the Earth shows the age of the moon and the ring above it, solar time. The moon turns on its axis in its sidereal period of 27⅓ days and completes its tour round the Earth in 29½ days. For demonstration purposes the orrery can be disconnected and turned by the handle such as that seen in Fig. 391.

RAINIERI, GIAMPAOLO (FATHER) AND GIAN CARLO (SON). These two from Reggio received the contract in 1493 to make the clock in St Mark's Square, Venice. They did the work in Reggio and in 1496 the clock was transported to Venice.[16]

RAMSAY, DAVID (?1575-?1655). According to the Dictionary of National Biography, David Ramsay was of the family of Dalhousie. He was a friend of Master Heriot 'Gringling Geordie', Jeweller to King James I. According to Ramsay's son William, when James I succeeded to the Crown of England, he sent for Ramsay, who was in France, and made him Groom of the Bedchamber to Henry, Prince of Wales. In 1610-1612 he made three watches for the Prince of Wales. The following details are from the Records of the Clockmakers' Company.[86] 'In the Accompte of the Money expended by Sir David Murray Kt as Keeper of the Privie Purse to the late Noble Prynce Henry, Prynce of Wales, from the first of October 1610, to the sixth of November 1612 (the daye of the decease of the said Prynce), as likewise for certaine paymentes made after the deathe of the said Prynce in the monthes of November and December 1612.

'Watches three bought of Mr Ramsay the Clockmaker lxi[li] (£61). In the list of Guyftes and Rewardes in the same account will be found, Mr Ramsay the Clockmaker, xjs.'

On the death of Prince Henry Ramsay was given a pension of £200 a year in 1613, King James also gave him a pension of £50 a year and the title of Clockmaker Extraordinary. In 1616 he was paid £234.10s. for the purchase and repair of clocks and watches for the King. On 26th November, 1618 he was appointed Chief Clockmaker to His Majesty, which indicated that there were other Clockmakers to the King, and on 27th July, 1619 a Grant of Denisation was made to The King's Clockmaker, born in Scotland. On 30th March, 1622 he was paid £113 for work for the late Prince Henry and for watches and clocks for the King. On 30th September, 1622 he received £232 15s. for repairs to clock and making a chime of bells. He appears to have succeeded in the appointment as Clockmaker to King Charles I, although no official record has been found. On 17th March, 1627 David Ramsay, Page of the Bedchamber and Clockmaker was paid £441. 3s. 4d. for work done for his late Majesty, and £358 16s. 1d. in lieu of diet and bouche at the Court. On 10th July, 1628 he received £415 for clocks and other necessaries delivered for the King's service, and in 1632 he received £219 for one year's bills. On 26th January, 1626 he was paid £150 for coins to be distributed at the King's (Charles I) Coronation. A receipt dated 18th February, 1649 was for 'one clocke with divers motions, two globes, one case for a clocke and a glasse, one Bullet Clocke, one clocke with five bells, and one other clocke, all which were lying at Whitehall late in charge of David Ramsay'.[87] From this it appears that Ramsay held the appointment to Charles I right up to his death.

393. *Anonymous lantern clock with hooded bracket bearing the arms of Charles I, c. 1630. Possibly by David Ramsay, London. (Mr L. H. Moore)*

394. *Detail of the David Ramsay clock dial.*

When one considers the value today of the £2,000 odd paid between 1616 and 1632, perhaps £80/100,000, it is strange that so little of his work survives. There is the well-known table clock in the Victoria and Albert Museum on which is engraved a scene showing the 'grinding of the Pope's nose' and also a fine five-pointed star watch, recently presented to the Master of the Clockmakers' Company and worn by him on the occasion of the Annual Livery Dinner. There are about half a dozen watches by him in the British Museum and elsewhere, but we know of no other clock, for which reason the clock shown in Figs. 393 and 394 is included. David Ramsay must have held a position of considerable esteem in London as, when the Clockmakers' Company was founded in 1631 he was the Foundation Master, being sworn into Office on 12th October, 1632. He does not seem to have been very active in the affairs of the Company, the Deputy Master, Henry Archer (q.v.) presided at many of the Courts held during Ramsay's year of Office.

The clock illustrated is not signed, but as it bears the arms of King Charles I it may well have been made by Ramsay. On the other hand, as we have seen above, there was more than one Clockmaker to the King and we know that Edward East (q.v.) was also Clockmaker to King Charles I. At all events, it is a beautiful clock in silvered brass, and well worth illustrating.

The corners of the dial are decorated with figures representing the four seasons. The two holes in the lion's mask would have been to allow the rotation of the balance, with which the original movement would have been furnished, to be seen. The clock now has a verge pendulum movement. The original weight would have been brass encased, and probably engraved.

The date of Ramsay's death is not known, but was probably the mid-1650's.

RATE. In Observatory clocks, chronometers and other specially accurate timekeepers one does not aim at their keeping absolutely correct time daily. If the clock *regularly* gains or loses a constant small amount the performance is considered satisfactory. The clock is then said to have a gaining or losing rate of so much a day, which is taken into consideration when checking the clock against observation.

RATING NUT. The nut below the pendulum bob (q.v.) which is screwed up or down, altering the length of the pendulum for regulation.

REEDING. The decoration of columns or other surfaces with a series of semi-circular line carvings which resemble reeds in the marshes. (*See* the hood columns in Fig. 387).

REGULATING DIAL. (*See* DIAL).

395. *French Religeuse clock by Thuret (presumably Isaac). Paris c. 1680 (Victoria and Albert Museum)*

REGULATOR. The name given to a specially accurate clock, usually a timepiece (q.v.), only with temperature compensated pendulum, jewelled pivots and perhaps pallets. To give the best results regulators should be fixed to a wall. (*See* Fig. 30).

REID, THOMAS (1746-1831). A celebrated Edinburgh clockmaker, in partnership with Auld from 1806. He published *Treatise on Clockmaking and Watchmaking* in 1826 which went through six editions. He also wrote the article on Horology in the *Edinburgh Encyclopedia* of 1818 and 1830. He was made an Honorary Freeman of the Clockmakers' Company in 1825.

RELIGEUSE. These clocks are usually referred to as Louis XIII clocks, however, this King died in 1643 and the Religeuse is a pendulum clock, which cannot have been made before the latter half of the 17th century. Religeuse clocks are usually beautifully inlaid (Fig. 395), and have more simple lines than the clocks of the Louis XIV styles.

REMONTOIRE. A system for the frequent rewinding of a spring-driven clock, so that it is constantly being brought up to the fully wound state and thus will exert a constant force. For the first example see under JOST BURGI, whose remontoire operated every 24 hours; in the Harrison (q.v.) No. 4 the remontoire operates every $7\frac{1}{2}$ seconds.

RENAISSANCE (OR RE-BIRTH). A period of great artistic activity and revival in the Arts and Letters on the Continent. In horology this activity was practised mainly in Italy and Central Europe during the 14th to 16th centuries.

REPEATER. A clock that, by pulling a cord or other device, will sound at will the last hour struck, sometimes also the quarter hour and in rare cases $7\frac{1}{2}$ and even single minutes. Not to be confused with dual striking clocks (q.v.). Repeating action was invented by Rev. Edward Barlow (q.v.), who also invented the rack and snail strike (q.v.).

RETE. Literally 'Net'; this is the term applied to the pierced dial on which are engraved the principal stellar positions, and which lies above the base plate, or mater, of an astrolabe (q.v.). (*See* Fig. 441).

REUTTER, J. E. (*See* ATMOS CLOCK).

RICHARD, DANIELL JEAN (1672-1741). Reputed to have introduced watchmaking into Neuchatel, Switzerland, in 1692.

RIGHT ASCENSION. The longitude of a celestial body. It is measured in hour angles with the body at the apex and the base starting from the first point of Aries (q.v.) and terminating at a Great Circle (q.v.) through the body at the time of observation. This will be expressed as so many degrees, but right ascension is usually converted into time at the rate of 4 minutes of time to 1 degree of arc, or 15 degrees to the hour. (*See* ANGULAR MEASUREMENT).

RISE AND FALL. (*See* DIAL, REGULATING).

RITTENHOUSE, DAVID, F.R.S. (1732-1796). The most celebrated American clockmaker of the late 18th century. He was born at Norriton, Pennsylvania and began making clocks and mathematical instruments at the age of seventeen. In 1770 he moved to Philadelphia, by which time he had established a reputation for himself as a maker of scientific instruments; he also helped to survey the boundaries between the States of Pennsylvania and Maryland in 1763 and between New York and New Jersey in 1769. From an observatory in his garden at Norriton the transit of Venus was observed on 3rd June, 1769, Rittenhouse making some of the observations and calculations. One of his chief claims to fame are the orreries (q.v.) that he made for the Princeton University and for the College of Philadelphia. He was paid £300 for the former and £400 for the latter. Both machines were hand operated. He does not seem to have proceeded much with clockmaking after he came to Philadelphia, turning his attention to scientific instruments and politics, being elected to the Pennsylvania Assembly in 1776. In 1791 he succeeded Franklin as President of the American Philosophical Society and in 1795 he was elected a Fellow of the Royal Society, London.

Fig. 396 shows a clock by him; the examples known are generally of a standard much above that of his contemporaries.[88] Fig. 397 gives the detail of the complicated dial. It is a three train having in the arch a planetary dial with the five planets and the moon encircling the sun. The main dial shows hours and minutes with an annual calendar hand concentrically fixed. Below is an aperture for the day of the month. The lunar dial with a two lunation period of the disc is marked in an unusual way; reading from the right, 1-6 days after new moon, 6-1 days before full moon, 1-6 days after full moon, and 6-1 days before new moon. The subsidiary dials indicate, top left, the position

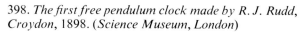

396. *Long case clock by David Rittenhouse, Philadelphia, c. 1775. (Drexel Institute of Technology, Philadelphia)*

397. *Detail of the dial of Rittenhouse's clock.*

398. *The first free pendulum clock made by R. J. Rudd, Croydon, 1898. (Science Museum, London)*

of the sun and the moon in the zodiac (q.v.), right, the equation (q.v.), bottom left, the Earth's elliptical orbit and right, pendulum regulation. At each side are slides to regulate the frequency of striking.

ROCOCO. The author's dictionary defines this as 'With much conventional decoration, tastelessly florid in the Louis XIV or Louis XV styles. The term derives from Rocailles which was used to describe the artificial rock grottoes of Versailles'.

ROLLER BEARINGS. These were first introduced into horology by Eberhard Baldewin (q.v.), but their use was not generally adopted until the second half of the 18th century, when they were used by John Harrison (q.v.). They were also used by Justin Vulliamy (q.v.). By supporting the ends of arbors on the intersection of the circumferences of two loosely pivoted wheels the friction of the pivot holes is avoided. If the ends of the arbor of the remontoire fly in Fig. 276 be followed through, it will be seen that they are resting on the circumferences of two wheels, where they intersect.

ROLLING BALL CLOCKS. (*See* BALL CLOCKS.)

ROMAN STRIKING. (*See* KNIBB, JOSEPH.)

RUDD, R. J. R. J. Rudd of Croydon was the first man to construct, in the year 1898, a clock with an absolutely free pendulum. His pendulum was suspended above a slave clock

(Fig. 398) and received from the clock an impulse of constant force at its dead point (q.v.) every two minutes. Having given the impulse, the same arm gave the synchronising signal to the slave clock. Rudd does not seem to have realised the importance of his invention, as in his description in the *Horological Journal* for August, 1898 and July, 1899, he only lays stress on the cumulative regulation of the clock; however, he must be given the credit for making the first free-pendulum clock, which is now in the Science Museum, London.

RYE CLOCK. (*See* PENDULUM, 2 SECONDS.)

SAEGE UHR (SAW CLOCK). The German term for a rack clock (q.v.).

SALISBURY CLOCK. This clock is the oldest surviving mechanical clock in the world; in the course of time it was converted to anchor escapement (q.v.), which is not surprising since it was in continuous use in the cathedral until 1844. In recent years it has been restored to its original verge escapement (q.v.) and is now exhibited in the north aisle of the Cathedral (Fig. 399).

The earliest record we have of the clock is a Deed in the Salisbury archives dated 1386, which mentions the building of a house for the Keeper of the Clock. The next oldest clock to survive is that at Rouen of 1389, the first to have a quarter strike, and then comes the Wells clock of 1392 (q.v.), now in

153

399. *Salisbury Cathedral clock. 1386. The oldest surviving mechanical clock in the world.* (*Messrs Smith, Ltd. Derby*)

the Science Museum, London.[6] The late Mr Howgrave-Graham, a well-known authority on early turret clocks (q.v.), considered that the Salisbury and Wells clocks were by the same maker. We do not know who he was, nor his nationality, but we do know that Bishop Erghum of Salisbury (1375-1388) was consecrated in Bruges, and was transferred to Wells in 1388. It is quite possible that he brought over a Continental craftsman. Burgundy was a leading scientific area at that time, and it may be that a Burgundian made the two clocks. Comparison should be made between the coarseness of the blacksmiths' work of the Salisbury clock and the delicate wheel work of Giovanni Dondi (q.v.) who, working in brass, made his clock in 1364, before either of the clocks mentioned here.

SCALLOP. Decoration in the form of scallop shells.

SCHWILGUÉ, JEAN BAPTISTE-SOSIME (1776-1856). Schwilgué is another example, with Jens Olsen (q.v.), of a man, who, as a child, took a decision to reconstruct a complicated clock to replace one that no one could repair. When ten years old Schwilgué was listening to a verger at Strasburg Cathedral who was describing the past glories of the second Strasburg Clock, made by Isaac Habrecht (q.v.) to the designs of Dasypodius (q.v.) and who was saying that there was no one capable of making it go, the lad piped up 'I will make it go' and therefrom he devoted his life to acquiring the necessary knowledge to give effect to his resolution. Soon after, he was obliged to leave Strasburg as his widowed mother moved to Silestat, but here, as all the schools and colleges were closed in those troublous revolutionary times, he concentrated, without outside assistance, on designs and mechanical productions, especially horological. This resulted, some years later, in his being appointed Professor of Mathematics at the College of Silestat, where he remained till about 1827.

Before undertaking the manufacture of the Strasburg clock, Schwilgué was in business with a partner, Rollé, making portable scales and balances of his own design as well as making turret clocks (q.v.). The problem of the big clock was now out of his thoughts. However, whilst studying the perpetual calendar of the 1574 clock, which was only valid for 100 years before it had to be repainted, Schwilgué conceived the idea of making a calendar which would show automatically the movable feasts of the Church, this he did in 1821. This model attracted so much attention that it secured him an audience with Louis XVIII. His perpetual calendar inspired the Mayor of Strasburg to invite him to give an estimate for the repair of the 1574 clock. Schwilgué made three proposals, 1) to repair the old clock, which would then still be clumsy and inaccurate, 2) to replace some of the old clock with new and more accurate pieces, 3) to build a new clock. The third proposition was accepted, but because of the cost the proposal was shelved. In 1832 the project was renewed, but the contract was not signed until 1838 and Schwilgué commenced work on 24th June, 1838. He complains that he was restricted to fitting his movement into the existing case, already *in situ*. This prevented him from designing his clock so that it could be seen from the outside. The clock was going for the first time on 2nd October, 1842 at the time of the 10th Scientific Congress in France. Fig. 400 shows the general view of the third Strasburg clock. In the foreground centre is the celestial sphere which shows sidereal time on the dial at its north pole. The movement of this sphere takes into account the precession of the equinoxes (q.v.), involving a gearing of 1:9,451,512. Behind this, in the centre, is the annual calendar wheel dial which revolves once a year and is read off an arrow held by the figure on the left. The date ring adjusts itself automatically on the 31st December of each year so that the indications for Easter and the other movable feasts of the Church come against the days on which they will occur in the succeeding year. The hands on this dial indicate apparent or solar time, the position of the moon and the times of the rising and the setting of the sun. On the left is the very complicated arrangement for ascertaining the date of Easter and transmitting this date to the annual calendar dial. On the right are the three sets of profiled discs that portray the equation of the sun, the moon and the nodes (q.v.). Schwilgué adopts quite a different method from all others. He takes each influencing effect separately and works out a profiled curve for it, these he superimposes one above the other, 'feeding' the results from one into the next, so that the combined effect of all the curves is transmitted from the topmost to the dial concerned. For the sun there are two curves, one for the elliptical orbit of the Earth and one for the effect of the inclination of the Earth's axis; for the moon there are five different perturbations taken into account. For the nodes there is only one.[5,6]

Continuing the survey upwards, above the annual calendar dial is a representation of the planetary deity of each day of the week, in the photograph, Apollo, for Sunday, is shown riding his chariot across the heavens. Above this there is a small dial giving mean time and seated on either side are two small boys, the one on the left strikes a bell and that on the right turns a sand-glass over at each quarter of an hour, the twelve signs of the zodiac (q.v.) surround the central dial, which is a planetary dial, surmounted by a lunar globe which shows its phases. Schwilgué made fresh calculations for the planets and

400. *General view of the Third Strasburg Clock, by Schwilgué, 1842. (Oeuvre de Notre Dame, Strasburg)*

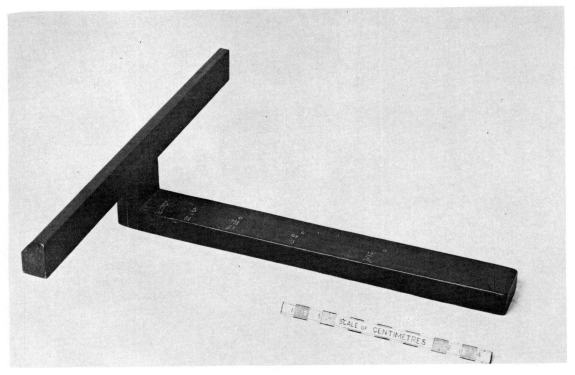

402. *A shadow clock from Egypt, c. 1000 B.C. Shadow clocks are first mentioned about 2000 B.C. (Science Museum, London)*

401. *Three train long case clock, London made, in seaweed marquetry case. c. 1710.*

achieved the following degrees of accuracy, Mercury +0·79 secs. in 78 days, Venus +0·68 secs. in 224 days, Mars −0·13 secs. in 681 days, Jupiter +13·5 secs. in 4,330 days and Saturn −7·85 secs. in 10,746 days. These calculations must be accorded very great reverence. Unfortunately the photograph does not show any detail of the planetary dial except the surrounding signs of the zodiac.

Next comes the region of the automata, first for the hour and the quarter-hour strike; Death, with his scythe, stands in the centre and at the quarters pass before him a child, a youth, a mature man and finally an old man with his crutches, these strike the bell on the left one to four times and the hour is struck on the bell on the right. Above, at the hour, the twelve apostles pass before Christ making an obeisance as they do so; Christ, in turn, raises his hand in blessing. Finally, top left, is the cock that crows at 12 o'clock. It opens its beak, flaps its wings, extends its primary feathers, and crows. Fig. 50 shows the mechanism of the first cock in the clock of 1354, now in the museum in Strasburg. It used to be thought that the cock crowing was connected with St Peter, but now the thought is that perhaps he is the Herald of the Morn.

SEAT BOARD. The board to which the movement (q.v.) is secured. In some early mantel clocks the movements are on seat boards, in long case clocks (q.v.) they are essential and rest upon 'cheeks' (q.v.) fastened to the sides of the trunk.

SEAWEED MARQUETRY. Marquetry in the pattern of fine and flowing lines. (*See* Fig. 401.)

SECOND MINUTES. At the time of the Restoration time-keeping was becoming much more accurate because of the invention of the anchor escapement (q.v.) and the pendulum (q.v.). The general public became aware of seconds; these were at first called second minutes, indicating a second division of the hour by sixty, the word minutes was later dropped and the word second put into the plural. Writing in 1670 John Wilkins, Bishop of Chester, says 'Four flames of equal magnitude will be kept alive for the space of sixteen second minutes'.

SEDAN CLOCK. A large watch, some 6 inches in diameter, used for hanging in a sedan chair or coach.

SERPENTINE. When the front of an object follows alternately concave and convex curves.

SFORZANI, CHERUBIMO. The most famous of a family of clockmakers. In 1518 the Duke of Ferrara commissioned a clock worth twenty gold scudi for a present. In 1524 he entered the service of Pope Clement VII and in 1527 was appointed clockmaker to the Palace.[16] He made gold cased clocks studded with precious stones which the Pope presented to foreign royalties.

SHADOW CLOCK, EGYPTIAN. The first mention of the measurement of time by a shadow clock is in a text of the Middle Egyptian Empire of about 2,000 B.C. Since the Exodus is reputed to have taken place during the reign of the Pharaoh Meneptah (1210-1200 B.C.)[89] and nearly all biblical history dates from after the return of the Israelites from their Egyptian bondage, it follows that this shadow clock far ante-dates the much quoted Dial of Ahaz in the time of King Hezekiah

(726 B.C.)[90] and other graduated shadow-time measuring devices.

The passage referred to can be translated 'One cannot tell when it is midday, one cannot record the shadows'. This seems to imply a reference to a solar eclipse.[91] Fig. 402 shows an Egyptian shadow clock. The tail was placed in an east-west position with the T piece north and south. It would have to be turned round at midday.

SHARP GOTHIC. A term used in America to describe clocks with a sharply pointed top to the case. (*See* Fig. 295).

SHEEPS HEAD. A type of English lantern clock (q.v.), made at the turn of the 17th century, where the diameter of the dial is appreciably greater than the width of the clock frame and protrudes all round.

SHELF CLOCK. An American term which corresponds roughly to the English mantel clock. (Fig. 403).

SHORTT, WILLIAM HAMILTON. To W. H. Shortt must be given the credit for the invention of the most accurate pendulum clock ever constructed. It is, in the author's opinion, very sad that such a fine invention should lose its supremacy after about twenty-five years, due to the invention of the quartz crystal clocks and still further developments therefrom that find no place in this book. It has, however, only been superceded in the larger observatories of the world and is still the reliable timekeeper for many of the smaller observatories. Its accuracy is such that the effect of nutation (q.v.) had

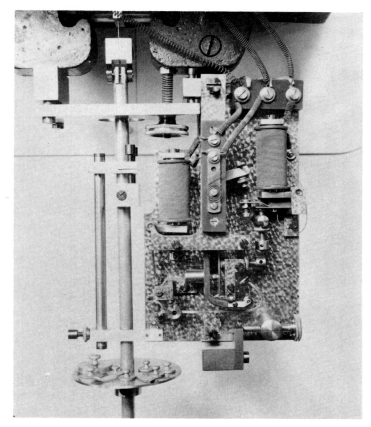

404. *W. H. Shortt's free pendulum clock*, 1920. (*Science Museum, London*)

to be taken into account when making calculations. Never before had this been necessary.

Fig. 404 shows the Shortt clock in the Science Museum, London. The pendulum is suspended on an elinvar spring and has no work to do at all, this is all done by the slave clock (not illustrated). Every half minute the pendulum of the slave clock receives an impulse; the current that performs this passes also to the gravity arm, seen low left on the burnished plate, which carries a D shaped ruby pallet, of which, at first, the flat face is tangential to the circumference of the small brass wheel and effects no impulse until the pendulum has swung a little further to the left, bringing the centre of the wheel directly under the jewel. The slave clock contact is made about 8/10 second before the pendulum reaches its synchronising position, which results in the gravity arm of the master being released when the pendulum is momentarily at rest at the end of its excursion to the right. Attached to the slave pendulum is a free standing vertical spring and positioned near to its tip is a horizontal spring (Fig. 405). The position of the tip of this horizontal spring is controlled by the current which re-sets the gravity arm with its jewel. If the slave pendulum be in advance the tip of the vertical spring will have passed the tip of the horizontal spring before it is re-set, but if the slave be slow, the horizontal spring will meet the vertical spring and give it a slight extra impulse. The slave pendulum is rated (q.v.) to lose 6 seconds a day on the master, so that it drops back 1/480 second in half a minute and the advance caused by the buffer spring is 1/240 second. Engagement and missing usually occur alternately, hence the term, 'Hit and Miss' synchroniser. The records for the Shortt Clock No. 3 at Greenwich show a

403. *American shelf clock by Jerome, c. 1845. (Smithsonian Institution, Washington D.C.)*

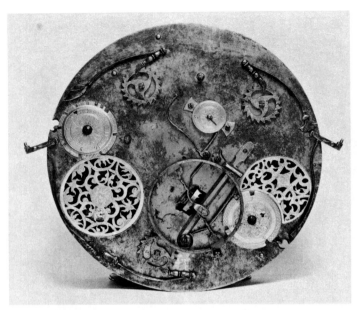

421. *Bottom plate of clock in Fig. 420.*

Kings and the Shepherds. On either side are free-standing figures of Moses with the Tablets and David with his harp, under these (not illustrated) are the Baptism in Jordan and the Last Supper. At the four corners sit the four Evangelists and under them, at their feet, their respective 'beasts'. Below the clock on the walls of the bell chamber are the Martyrs at the Tomb and the Incredulity of Thomas. The whole front panel is removable to reveal a gilded brass interior with an engraving of Christ preaching in the Temple.

The whole is damascened with gold and silver and it would be hard to find a more beautiful example of craftsmanship.

TABLE CLOCK. A table clock is a spring driven clock with a horizontal dial; a form frequently found on Continental clocks, but only rarely used by English makers. Some were made by foreign makers living in London before 1600. East (q.v.) and Fromanteel (q.v.) are believed to have made a few, one signed by both of them exists.[94] In the Science Museum,

London and in the Museum at Banff are table clocks by Nicholas Vallin (q.v.). A recent sale in London has aroused interest in a series of very fine table clocks in exquisite cases, which show that as early as the middle of the sixteenth century one case maker was working for several different clockmakers, as the movements of these clocks have markedly different characteristics.[96] Three of this series are illustrated here. These cases are not signed, but they are believed to be the work of Wenzel Jamnitzer of Nuremberg (1508-1585) .Fig. 419 shows two views of the one believed to be the earliest of the series. The clock is most unusual in that the hour hand has a six hour period of revolution, so it is presumed to have been made for Italy, where six hour dials are most generally found. It has a ting-tang quarter strike and an alarm. The wheels of the clock are of fire gilt brass and the fusees (q.v.) are covered with a lead alloy. There is grande-sonnerie striking (q.v.), its six slotted locking plate (q.v.) being quadrupally cut, (the only other locking plate with this type of strike known to the author is that illustrated in Fig. 255). The balance, locking plate release lever and other small items are in highly polished steel. The dial, which has six hour marks with $\frac{1}{2}$, $\frac{1}{4}$ and $\frac{1}{8}$ hour intervening marks, has an elaborate and complicated design consisting of vine leaves and tendrils interwoven among birds and snakes, and is hand-beaten, a wonderful piece of craftsmanship. Proceeding from a central boss of vine leaves is the single hand in the form of a snake twined along a vine stem. This can be just distinguished at a quarter to two in the side view and with the tail of the snake at the quarter past four mark in the vertical view. A beautiful piece of goldsmith's work, if somewhat difficult to read. The side decoration of this clock will be dealt with later. Another, as fine horologically, if not from the gold smiths' point of view, is seen in Fig. 420. This is the earliest known spring driven clock to record hours, minutes and seconds. The date of the 1st point of Aries (q.v.) is shown as 11th March so that the clock should be before 1582 when the Gregorian calendar was introduced; however, if it were made in a Protestant country it could be later. (There is a weight driven clock in the Germanisches Museum, Nuremberg which shows these three indications on separate dials, and was made about 1550.[95])

422. *Another late 16th century German table clock. (Sir Harold Wernher, Bart)*

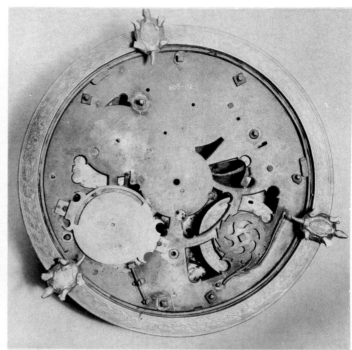

423. *Dial of clock in Fig. 422, which has been partly renewed.*

424. *Bottom plate of clock in Fig. 422.*

425. *Side view of clock in Fig. 422. Compare with Fig. 419. Note piece inserted.*

426. *Another side view of clock in Fig. 422.*

427. *Magnificent table clock by Jost Burgi, c.* 1610. (*Hessisches Landesmuseum, Kassel*)

The case of the clock illustrated is of brass gilt with silver dial rings, the whole movement being of iron. In the centre of the dial (Fig. 420) is the hour hand with a I-XII chapter ring with touch knobs and subsidiary dials for minutes and seconds. Around this are the twelve signs of the zodiac (q.v.), each divided into 30°, which in turn merge with the days of the month, each month being represented by an agricultural or homely scene. January the Lord and his Lady having a meal, watched by their dog, February, cutting saplings, March, sowing, April, milking and butter making, May, a boating and bathing party, June, sheep shearing, July, haymaking, August, harvest, September, ploughing, October, wine making, November, beating flax, and December, cutting off the boar's head for the Christmas dish.

On the extreme edge the days of the week are marked, these are not indicated by continuous motion, but by intermittent action which is connected with an extra spring drive and set off by the striking train, when the hand, missing in the photograph, jumps from the middle of one day to the middle of the next. The clock has hour and quarter striking, the locking plates (q.v.) for these, with the pierced plates, are the only parts in brass, and are seen in Fig. 421, also the regulation control which acts directly onto the crown wheel, altering its depthing in relation to the pallets.[147] (*See* HANS KIENING). There is a dumb-bell foliot (q.v.); the pierced brass plates cover the bells.

Besides those illustrated, other examples of these cases are one in the Bayrisches National Museum, Munich, one in the British Museum, which is square, one in the Adler Planetarium in Chicago and one at Luton Hoo, which is fully illustrated (Figs. 422, 423, 424, 425 and 426). The dial of this clock has been renewed at some later date, the outer hour ring is original, but the zodiac and the rete (q.v.) are renewals. Below an astrolabe mater has been inserted. It will be noted that the

hands, except for the long hour hand, do not fit any dial. On the subject of hands this is a very fine example of the Continental practice of indicating the nodes (q.v.) by a dragon hand, the dragon's head and tail being to indicate the ascending and descending nodes respectively. The bottom plate is seen in Fig. 424. The clock bears the maker's mark /A\ (not visible in photograph), but the identity of this maker eludes us.

The sides of the cases of the clocks will be examined together (Figs. 419, 420, 422, 425 and 426). In Fig. 422 we see Orpheus with his Lute, which has become a viol-gambia, and Eurydice on his right with the Cerberus, the three headed dog guarding Hades, squatting between them. Orpheus was inconsolable on the death of his wife Eurydice and went down into Hades to see her. His music so softened the heart of the devil that he allowed Eurydice to return to Earth with Orpheus, on condition that she follow behind him and that he did not look back. This condition Orpheus did not keep, and Eurydice again became a ghost.

If we compare Fig. 420 with Fig. 425 we see a lion, a unicorn, a camel and a bear in front of a tree. In Fig. 425 we see that between the camel and the bear there has been inserted a small piece with a stork and a squirrel, which one finds on the other side of the case (Fig. 426), behind a ram and a stag. To the right of the squirrel is a bird that the author first took to be a Dodo, and he was therefore excited to know how the knowledge of this now extinct bird, which was only found in Mauritius and Reunion in the Indian Ocean, came to Europe and South Germany at this early date. On further reflection however, he puts it at a badly designed ostrich. The insertion of this small piece indicates that the clock in this case is slightly larger than that in the other case.

Another example of the care and love lavished on these Renaissance table clocks is seen in Fig. 427. This one is by

428. *An Eli Terry shelf clock, Plymouth, Connecticut. c. 1815.*

429. *The author's largest and smallest long case clocks. The latter is 2 ft. 11 in. high, 30 hours and is dated 15th June, 1817.*

430. *A 30 hour lantern clock by John Drury, London, c. 1710, late cased in a lacquer case. (The late Mr Percy Webster)*

Jost Burgi (q.v.), and a notable feature of it is that the solar and lunar dials are connected and are on either side of the lid; both can be kept in motion with the lid open or shut by means of the pair of bevel wheels seen, so that the lunar dial can be studied without upsetting the going of the solar dial. Of the side dials, the one seen in the front indicates mean time with an adjustable ring for the Italian hours (q.v.) and also for the length of day and night; that on the side is used, when the lid is closed, to set the alarm and, by means of the hand with the knob, to set the clock to the correct date.[6]

TAVERN CLOCK. A type of Act of Parliament clock (q.v.), but with a plain circular dial and undecorated trunk.

TERMINAL. (*See* FINIAL).

TERRY, ELI (1772-1852). Terry is the man who introduced the mass production of clocks into America. He was apprenticed to Daniel Burnap at his shop in East Windsor, Connecticut, where Terry set up for himself in his own shop in 1792. At this time in America brass was very expensive, so Terry's first clocks were all made of wood. Terry realised that there was an enormous potential demand for clocks if the price could be considerably reduced and about 1806 he ceased making individual clocks and made interchangeable parts. For this he employed two hands, Seth Thomas and Silas Hoadley, both of whom were later to make their mark in American clock and watch making. Employing water power he first made wooden movements for long case clocks (q.v.), which were then cased or hung on the wall as 'Wag on the Wall' clocks (q.v.). In 1805 Terry began at first thinking in terms of twenty-five at a time; by 1807 he was making 500 and in 1808 he contracted for 4,000 clocks. He sold all these without cases, which were to be found by the buyer.

Terry now sold his plant to Thomas and Hoadley and set up in Plymouth, Connecticut where he developed his 30 hour going and striking clock to sell for $15 (£3). This design finally developed into the now much sought after 'Pillar and Scroll' type (Fig. 428). These clocks have brass escapements

and the pendulum hangs down in front of the dial. The glass panel in the bottom is painted on the reverse side. There is a report that Terry made a clock with two minute hands to show the equation of time (q.v.), but no example of this type by Terry has survived and the author very much doubts if there is any truth in the report. To have two concentric hands showing mean and solar time simultaneously involves complicated epicyclic gearing, for which wood would be quite unsuitable; further, it is most improbable that Terry would have had the necessary mathematical knowledge to make such a movement, of which very few are known in Europe. Terry's success in Connecticut started a rush of clockmakers to that state and many new factories were opened up.

THIRTY HOUR CLOCKS. The general description of a clock that needs winding every day, with a twelve hour margin to prevent too frequent stoppings. Clocks made in all countries prior to 1600 are almost invariably of thirty-hour duration, or less, and the need for daily winding is not regarded as a drawback in older specimens as they are rarely kept going, even if able to do so. However the price of a thirty hour clock is always considerably lower than one of eight days directly productions later than the mid-17th century are reached. When one

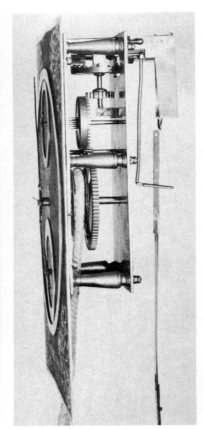

431. *Pendulum clock showing hours, minutes and seconds by Isaac Thuret, Paris, c. 1665, made for Christaan Huygens. (Museum for the History of Science, Leyden)* 432. *Movement of Thuret's clock* 433. *Bracket clock by Jacques Thuret, Paris, c. 1710. (Wallace Collection, London)*

speaks of thirty hour clocks one is usually referring to the period where eight day clocks are general.

The author's advice to anyone who wants to keep a thirty hour clock constantly going is to have it in the principal living room or else on the stairs where it will be passed on the way to bed. The zeal for winding a clock daily soon evaporates if it entails going specially into another room. The author has a miniature 'Grand-child' clock (Fig. 429) 2 feet 11 inches high which has to be wound daily, this is in the main living room and rarely gets forgotten. Another little thirty hour clock is seen in. Fig. 430, here an English lantern clock (q.v.) has been encased in a lacquer case of about 1710 and, probably had the minute hand and spandrels (q.v.) added at the same time. Genuine lantern clocks with both hour and minute hands original are so rare as to be considered almost non-existent.

THURET, ISAAC (?-1700). Isaac Thuret was Clockmaker to King Louis XIV, he was an eminent maker and is sometimes referred to as the Tompion (q.v.) of France. He was employed by Huygens (q.v.) to make clocks and watches to his design and, under a pledge of secrecy, made Huygens' watch with his design of balance spring (q.v.). It is reported that later Thuret claimed to have invented the balance spring himself, but that he withdrew his claim in a letter to Huygens written in. 1675.

He also made a clock to Huygens' design showing hours, minutes and seconds, with cycloidal cheeks (q.v.) guiding the

pendulum. This clock also had a pinion taking into the contrate wheel, which has the effect of reducing the amplitude (q.v.) of the seconds pendulum with verge escapement (q.v.) (Figs. 431 and 432). In Fig. 432 the pendulum has become unhooked from its silk suspension. A somewhat similar design for a spring driven clock is shown on p.10 of Vol. XVIII of the *Oeuvres Complètes de Christaan Huygens*, published by the Société Hollandaise des Sciences. (*See* RELIGEUSE).

THURET, JACQUES (d. 1712). The son of Isaac Thuret (q.v.), he succeeded to his father's appointments in 1694 as Clockmaker to the King, Louis XIV. Fig. 433 shows one of Jacques Thuret's clocks, the quieter lines of the clock (Fig. 395) made in the reign of Louis XIV, but generally referred to as Louis XIII clocks, have disappeared and we have the influence of the decorations at Versailles under Mansard, and the conception of the Roi Soleil. The whole is surmounted by Diana, the Huntress, with her hounds at the base. The case is veneered with tortoiseshell with a little boulle inlay (q.v.). The dial is early with every minute marked and the quarter hours on the inner side of the chapter ring. Although the coming of the pendulum has made the marking of the minutes worth while, tradition and conservatism have retained these quarter hour divisions which were really only necessary on the earlier single handed clocks. The hours are shown on shaped enamel insets, which later become straight sided and fit round the chapter circle with a thirteenth piece, a central disc, known as the dial of thirteen. If the pendulum bob (q.v.) could be seen, it would probably take the form of the sun's disc with radiating rays, a reference to the Roi Soleil.

TIDAL DIAL. (*See* DIAL and JANVIER, ANTIDE).

TIMEPIECE. A clock that has only a going train (q.v.), and does not strike.

TOMPION, THOMAS (1639-1713). Thomas Tompion was born at Ickwell in the parish of Northill, Bedfordshire. A plaque was placed on his birthplace, a cottage near the forge in Ickwell by the Clockmakers' Company in 1952. Where he was apprenticed or where he worked between the time he left his home and the time he was elected as a 'Brother' by Redemption in the Clockmakers' Company in London in 1671, is not known. Election as a Brother means that he had served an apprenticeship and was Free of some other Company, but the Blacksmiths' have no record of him. By Redemption means that he paid for his admission instead of gaining it by servitude as an apprentice to a Freeman of the Company. Tompion was admitted to the Livery of the Company in 1674,

434. *Dial of year clock made by Thomas Tompion, London, for Greenwich Observatory in 1676. (British Museum)*

435. *Engraving of the 'Octagon Room' Greenwich, c. 1680.*

in 1691 he was admitted to the Court of Assistants, in 1700 he was appointed Junior Warden, and Master in 1703.

Edward East (q.v.) was born in 1602 in Southill, Bedfordshire, which is only a mile or two distant from Northill. By 1650-1660, the time when Tompion may be supposed to have left Northill, East had been established in London as a clockmaker, having been appointed Clockmaker to King Charles I. Politics would not have lessened his reputation under the Commonwealth. It is tempting to speculate whether East's success had any influence in bringing Tompion to London and in his choice of calling.

Tompion was a first rate craftsman and an ingenious designer of complicated clocks. His fine workmanship raised English clockmaking to the peak of fame, for inherent in his careful work was much improved timekeeping, but no specific invention for increased accuracy in timekeeping stands to his credit, such as those of George Graham (q.v.) and John Harrison (q.v.). Their inventions still are used to-day, whereas Tompion's fine creations are just collector's pieces. Whilst Tompion should, and must, be accorded the honours of raising the standard of English clockmaking to its high peak, his journeyman, friend and partner, George Graham, had a much more lasting influence on the horology of the world. Tompion worked at the Dial and Three Crowns in Water Lane,

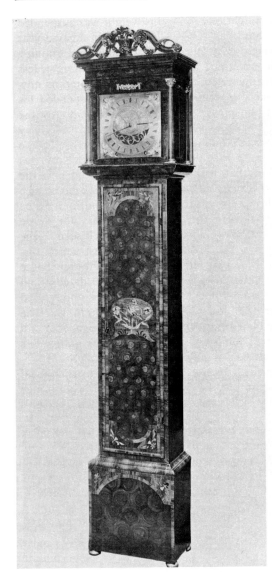

440. *Astronomical clock by Thomas Tompion, London, c. 1677. (The Syndics of Fitzwilliam Museum, Cambridge)*

441. *Dial of Tompion astronomical clock.*

effigy goes round in 24 hours and shows the sun's position in the ecliptic (q.v.) and the date, the minute hand goes round once in two hours. The astrolabe (q.v.) rete turns once in a sidereal day and makes $1 + 1/365$ turns a day, thus making 366 revolutions in 365 mean days. The principal stars are engraved on the spurs of the rete (q.v.) and when these cross the curved line seen below representing the horizon, the star in question rises or sets. Above are the almacantars (q.v.) or lines of equal altitude, the stars crossing any one of these circles are of equal altitude. In the centre is a lunar dial, outside, $1-29\frac{1}{2}$, the days of the moon's age, inside 1 to 12 twice over. This is a tidal dial (q.v.) designed for London Bridge. In the centre are the astrological signs (*See* DIAL, ASTROLOGICAL). The equation clock made by Tompion for King William III, c.1695, and now in Buckingham Palace is thought to be the first made in England (*see* Quare and Williamson). Tompion made a year spring driven clock some time before 1700.

Tompion took Edward Banger, who married his niece Margaret, into partnership about 1701; the partnership lasted until 1708 and many beautiful clocks are signed Tompion and Banger. Later Tompion took George Graham into partnership. Graham was NOT an apprentice of Tompion, as is often stated; he had worked for Tompion since about 1696 and had

married his brother James's daughter. Tompion was never appointed Clockmaker to Queen Anne or William III. He died on 20th November, 1713, and was buried in Westminster Abbey; his grave was later opened to receive the body of George Graham, who died in 1751. Burial in Westminster Abbey in those days, although an honour, was not the great honour that it is today.

TORQUE. The power derived from the coiling of a spring or the twisting moment of a rod.

TORRIANO, GIANNELO (1518?-1583?5). A noted clockmaker of the 16th century. He was Clockmaker to the Emperor Charles V of the Holy Roman Empire and accompanied him to Spain when in 1556 the Emperor abdicated and retired to the Monastery of San Juste. He was first brought to the notice of the Emperor when the latter, in 1529, on the way to his coronation in Bologna, passed through Padua and saw the clock of Giovanni Dondi (q.v.) which was out of order and expressed the desire to see it restored. The Gerence of Milan, Ferdinando Gonzaga, introduced Torriano to him. One of his principal duties was to look after the Dondi clock.

Torriano was born in Cremona at an uncertain date; besides being a clockmaker, he was a civil engineer of no mean

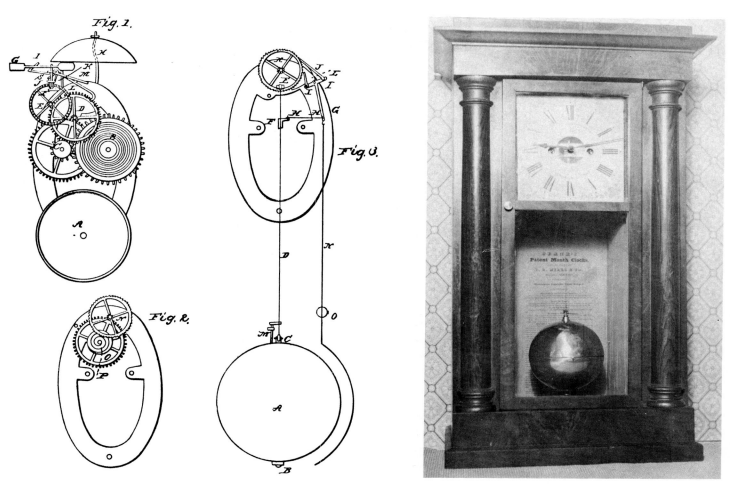

442. *Aaron D. Crane's patent specification for his torsion clock*, 1841. (*U.S. Patent Office*)   443. *A month torsion clock by Aaron D. Crane, c.* 1850. (*Photo loaned by Mr M. Selchow*)

importance and constructed a water works on the Tagus at Toledo.[99, 100]

TORSION CLOCK. Whilst in most cases the young United States gained their ideas and inspirations from European sources, in the torsion clock we have an example where the States led the world. Aaron D. Crane took out a patent on 18th March, 1829, for a clock, the details of which are now lost, presumably in one of the two big fires that took place at the U.S. Patent Office. All that is known is that it was a patent for a clock, it had no number, as was the practice in the early days, and we can only assume that this was for a torsion clock, since Crane's name is not associated with any other horological invention. There is a second patent in his name dated 10th February, 1841, of which the drawing is reproduced in Fig. 442. This provides for a year striking movement. The method of striking is unique in that the hammer is placed horizontally on a counterbalanced rod; it is claimed that in this way much less power is needed. When the count wheel (q.v.) is released the contrate wheel E turns the pivot F carrying the support for the hammer arm. The hammer revolves clear of the bell until the inclined piece I is brought into action by the count wheel release L when it raises the hammer to strike the bell at each revolution, until the count wheel is again locked. Crane provided for 58,968 strokes of the bell, which is 2,068 more than is needed for a clock of a year's duration. The bob is a hollow copper ball; the method of imparting the impulse is seen in Fig. 3 in the drawing. Another clock of this type, but of a month's duration is seen in Fig. 443.

TORTOISE CLOCK. A table clock (q.v.) in which the centre of the dial is filled with water. On this a figure of a tortoise floats, with a small steel prong in its mouth. A clock movement carries round a magnet under the chapter ring, so that the tortoise follows it around pointing to the hour (Fig. 444). This device was first conceived by Grollier de Servière of Lyons about the end of the 17th century.[101]

444. *Reproduction of Grollier de Servière's tortoise clock.* (*Mr Bernard Hawkins*)

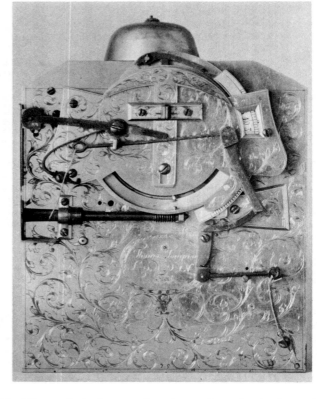

445. *Thomas Tompion Clock No. 79, c. 1695, fitted with both spring and pendulum control. A second clock on this principle exists, dated 1693. (Hessisches Landesmuseum, Kassel)*

446. *Back plate of Tompion travelling clock, showing pendulum suspension arrangement.*

TOUCH KNOBS. The difficulty of telling the time in the dark was first overcome by providing touch knobs on the dial, with an extra big one at twelve o'clock (Fig. 9). These will be found on many of the clocks illustrated in this book up to the middle of the 17th century; they were not, as has often been supposed, placed there for the convenience of the blind. Usually they are placed below the 1-24 numeration for the Italian hours (q.v.), which is so frequently found within the 2×1-12 dial of early clocks. They went out of use for clocks after the middle of the 17th century and re-appeared in watches by Breguet (q.v.) in the early 19th century (Montre à Tact).

447. *Balance of Tompion's travelling clock showing amplitude screw.*

TRAIN. The technical term for the series of wheels and pinions interconnected to perform a particular function in a clock, e.g. going train, striking train, chiming train, astronomical train, etc.

TRAVELLING CLOCKS. A clock adapted for travelling. In the late 17th and early 18th centuries they often took the form of a large watch and are referred to as carriage or sedan clocks. Various devices were used to make clocks portable and suitable for the rough travelling by coach. Thomas Tompion (q.v.) made one or two clocks designed for travelling quite early in his career, for that illustrated is only No. 79 (Figs. 445, 446 and 447), and another similar clock, the only known clock by Tompion to be dated, was made in the year 1693. These clocks could be actuated either by pendulum or balance; the pendulum would be suspended between the cheeks seen in Fig. 446 and the spring held in place by the pin seen. Another method was to hang the clock on a universal ball joint; one beautiful example is seen in Figs. 448, 449 and 450. It will be seen that the suspension loop ends in a ball socket. The very fine champlevé dial should be noted, also the central alarm disc and the day of the month dial read off a fixed pointer in the arch. This clock is fitted with a balance only. Another clock with universal joint suspension is seen in Fig. 451. This clock is by Daniel Quare (q.v.), and only has a pendulum. Fig. 452 is not so much a travelling clock as a clock packed for travelling; a George Graham (q.v.) short pendulum alarm lantern clock (q.v.) with going and alarm weights is snugly fitted into a strong oak travelling case. Note the slot between the weights to accommodate the spire.

The real vogue for travelling clocks came in the latter half of the 19th century. They were nearly all French and were called 'pendules de voyage', although here in England they were always referred to as carriage clocks. However, their form and shape were preceded in England by nearly half a century and two examples are illustrated; Fig. 453 shows a travelling clock by Benjamin Vulliamy of London (q.v.). This is in a rosewood case with a hinged handle, and is an eight day clock with strike/silent mechanism. It is interesting to know that we have Vulliamy's full record of the cost of making this piece. It was commenced on 30th June, 1830, finished in May, 1834 and cost the maker £34 2s. 3d., it was delivered on 23rd May, 1834, to Mr Shafto Adair, whose arms are on a plate on the top of the case. Another lovely little travelling clock of about the same period is seen in Fig. 454. It is an eight day timepiece (q.v.) by Arnold and Dent. The case has side panels and top plate of finely engraved mother-of-pearl and is housed in a gilt vase with ebony corner uprights.

It was, however, in the last quarter of the 19th century that the French 'pendule de voyage' reached its peak. The two principal makers were H. Jacot and A. Droucourt, both of whom had factories at St Nicholas d'Aliermont, near Dieppe, for producing movements, and factories in Paris for assembling and casing. The platforms or escapements were usually made at Besançon, near the Swiss border. Clocks by these and other makers were made in great variety, both as regards striking and repeating mechanisms, also as regards design and finish of dials

448. (*Above*) *Magnificent silver travelling clock with ball suspension by Paulet, London, c. 1720, with calendar and alarm.* (*Messrs How of Edinburgh*)

449. (*Left*) *Back view of Paulet's silver clock.*

450. (*Right*) *Side view of Paulet's clock.*

451. *Bracket clock by Daniel Quare, London, c. 1690 with universal ball suspension. (Lord Harris)*

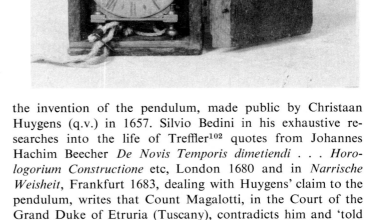

452. *A lantern clock by George Graham, London, c. 1720, in an oak case for travelling.*

and cases. Paul Garnier was a mid-19th century maker who worked in Paris and his clocks occasionally featured his own escapement patented in the 1830's. Fig. 455 shows a French travelling clock of the late 19th century, with alarm.[148]

TREFFLER, JOHANN PHILIP (1625-1697). An Augsburg clockmaker who was at the Court of the Grand Duke of Tuscany during the years 1656 to 1658, the important years for

the invention of the pendulum, made public by Christaan Huygens (q.v.) in 1657. Silvio Bedini in his exhaustive researches into the life of Treffler[102] quotes from Johannes Hachim Beecher *De Novis Temporis dimetiendi . . . Horologorium Constructione* etc, London 1680 and in *Narrische Weisheit*, Frankfurt 1683, dealing with Huygens' claim to the pendulum, writes that Count Magalotti, in the Court of the Grand Duke of Etruria (Tuscany), contradicts him and 'told

453. *Travelling repeating clock in rosewood case, by Vulliamy, London, 1834. (Mr Charles Hobson)* 454. *Engraved mother of pearl travelling clock by Arnold and Dent, London, 1835. (Mr Harry Ross)* 455. *French travelling clock of the type popular in the latter half of the 19th century. (Dr A. B. Dickie, photo by Mr F. G. Agius)*

456. *Drawing of a pendulum clock sent to Huygens from Italy in* 1659. (*Leyden University*)

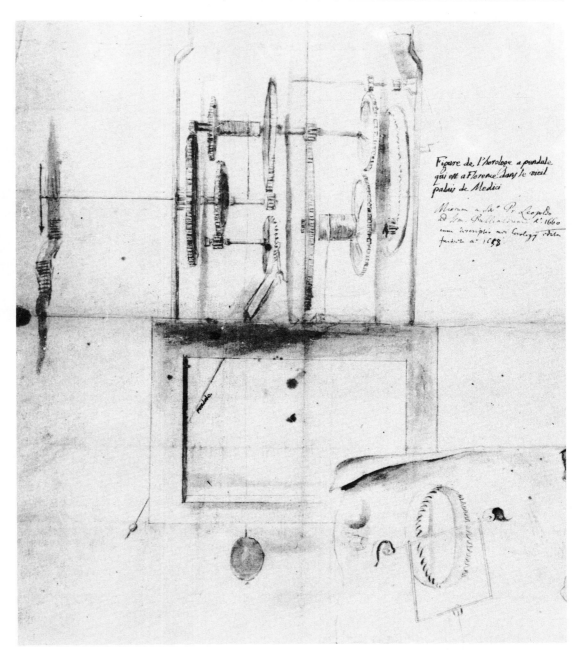

me with his own lips the whole history of the horologe. A clockmaker to the father of the present Grand Duke of Etruria, by name Triffler (sic) narrated to me, about three years ago, at Augsburg, a similar history and confessed that, by command of the Grand Duke and the urging of his mathematician, Galileo, he made at Florence the first pendulum horologe: a patten of which came into Holland'. A letter, 22nd May, 1659 from Prince Leopold to Huygens' friend, Israel Bouillian, says that the Prince had discussed a model made by Vincenzio Galileo (a son of Galileo) of a clock and that three years ago (1656) a clock was made from it by an expert who in all probability was Treffler.

Bedini's claim that Treffler completed a model by Vincenzio Galileo is confirmed in a book *Discorso di Guiseppi Campani* (q.v.) *in torno a suoi muti Orinoli* Rome 1660 in which Campani states that the Archduke of Tuscany showed him *three* clocks; 1) a clock which the Archduke said was his own invention, 2) a clock with a pendulum of a dissimilar type to that designed by Huygens, in the form of a printed drawing, and 3) a large old chamber clock that was regulated by a pendulum, quite different to Huygens' clock and not as well designed as the Archduke's clock. This clock Bedini claims is Treffler's completion of Vincenzio's model of his father's clock. Bedini also points out that the inventory of 17th November, 1690 shows that the Archduke Ferdinand II owned a clock by Salomon Coster (q.v.) of Huygens' design, which he surely would have shown to Campani had he then possessed it. After describing it the inventory says that 'this clock was sent by Signor Tito Livrio Burattingij to his Serene Highness the Gd Duke Ferdinand on 25th September, 1657, made in Amsterdam in Holland and was the first pendulum clock brought into Italy.'

A report that Viviani, a pupil and a collaborator with Galileo, wrote on 20th August, 1659, to Prince Leopold de Medici refers to an instruction to Treffler to reconstruct the clock of the Piazza of the Pitti Palace and states that Treffler 'bounced' from one invention to another to reduce this clock

179

457. *A day and night clock by Johann Philip Treffler, Augsburg. Late 17th century. (Hessisches Landesmuseum, Kassel)*
458. *Back plate of Treffler's clock showing lamp and underhung escapement.*
459. *Night dial of Treffler's clock.*

to its present form (1659). A drawing of this clock was sent to Huygens (Fig. 456). It will be noticed that here the verge escapement (q.v.) is underslung, a method known to be adopted by Treffler, one of whose clocks is seen in Figs. 457, 458 and 459. This is a day and night clock, a small glass disc set above the movement carrying a hand rotates before a glass disc marked with the hours and is illuminated by the lamp seen in Fig. 458; this dial can be covered up in the daytime by the flap seen in Fig. 457.

TREFOIL. The three 'foils' that form the Gothic decoration of a clover leaf type in a circular window or other orifice.

TROPICAL YEAR. The period between two successive passages of the sun through the vernal equinox (q.v.). That is from the first day of spring in one year to the first day of spring in the next. The tropical year is 365·2422 mean solar days, the mean solar year having 365·2464 mean solar days.

TRUMPETER CLOCK. A type of Black Forest clock (q.v.) in which the cuckoo is replaced by a trumpeter who plays a tune (Fig. 460).

TRUNK. That portion of a long case clock (q.v.) between the hood and the base or plinth.

TURKISH MARKET. Towards the latter part of the 18th century quite an extensive trade was developed with Turkey and clocks made for that market were supplied with Turkish numerals. One such clock is seen in Fig. 461, made by George Prior of London *circa.* 1770. This is a fine clock about 2 feet 7 inches high. The hour numerals are about the only concession that had been made to the Turks, for the tunes it plays could hardly be more English; God Save the Queen, a minuet, The Blue Bells of Scotland, and a chorale from

Handel's Joshua. Queen Elizabeth I sent an elaborate organ clock (q.v.) to the Sultan Mahomet III in 1599.[76]

TURRET CLOCK. A large clock made for a church or other tower. Originally of what is known as the birdcage type (*See* SALISBURY CLOCK and WILLIAM CLEMENT), they are now usually made on a horizontal bed (*See* BIG BEN). Occasionally one finds very early vertical clocks such as Fig. 462. This unique piece is in Cotele House, a National Trust Property in Devon, it dates from about 1485 and has recently been fully described by Mr Clutton, who first discovered it in 1955 and through whose efforts it has now been repaired.[103] Except for the foliot (q.v.) weights, all is believed to be original. Its underslung verge escapement (q.v.) would have made conversion to pendulum impossible and as the double swing of the foliot takes twelve seconds, the whole clock would have required rebuilding to provide for a pendulum of reasonable length. The escape wheel revolves once in five minutes.

TWIST PILLARS. (*See* BARLEY TWIST).

TYMPANUM. The triangular space enclosed by the top of an architectural clock (q.v.). (*See* ACANTHUS, EDWARD EAST, etc.).

460. (*Above*) *Wooden black forest trumpet clock, c.* 1870. (*Messrs Camerer Cuss*)

461. (*Left*) *Bracket clock by George Prior, London, c.* 1770. *for the Turkish market.*

462. (*Right*) *Vertical turret clock, c.* 1485, *from Cotele House.* (*National Trust*)

463. *Table clock by John Vallin, London, c. 1590.* (*Chaux de Fonds Museum, Switzerland*)   464. *Travelling case for the Vallin clock.*

465. *Carillon clock by Nicholas Vallin, London, c. 1598.* (*Ilbert Collection, British Museum*)

UNIVERSAL CLOCK. One which records the hour simultaneously all over the globe. (*See* GLOBES, MECHANICAL).

UNIVERSAL TIDAL DIAL. (*See* DIAL, TIDAL).

UP AND DOWN DIAL. (*See* DIAL).

VALLIN, JOHN (1530?-1603?). John Vallin was born at Ruyssel in Flanders, a town now known as Lille. The date of his birth is unknown, but is believed to be about 1530-1535. The Vallins were Flemish, not French; John's will, made in 1593 is described in the register as being translated 'oute of Dutch' (i.e. Flemish). There was a John Vallin who went to Spain with the Emperor Charles V when he abdicated (*See* TORRIANO), but as Charles died in 1558 and left Vallin a legacy of 200 Gulden which suggests long service, it is doubtful if the two are the same man. One clock definitely by John Vallin is known to the author from a drawing in Britten, Sixth Edition, Fig. 109; it is believed that this clock came up for sale a year or so ago. Another, exactly similar in design, only varying in decorative detail is seen in Figs. 463 and 464, with its travelling case.

John had three children, John, Margaret and Nicholas Vallin (q.v.), the last worked with his father and was still working with him when John made his will in 1593. John is thought to have died from the plague in 1603, shortly after Nicholas, as the latter never took up the appointment as executor to his father and the grant of Nicholas's will was later accorded to his widow.

VALLIN, NICHOLAS (1565?-1603). Nicholas was the second son of John Vallin (q.v.). We have no record of the date or place of his birth. He married at the Dutch church in Austin Friars in 1590 and had three daughters. The Vallins were Protestants and earlier persecution in the Spanish Netherlands may have accounted for their coming to England. At first he worked

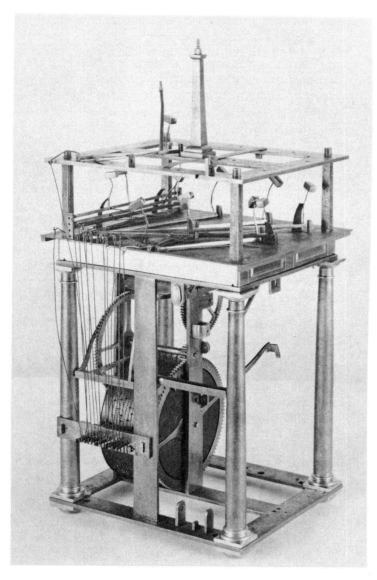

466. *Carillon Movement of Nicholas Vallin's clock.* (*Crown copyright*)

467. *Table clock with globe by Nicholas Vallin, London, c.* 1600. (*Banff Museum*)

468. *Base plate of Vallin's clock.*

with his father, as indicated by John's will made in 1593; when he set up for himself is uncertain, possibly in 1593. Two dated clocks by Nicholas are known, one dated 1598 (Fig. 465) and one 1600, which is one of two Vallin cases with later movements in the British Museum. The clock dated 1598 and marked N. Vallin is one of the earliest known English clocks with a carillon (q.v.) of thirteen bells. The hands are a restoration. The pins of the carillon drum were missing and much research was necessary to reinstate a contemporary tune. This clock is now in the Ilbert Collection at the British Museum. The perspective type of decoration is also found on one of the cases in the British Museum and shows Flemish influence.

Another very interesting piece is that shown in Figs. 467 and 468, now in the Banff Museum. It is there because it once belonged to James Ferguson, the 18th-century astronomer and designer of astronomical clocks (q.v.), of which few, if any, were made. The central wheel revolving once in twelve hours

469. *Small astronomical clock by Nicholas Vallin. (Science Museum, London)*

has every appearance of being original; it takes into a wheel with twice the number of teeth, thus making the globe revolve once in 24 hours. The actual map on the globe is mid-19th century; it is suggested that the clock, had it been a simple 24 hours table clock, would not have been sufficiently distinctive to attract the attention of its illustrious owners, whose names are engraved on the bottom cover: John T. De Saugliers. LLD Lecturer on Nat. et Exp. Phil: London: MDCCXXIX. Benjamin Franklin LLD, FRS, 1757, James Ferguson F.R.S. 1766. Kenneth McCulloch (Ferguson's assistant) 1774. Vallin's signature is seen on the bottom plate (Fig. 468). The movement of the clock is seen in Fig. 146. A small astronomical clock by Vallin is seen in Fig. 469, this is now in the Science Museum, London.

Nicholas died of plague which raged in his parish in London, St Annes Blackfriars, from May till the middle of December, 1603, claiming over two hundred victims, including two of Nicholas's daughters on 10th and 18th August. On 17th September Nicholas himself died, being followed by one of his journeymen later in the month, and another on 1st October.[104]

VENEER. Very thinly cut sheets of a good quality wood, used to cover a more common base, frequently oak.

VERITÉ, AUGUSTE LUCIEN (1806-1887). Verité was born in the town of Beauvais, France, the capital of the Departement of the Oise. He established himself there as a clockmaker and made such a reputation in his home town and throughout France that he was commissioned in 1856 to make a monumental astronomical clock (q.v.) for the Cathedral at Besançon (Fig. 470). This occupied him until 1860. The success of this clock inspired Mgr. Gignoux, Bishop of Beauvais, to have his Cathedral equally enriched, and in 1865 he ordered a monumental astronomical clock for the Beauvais Cathedral, which was finished in 1868 and in 1869 sent to the exhibition in the Palais de l'Industrie in Paris. The clock remained in Paris

during the war of 1870 and it was not till 1876 that it was installed in the Cathedral in Beauvais.

Taking first the Besançon clock, mean time, hours and minutes are shown by the dial above the collection of subsidiary dials. Below, in the centre are the calendar dials, in the middle of the central group are month and date and, clockwise, starting at the bottom, the dials show year, day of week, daily deity, the seasons, the signs of the zodiac (q.v.), length of daylight, length of darkness, and the equation (q.v.). The outer central group of dials show, clockwise from the top, seconds, sunrise, sunset, the remaining five giving the indications necessary for the calculation of Easter, (*See* Beauvais Clock below). The side panels show, top left, the number of solar and lunar eclipses and on the right leap years and centennial leap years. The remainder of the dials show local time at sixteen different places. Installed in the sides, and not visible in the photograph, two dials show the passage of the moon across the meridian and its phases at Besançon, and there is a group of dials indicating morning high tide at eight different places and

470. *Verité's clock at Besançon Cathedral, 1856.*

471. *Verité's clock at Beauvais Cathedral*, 1870. (*Photo, Barette*)

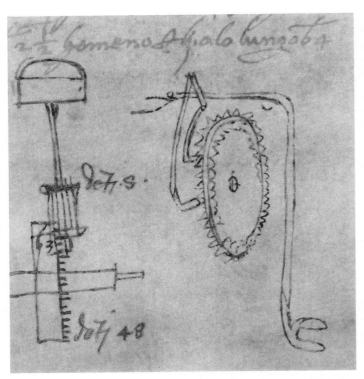

472. *Escapement design by Benvenuto della Volpaia, c. 1520.* (*La Clessidra, Rome. Illustration from* L'Orologio e il Pendolo, *Morpurgo, pp. 2, 4, 29*)

the age of the moon at the meridian of each port.

Illuminated in the base is the planetary dial, with the signs of the zodiac outside and the sun shown centrally, with the Earth and moon and five planets revolving around it. The pendulum bob (q.v.) can just be seen in the aperture below the central group of dials, with the maintaining power (q.v.) lever below it. Of the automata, on the summit, the Virgin raises and turns a sceptre. In the canopy beneath, the Resurrection, with the tomb stone rolled away and soldiers at the grave. In niches on either side at the front and on the sides, the twelve apostles appear in sequence, striking the hours, and above these, on either side, an archangel sounds the quarters. Other statuettes represent Faith, Hope, and Charity. At the hour Hope and Charity turn towards Faith who raises a chalice in benediction. Besides these indications there are four dials on the exterior of the bell tower which show the month and the date, these are self adjusting for the long and short months, and the hour and day of the week. The three other dials show, besides the hour, the days of the week, the phases of the moon and the month of the year. The Resurrection scene is enacted at midday. Two soldiers stand on guard over the tomb, midday strikes, the stone covering the tomb falls off, Christ rises and the soldiers retire to the back. At three o'clock the scene is restored, Christ re-enters the tomb, the stone is replaced and the soldiers reappear. The tidal dials at the side of the clock are provided with marine scenes. The waves are constantly in motion, a cloud appears on the horizon, a storm breaks, the sea is agitated, rocking little boats; the sky brightens and the sea calms. These scenes take place at irregular times, the actual time of high tide is shown on little clocks at the side of the animated dials.

The clock at Beauvais is seen in Fig. 471. In the centre of the main dial is the mean time dial $2 \times \text{XII}$ surrounding a picture of Christ, in the arch above are twelve medallions for the twelve apostles. In the centre of the arched design below is a dial with five hands showing, in five circles, the five indications necessary for the calculation of Easter day, the solar cycle (q.v.), the lunar cycle (q.v.), the dominical letter (q.v.), the epact (q.v.), and the indiction (q.v.). The dial immediately above shows sidereal time. Taking the series of dials downward, on left and right respectively, they show the equation (q.v.), and the declination (q.v.), the length of daylight and darkness, the seasons and the signs of the zodiac, the rising and the setting of the sun and the day of the week with its planetary sign. In the bay on the left, at the bottom, is a calendar dial with correction for leap year every four years and the correction introduced by the Gregorian calendar, i.e. the omission of leap year in those centennial years which are divisible by 400. Three smaller dials indicate the age of the moon and its mean time of passing the meridian at Beauvais. The dial above this shows local time at eight principal places in France west of Paris, but this is now obsolete since the introduction of the international time zones in 1873. The next dial above shows the time of the rising and the setting of the sun accompanied by a mechanical sun which rises and sets in harmony. In the bay on the left the bottom dial has its rim divided into the days of the month, each with its patron saint. There is an automatic adjustment for Easter valid for 300 years, when a slight adjustment makes it valid for another 300 years, however since 300 years is a long way ahead for any of us, we need not be unduly alarmed. In the centre of the calendar dial are three others indicating the age of the moon, the age of the world after the Mosaic calculation and the date of the current year, with the indication if it be leap or not. Above this is shown local time for eight principal cities east of Paris, and again above this a dial showing the phases of the moon and the times of its southing (q.v.) at Beauvais.

The sides are provided with dials, not visible in the illustration. On one side are dials showing all the solar eclipses that will be visible at Beauvais, the tidal movements at Mont St Michael in northern France, and one showing the apparent motions of the stars as seen at Beauvais. On the other side are dials for the motions of the planets, the tides at Mont Orgeuil in Jersey and a dial showing the sky at the zenith at Beauvais. Thus the whole of the lower part is devoted to terrestrial indications, while the upper part is given over to celestial conceptions, Christ enthroned in a rainbow sits with his feet on the Earth, the Virgin and Joseph kneeling beside him. Below, a cross is seen between angels holding the instruments of the Passion, on the central turret stands St Michael holding the scale of Judgment and the cock as a symbol of vigilance.[105,106] These two clocks at Besançon and Beauvais are veritable masterpieces and deserve to be as well known and as often visited as the clock at Strasburg.

VERNAL EQUINOX. The first day of Spring, 21st March.

VINE TENDRILS. A form of twisted wire decoration (*See* Fig. 123).

VOLPAIA, FAMILY (1446?-1550?). A noted Florentine family of clock and instrument makers. The founder was Lorenzo, *circa* 1446-1512, his sons were Benvenuto, 1486-?,

Frosino and Camillo; Girolamo was the son of Camillo. Lorenzo made a wonderful astronomical clock (q.v.) in 1484 which Camillo was instructed to restore on the death of his father in 1512. Benvenuto was mechanic, designer, horologist, military architect and engineer. He invented tools for sawing, mangling, weight lifting and milling. The item that most interests us here is seen in Fig. 472, which shows the sketch of a double toothed crown wheel in which may lie the germ of the anchor escapement (q.v.) or pin-pallet escapement (q.v.). This sketch can be dated *circa*, 1520-1530. Whether this was ever intended to be applied to a clock or whether it was to be used in one of Benvenuto's many inventions we do not know. In any event it is an interesting design.[107]

VULLIAMY, BENJAMIN (1747-1811). Benjamin Vulliamy was the son of Justin Vulliamy (q.v.); he had inherent ability, and at the age of 11 he obtained a Society of Arts premium for drawing; however, he is reported to have been too much of a gentleman to make a good tradesman.[108] Many pieces by him are in Buckingham Palace and Windsor Castle, one of the best known being the regulator he made George III for his observatory, where it stood in the mural quadrant room; it is now in the British Museum. In this clock he used Harrison's grasshopper escapement (q.v.) (Fig. 206). The type of escapement used is that version with the pallets on separate arbors, as was used by Harrison in his Nos. 1, 2 and 3 (*See* HARRISON). There are several clocks by him illustrated by Clifford Smith.[109]

Benjamin was the first member of the family to be connected with the Clockmakers' Company, being made an Honorary Freeman. On 8th January, 1781, it was 'Resolved that a special Court be summoned to meet on Monday, 5th of February next at 9 o'clock in the morning in order to admit a number of Gentlemen of the trade and profession into the Freedom of the Company. Ordered that Mr Martin, who attended, be acquainted with the foregoing resolution for the information of the Trade who meet at the Devil Tavern.' On 2nd April, 1781, Benjamin Vulliamy, who worked in Pall Mall, in Westminster, heads the list of thirty-eight names. It would seem that the hold of the Company on the Trade was lessening and that these, recognised as leading figures in the trade and eminent in their profession, were holding separate meetings at the Devil Tavern, for, in 1781 the meeting place of the Clockmakers' Company was either the Paul's Head Tavern in Cateaton Street or the Queen's Arms Tavern in St Paul's Churchyard.[110]

VULLIAMY, BENJAMIN LOUIS (1780-1854). A celebrated clockmaker of the 19th century, the son of Benjamin (q.v.) and the grandson of Justin (q.v.), both eminent in their time; between them they held the Royal Warrant as Clockmakers for 112 years, under five sovereigns. A man of good education, his clocks, in themselves fine pieces of workmanship, were housed in cases which bore witness to his knowledge of the Fine Arts and classical learning. He designed many turret clocks (q.v.) and it was claimed that he was the first to use a two seconds pendulum,[111] but the claimant overlooked the two seconds pendulum clocks made for Greenwich Observatory by Thomas Tompion (q.v.).

His reputation as a designer of turret clocks led to his being asked to produce a design for the 'Great Westminster Clock' (*See* BIG BEN), which he duly submitted. When it was not

473. *Grande Sonnerie movement by Tompion, London, c. 1676, removed from its case by B. L. Vulliamy, who substituted a movement of his own.*

accepted outright and a competition called for, he withdrew, mortified.[112] He entered the Clockmakers' Company in 1809 and was Master in 1821, 1823, 1825, 1827 and 1847. In 1849, in recognition of his having served the Company for forty years, being Master five times, he was presented with a piece of plate.[112] He was a Fellow of the Royal Society, Geographical Society, Zoological Society, and an Associate of the Institute of Civil Engineers, to whom he left his library of 270 books. Like his father and grandfather, he was Clockmaker to the King and there are clocks by him in Buckingham Palace and Windsor Castle. In 1824 he installed the turret clock in the Tower at Windsor Castle.

We must remember that in the middle years of the 19th century there was not so much attention paid to the value of antiques, this coupled with Vulliamy's belief that he could make better clocks than anyone else, as evidenced by his withdrawal from the Great Westminster Clock competition on others being invited to compete, led to his replacing with movements of his own those of earlier makers that would today be highly prized. The outstanding example of this, for which he must be severely criticised, was the removal of a Tompion Grande Sonnerie (q.v.) movement with silent escapement (*See* Fig. 211) from its magnificent fire gilt (q.v.) bronze case with silver mounts and the replacement of it with a movement of his own. He added his name to that of Tompion on the dial, but was made to remove it by the owner, the then Duke of Grafton. This clock had been given by Charles II to his mistress, Barbara Villiers, later Duchess of Castlemain, one of whose sons was created Duke of Grafton. In a letter to the Civil Engineers dated 21st June, 1847, Vulliamy speaks of

474. *Long case clock bearing the signature Vulliamy, London. Believed to be a clock by George Graham which Vulliamy converted to grass-hopper escapement and added his own name.* (*Messrs Sothebys*)

475. *Detail of the dial of the 'Vulliamy' clock.*

the Tompion clock as being in poor repair and spoilt. How-ever, Vulliamy must have been aware that the movement, which he left to the Institute in his will, was of value, for he seemingly repaired it, since it is now in first class order (Fig. 473).

Symonds suggests that Vulliamy made more profit by supplying new movements than in repairing antiques.[113] The author does not know whether Vulliamy replaced the Tompion movement with an equally complicated Grande Sonnerie movement. It would seem that Vulliamy, at times, used a gut pallet for a silent escapement, as the author has been told that Vulliamy was the inventor of this type of escapement. Since the Tompion movement he discarded has this escapement, it is hardly likely that Vulliamy would discard his own invention. No, if Vulliamy made any gut escapements he copied Tompion.

A very fine clock now bearing the name of Vulliamy, London, is included under this heading, although it is not, actually, by any of the Vulliamys (Figs. 474, 475 and 476). Since the greater part of the production by all three, and especially that of the two Benjamins, was only signed Vulliamy, London, it is often difficult, as in this case, to say which of the three substituted his name at the time of repair or conversion. In the present case there are signs that the original maker's name has been 'stoned' out and Vulliamy's inserted. On the basis of 'giving a dog a bad name and hanging him', the

476. *View of the grasshopper escapement in the 'Vulliamy' clock. The pendulum regulation dial and its mechanism can be clearly seen.*

author has included these illustrations under B. L. Vulliamy, since he is the one most often guilty of this practice. The dial of this clock is distinctly 'Graham', especially the diamond marks between the hour numerals. The date of the dial 1730-1740, is long before any of the Vulliamys; it will be noticed that the quarter hour divisions on the inner side of the chapter ring still persist, a stubborn relic of the single handed lantern clock (q.v.) dial nearly a century earlier. The spandrels (q.v.) are also of the same period. There is a pendulum regulation dial in the arch, the functioning of which will be seen in Fig. 476. Against this theory, Graham usually signed in a cursive script with the tail of the L passing under the word London, and ending in a curve above the first n, but this is not invariable.

The clock now has a gridiron pendulum (q.v.). Other grasshopper escapements (q.v.) used by Vulliamy also have gridiron pendulums and it is assumed, if the clock be a Graham, that the mercury pendulum he would have used was replaced when the escapement was changed; at the same time the 'pockets' on each side of the case would have been added to accommodate the wide arc of swing, $12\frac{1}{2}°$, needed by the grasshopper escapement. The clock has a month movement and the dust proof grooves for the fitting of the hood are indicative of the great care bestowed on the clock. Whilst Vulliamy had his faults and his failings, we must admit he was a fine craftsman; many of his clocks are to be found in Government offices (*See* TRAVELLING CLOCKS).

VULLIAMY, JUSTIN (1712-1797). Justin Vulliamy was born in Switzerland and at some unspecified time went to Paris and later came to London to study Graham's (q.v.) cylinder escapement, it is believed about 1730. He joined Benjamin Gray (q.v.) some time after 1738 when the former went

478. *Movement of Justin Vulliamy's 'timer'.*

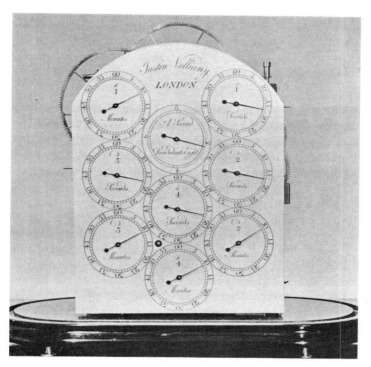

477. *Dial of a 'timer' made by Justin Vulliamy, c. 1770, believed to have been made for George III. (Mr R. K. Foulkes)*

to 'Yᵉ Sun Diall in Thatched House Court, St James'; he was taken into partnership in 1743. In 1746 he married Gray's daughter, Mary. In 1752 Gray removed to 74 Pall Mall, which remained the address of the Vulliamys until the death of Benjamin Louis Vulliamy (q.v.) in 1854. In 1742 Gray was appointed Watchmaker in Ordinary to George II and Justin continued in the appointment after Gray's death in 1764. Justin was not a member of the Clockmakers' Company, his place of work being in the City of Westminster, and therefore outside the jurisdiction of the Company. There are some clocks by Gray and Vulliamy in Buckingham Palace as well as several by Justin Vulliamy.

One interesting sequel to Justin's coming to London to study the cylinder escapement is the production of a curious 'Timer' (Fig. 477 and 478). The dial is $9\frac{1}{2}$ inches $\times 7\frac{3}{8}$ inches and shows nine subsidiary dials, minutes, seconds, $\frac{1}{8}$ seconds, 2nd, 3rd and 4th seconds and 2nd, 3rd and 4th minutes. One can only assume that it was intended for use in astronomical observations, as three of the dials can be put into, or taken out of, action at will by three spring clutches mounted like organ

479. *Thoth in the form of an Ibis-headed man. The god of writing, mathematics, the calendar, the seasons, in fact everything requiring exactness. (Methuen and Co. Ltd, illustration from* A Dictionary of Egyptian Civilisation, *p. 284)*

480. *Picture of Thoth in the form of a Cynocephalus Ape.*

stops. There are provisions for starting and stopping and for starting the $\frac{1}{4}$ second pendulum, which is suspended on friction wheels. It has a cylinder escapement and has been claimed as the largest cylinder escapement ever made as well as the only one to be weight driven.[114] The owner, Mr R. K. Foulkes, believes that he is on the track of showing that it was made for George III.

WAGON SPRING CLOCK. In the early days of clock-making in America practically all the clocks made were weight driven, the reason for this was the fact that homogeneous spring steel could not be produced locally. The types were either long case clocks (q.v.) or shelf clocks (q.v.). About 1825 Joseph Ives (q.v.) of Brooklyn, New York, adapted an ordinary laminated wagon spring as the motive power for a shelf clock (Figs. 297 and 298). These were made by Ives and others up to about 1855. Today they are much sought after by American collectors.

There is, however, nothing new under the sun, and the principle of a vertical pull from a horizontal spring as the motive force of a clock was applied as early as 1680. Fig. 299 shows a clock by Lagville à Chaalons, France.

WAG ON THE WALL. An American term for a long case clock (q.v.) with one seconds movement, frequently made of wood, which was hung, uncased, on the wall.

WALL CLOCK. *See* HANGING CLOCK.

WARN. The first step in the release of a striking train which precedes the final release at the precise moment.

WATCHMAN'S CLOCK. A clock that has provision for recording the time whenever a punch piece is pushed in, to see, for example, at what time a night watchman passed by. Several clocks at different parts of a building would give a complete record of the frequency of the watchman's rounds.

WATER CLOCKS. The earliest known reference to time measurement is the Egyptian shadow clock (q.v.) for use by day; this is about five hundred years earlier than the first reference to a water clock, for use at night. As the sun shines unfailingly in Egypt there was no need for water clocks by day.

The god Thoth was the god of writing; he was the scribe of the gods and controller of the seasons, the moon and the stars, writing, mathematics, the calendar, in fact everything requiring exactness.[116] He took two forms, that of a man with the head of the sacred Ibis (Fig. 479), and the form of the Cynocephalus Ape or Baboon (Fig. 480). The latter was more closely connected with the measurement of time. He was also the Herald of the Night and guarded the sun god's nightly passage through the underworld from sunset to sunrise, in the Cairo Museum are figures of Thoth adoring the rising sun.[117] In the tomb of Tutankhamen there are twelve representations of Thoth, one to guard each hour of the night.

Egyptian water clocks are of two types, outflow and inflow, of which the outflow is the older. The oldest surviving clock of

481. *Karnak outflow clock. The outlet, with Thoth broken off, is seen bottom right.* (*Science Museum, London*)

482. *Another view of the Karnack clock.*

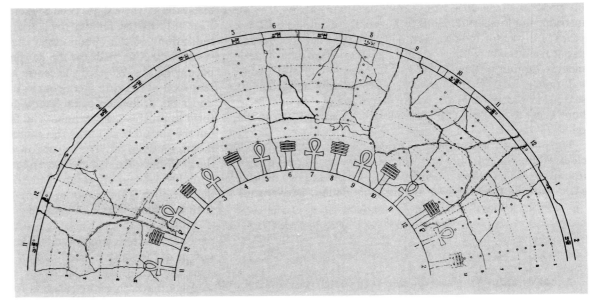

483. *Interior scales of the Karnak clock.* (*Borchardt.* Alt Egyptische Zeit-messung)

this type was found in pieces in a refuse dump in the temple of Amon in Karnak, near Luxor, on the east bank of the Nile in 1904, and pieced together by the Staff of the Cairo Museum, where it now is. There is a replica in the Science Museum, London. As an object it is now well known, but little has been published in English about it for many years, and as far as the author knows, with one brief exception,[121] nothing has yet appeared in horological literature. Of this outflow type no other complete clock is known, but there are fragments of other clocks, all modelled on the Karnak clock, in the British Museum, Paris Louvre, Moscow and Turin. Also, fragments in the Hermitage, Petrograd and the Naples Museum seem to be from the same type of clock. These have an inscription which may be translated 'Indicator of the hours by the god Thoth . . . so that therein (? within the hours shown) the offering may be brought.' Further reference to the bringing of offerings will be made later.

The Egyptians divided the year into three seasons of four months each, Flood Time, Winter Time, and Summer or Harvest Time. Each month had thirty days divided into three periods of ten days (decans) and the year consisted of twelve months plus five epagnomal days (q.v.). The Karnak clock was made by Amenemh't, Prince and Holder of the Royal Seals in the reigns of Amenophis I and Thotmosis I of the 18th Dynasty *circa* 1580-1560 B.C. In his tomb was an inscription, now largely lost, which read: 'The first time I was honoured was in the reign of the Majesty of the King of Upper and Lower Egypt, Amen-hotep I (alt. Amenophis I) . . . while reading in all the books of the divine words . . . I found that the winter night was 14 (hours long) . . . I found an increase in the length of the night) from month to month (and) decrease month by month. . . I (represented them on the vessels of the water clock) and the movements of (the sun god) Re (and of the moon god?) with the utterances of both. . . The sign of life and happiness is in their

492. *Saxon sinking bowl clock*, c. 800 A.D. (*Science Museum, London*)

experiment with volume and time as a measure of viscosity.[121] There is, in the Cairo Museum, another fragment of an outflow water clock with the figure of Thoth in position over the outflow orifice.

In 1901 an inflow clock was found in the Temple of Horus at Edfu (Figs. 484 and 485). This is now in the Cairo Museum, again a replica is in the Science Museum, London. The Temple at Edfu is much later, it was built between 237 B.C. and 57 B.C. so, assuming that the clock was contemporary it is some 1300-1500 years later than the Karnak clock. Here again we see Thoth seated and watching the outflow, although this is not now continuous, but only occurs once a day. In a clock of this type the direct reading of the hours on the internal scale (Fig. 485) would be very difficult, especially for the early hours at the bottom; a theoretical design by Borchardt for a scale to be placed above the clock to be read by a pointer floating on the surface of the water is seen in Fig. 486.[118] The water would be poured in in a very fine stream, or drop by drop. Fig. 487 shows another representation of an inflow clock, again with Thoth watching the outflow. It is about 4½ inches high and is much too small for any practical use. In Fig. 488 we see a hieroglyphic representation of Thoth seated before a 'nicked' column. The author was told that this represented some connection with time, but the exact meaning was uncertain. The 'nicked' column represents the word hn-tj (the Egyptians did not use vowels) which means the limits of a period of time.[118] As we saw earlier, a water clock was inscribed to the effect that it was to assist in ascertaining the hour at which the sacrifice should be brought and it is submitted that this little model is the representation of the offering by Pharaoh of a votive model of a water clock to be placed in the tomb so that the deceased may know the correct times to make his offerings, which would benefit him in the after life. On the right is Pharaoh with his false beard (made from the tail hairs of sacred bulls). In this case a Roman Emperor, Commodius (180-192 A.D.) has had himself depicted as Pharaoh and the goddess, who would normally be Isis, the goddess of Heaven and Earth, is in this case a later variant. This explanation of this hieroglyph is put forward as a basis of discussion.

When we come to classical times the oldest surviving clock in fragmentary form is the Greek klepsydra, found in the Agora in Athens in 1933 and now preserved in the Museum of the Stoa of Attalos in the Agora (Fig. 489). The date is late 5th century B.C. These klepsydra were used to limit the time of pleading in the Athenian courts. The one in Fig. 489 flows for six minutes. Fig. 490 shows a reconstruction of two of these clocks, the one flowing into the other; the marking on them indicated that they were used by the Athenian tribe of Antiochis. Professor Harris advises me that the first reference to these water clocks for timing pleading is in Aristophanes's Wasps (422 B.C.). In Demosthanes's legal speeches, in the first half of the 4th century B.C., there are frequent references to them, presumably the water flow would be stopped when laws or depositions were read as references are made to the turning off of the water. The Romans took the water clock from the Greeks and latinised it to clepsydra. The younger Pliny, prosecuting in a trial before the Senate, presided over by the Emperor Trajan (A.D. 100) claimed four extra clocks, above the twelve normally allowed, owing to the importance of the case. He says that he spoke for nearly five hours, which would give, in this instance, a period of 15/20 minutes per clock.[127]

Although in classical times water clocks were relatively well known, to the author's knowledge, no others have survived. The nearest approach to survival is the 'Tower of the Winds' in Athens, built by Andronicus Kyrrhestes (or Cyrrhus) about 100 B.C. and certainly before 35 B.C.[122] This is in the form of an octagonal tower; over each face is a representation of one of the eight principal winds. Four of the sides face the cardinal points and the intervening fronts face the intermediate directions. On each face is an inclined sun dial. The date of the dials is assumed to be the same as that of the Tower, as a marble block has been found at Tenos, in the Aegean Sea, inscribed with Kyrrhestes name, showing similar dials. The Tower contained a water clock, it was thought that Vitruvius described it, as he did

493. *13th-century MS. showing a monastic water clock.* (*Bodleian Library, Oxford. MS. Bod. 270b, fol. 183v*)

that of Cestibus (see later), but he confines his remarks to the architectural side of how to site a house or a town so as to avoid cold winds blowing directly in.[123] The only relic of the water clock is the bottom of the cistern, the circular stone adjunct to the tower seen in Fig. 491. Cestibus *circa* 300 B.C. is another much quoted maker of water clocks, their first application being attributed to him. There is a model of his clock in the Deutsches Museum in Munich. Here the principle is the same as in the Egyptian inflow clock, a float on the surface of the water carries a vertical indicator which rises and falls with the water level and is read off a vertical scale set above the clock. The clock is fully described by Vitruvius.[124] Another type is the Saxon sinking bowl (Fig. 492). This has a small hole at the bottom, and when floated on water, the bowl gradually fills, and sinks after a set period.

Before the invention of the mechanical clock in about 1300, water was used as motive power for monastic clocks, some more complicated than others with strike, alarm, automata, etc. The Arabs in particular were active in this respect, the clock of Medersa Bou Anania in Fez, made in 1337, is one of the most complicated; through twelve niches birds threw down balls into pans for the striking of the hour. Tardy illustrates many classical water clocks.[125] Fig. 493 is the representation of a 13th

495. *Water clock with conventional dial by Arnold Finchett, Cheapside, 1735. (British Museum)*

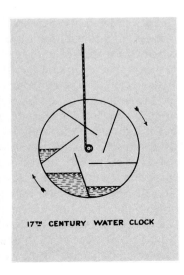

494. *English 17th-century water clock. The diagram shows the internal arrangement of the water clock. (Science Museum, London)*

17ᵀᴴ CENTURY WATER CLOCK

century water clock, discovered a year or two ago by Mr C. B. Drover.[115] A good deal of discussion has ranged around this picture, especially as there are only fifteen segments in the dial. The author inclines to the view that this is an artist's error, and that there should be sixteen, and that the clock is meant only for use at night, as was that at St Sebaldus Church, Nuremberg, (*See* Fig. 9). The holes in the dial may well be holes for the insertion of pegs to set off an alarm. Discussions as to how the clock worked are not very profitable however, the chief point being that it shows definitely that water clocks were, at that time, in use in monasteries. The MS. is dated in the 13th century. For this picture we have to thank the ignorance of the 13th century monk of earlier methods of time measurement. Not recognising that the dial of Ahaz recorded the time by shadows, in illustrating the healing of King Hezekiah (II Kings 20.5-11) and Isaiah 38.5-8) he has given us the only known representation of a 13th century monastic water clock, with the Prophet Isaiah indicating on the dial the return of the shadows by 10°. The translation of the text may be rendered 'King Hezekiah was sick unto death and prayed to the Lord and the Lord added fifteen years to his days and gave him a sign by the Prophet Isaiah that the sun would be moved back 10° in the clock.' Further proof that water clocks were used on monastic buildings is found in relation to St Edmund's Abbey in Bury St Edmunds in the year 1198. The wooden platform in the Abbey

496. *Italian 19th-century water clock. (Museum for the History of Science, Florence)*

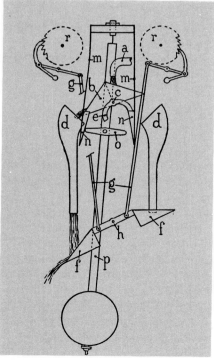

497. *Diagram of the water clock on Mount Pincio in Rome. (Horloges Astronomiques, Ungerer, Strasburg p. 373 1931).*

Church, carrying the shrine of Saint Edmund the Martyr, caught fire during the night. Luckily just then the clock struck for matins and the sexton immediately sounded the alarm. The Chronicle of Jocelin of Brakelond reads 'And we all of us ran together and found the flames raging beyond belief and embracing the whole feretory and reaching up nearly to the beams of the church. So the young men among us ran to get water, some to the well and others to the clock, while yet others, with the utmost difficulty, succeeded in extinguishing the fire with their cowls.'[126]

The introduction of the mechanical clock in about 1300 soon replaced the water clock, however we see some revival, on account of cheapness, in the 17/18th centuries when a drum with pierced radial plates was used (Fig. 494). (Compare with MERCURY CLOCK.) These were very unreliable, but have been subject to many modern reproductions. Authentic examples are very rare, the modern ones usually carry a 17th century date. Fig. 495 shows a rather later style with a conventional dial. A 19th-century Italian water clock is seen in Fig. 496. From the style of the clock it would seem to have been made about the same time as the well-known water clock on the Mount Pincio in Rome, which was first erected in 1872. The functioning of this clock is seen in Fig. 497. A stream of water *a* falls into a hinged trough *b*, connected with an arched piece *e* pivoted at *c*. Two springs *m* and the side pieces *n* keep the trough in position. *e* is actuated by a second pendulum *p* which, through the cross bar *o*, displaces the pieces *n*, causing the trough to trip and empty, through the funnels *d*, on to the pivoted trough *f* and thence to communicate to the movement through arbors *g*.[150]

WATSON, SAMUEL (*circa* 1635-1711.) Of Samuel Watson as a man we know very little. Presumably he was born in Coventry, where he lived till about 1689/90. He was Mathematician in Ordinary to Charles II, but there seems to be no record of the date of his appointment. It is recorded, however, that he made a complicated astronomical clock (q.v.) which he brought to London and sold to Charles II for £215. In the Accounts of the Secret Services of Charles II and James II[128] it states 'Paid to Wm. Chaffinch, for so much money he paid Samuel Watson for a clock he sold to his late Ma'tie, which shows the rising and the setting of the sun and moon and many other motions, £215.' This record was made after the death of Charles II, hence the reference to 'his late Ma'tie.' In 1683 Charles ordered another clock from Watson, still more complicated, and Watson returned to Coventry to make it, but he did not get it finished until 1689 (Fig. 498). By this time Charles II was dead and Queen Mary showed little interest in the clock. Watson came to London about 1689 and settled in Long Acre. He was admitted to the Clockmakers' Company as a Brother in 1692. Watson, finding no interest in his clock, decided to put it into a raffle to bring in £1,000. There were to be 100 tickets at £10 each, to be reduced in the first drawing to 10 tickets. The winner of the second drawing would have the clock and the other nine were each to have a watch worth £10. Actually the lottery never took place, Queen Mary relented and bought the clock for an unknown sum and the cypher of Charles II was replaced by that of William and Mary.

In the centre is a small dial recording only the hours and the quarters and the days of the week. The dials, top left, show the

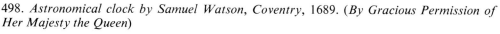
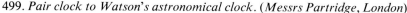
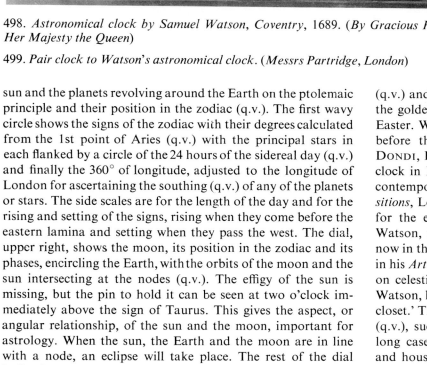

498. *Astronomical clock by Samuel Watson, Coventry, 1689. (By Gracious Permission of Her Majesty the Queen)*

499. *Pair clock to Watson's astronomical clock. (Messrs Partridge, London)*

sun and the planets revolving around the Earth on the ptolemaic principle and their position in the zodiac (q.v.). The first wavy circle shows the signs of the zodiac with their degrees calculated from the 1st point of Aries (q.v.) with the principal stars in each flanked by a circle of the 24 hours of the sidereal day (q.v.) and finally the 360° of longitude, adjusted to the longitude of London for ascertaining the southing (q.v.) of any of the planets or stars. The side scales are for the length of the day and for the rising and setting of the signs, rising when they come before the eastern lamina and setting when they pass the west. The dial, upper right, shows the moon, its position in the zodiac and its phases, encircling the Earth, with the orbits of the moon and the sun intersecting at the nodes (q.v.). The effigy of the sun is missing, but the pin to hold it can be seen at two o'clock immediately above the sign of Taurus. This gives the aspect, or angular relationship, of the sun and the moon, important for astrology. When the sun, the Earth and the moon are in line with a node, an eclipse will take place. The rest of the dial indications are the same as for those on the left.

Of the lower dials, that on the left is an annual calendar dial with four circles of 365 days, each circle being advanced $\frac{1}{4}$ day in relation to the former to provide for leap year. Next come the 28 years of the solar cycle (q.v.) and the dominical letter

(q.v.) and on the dial lower right we have the epact (q.v.) and the golden number (q.v.), all required to calculate the date of Easter. Whilst there were many clocks made on the Continent before this date, with all these astronomical details (*See* DONDI, BALDEWIN etc.) Watson was the first to make such a clock in England and his achievement was duly applauded in contemporary literature. John Smith in his *Horological Disquisitions*, London 1694 writes regarding the drawing up of tables for the equation of time (q.v.); 'and fifthly by Mr Samuel Watson, the curious contriver of that rare Celestial Orbitary, now in the present Queen Mary's possession.' William Derham in his *Artificial Clockmaker*, London 1696, writes in the chapter on celestial motions 'and of late, that elaborate piece of Mr Watson, late of Coventry, now of London, in her late Majesty's closet.' The clock was put in order in 1907 by the firm of Jump (q.v.), successors to the Vulliamys (q.v.) and converted from long case with a seconds pendulum to a $\frac{2}{3}$ second pendulum and housed in a square glass-sided bronze case. Its existence seems to have been lost sight of in the horological world until the author discovered it in 1942 in the Library of Windsor Castle. (Britten 6th Edn, 1932 only refers to the quotations given above.)

Watson's work is now much better known and appreciated.

500. *Sir Christopher Wren's weather clock*, 1663. (*By Permission of the Royal Society*)

He made at least another two less complicated astronomical clocks, which are believed to have belonged to Sir Isaac Newton, one is in the Museum of the Clockmakers' Company in the Guildhall, London, and the other is in the author's possession, the dial of the latter is seen in Fig. 171. Unfortunately the Clockmakers' Company have lost what little evidence they had that their clock belonged to Newton, but a study of the possibilities was made by the author.[129] Several bracket clocks by Watson are known and a few watches; the back plate (q.v.) of a Watson bracket clock is seen in Fig. 90. Only one long case clock (q.v.) by Watson is known to the author, and this, it would seem, was made to pair with the large astronomical clock (Fig. 499). Both have 20 inch dials, far too large for an ordinary domestic clock, whilst from a contemporary print it is seen that the Windsor Castle clock was originally housed in a case to pair with Fig. 499.

WEATHER CLOCKS. We are so used to self recording anemometers and barographs that we do not give time or thought to how they developed. Fig. 500 shows a design for a 'Weather Clock' by Sir Christopher Wren in 1663 and recorded in the papers of the Royal Society. Wren's description of it is as follows: 'Upon the index-wheel of the clock, within the plate, is fixed a little wheel A, which moves the rack B, annexed by the joint C, to the piece H C D E G which being made thin and light, passes through the basis of the clock at D and E, and through the slits in the pillars of the outward frame F, G; at the end it holds two black lead pencils, upon the points of which, (and not in the slits) the crooked piece depends. The pencil H, rests and draws lines on the cylindrical substance of the tumbril K, which is the weather wheel, moved by quicksilver after the manner I have formerly shown. The pencil I, resteth on the flat wheel L, moved by a Vane without. On both surfaces are described circular lines for hours according to the motion of the rack, and cross them straight lines, showing degrees of weather in the one and rumbs in the other: amongst these permanent lines the pencils describe irregular lines, compounded of the motions of the rack and the wheels, much like the motion of a ship described among the longitudes and latitudes of the chart: and from the tracks of the pencil may be collected the changes of the Wind and Weather, that have been in the twelve hours past. . . .'[130]

In 1679 the versatile Dr Hooke (q.v.) made a weather clock for the automatic recording of the barometric heights, temperature, humidity, rainfall, strength and direction of the wind, which was shown to the Royal Society on May 29th of that

501. *Wells Cathedral Clock*, 1392. *The quarter striking arrangement is a restoration.* (*Science Museum, London*)
502. *Hour striking train of the Wells Clock.* (*Science Museum, London*)

year. On 2nd April, 1684, the question of repairing the clock arose, so presumably it was made and functioned. Just how the layout was conceived it is difficult to assess.

WELLS CLOCK. The second oldest surviving clock in England was made in 1392; and would seem to have been made by the same craftsman who made the Salisbury clock (q.v.). It was in use until 1835, after which it was lent to the Patent Office, the forerunner of the Science Museum, London, in 1871, when certain worn out parts were replaced in brass. The clock has been converted from verge (q.v.) to anchor escapement (q.v.), and the whole is held together by mortices, tenons and cotters. The older parts of the clock now in the cathedral, dial and automata, are later than the 14th century; they show the hour, the age and phases of the moon. Opposite the aperture for the latter is an image of Phoebus, which is weighted so that it always remains upright. The next circle has a minute hand concentric with the hour hand, which carries an effigy of the sun, making one turn in 24 hours. Above the dial, in a niche, two pairs of knights circle round in opposite directions in combat and at each stroke of the hour one is unhorsed, regaining his saddle when out of sight. The hours are struck by 'Jack Blandifer' who sounds the quarters on two bells with his heels and the hours with a hammer and bell. There is a modern outside dial, with jacks for striking. Fig. 501 shows a general view of the clock with the later replacement of the quarter striking train, and Fig. 502 a good view of the striking train.

WESTMINSTER HALL CLOCK. There has been a legend current for the best part of a century, starting perhaps with the

first edition of Britten's *Old Clocks and Watches* in 1893, that this clock was paid for by a fine of 800 marks on the Lord Chief Justice, Randulphus de Hengham, imposed in the 16th year of the reign of King Edward I (1298) for having altered a record so that a poor man might pay only 6s. 8d. instead of 13s. 4d.[131] However, recent researches into the records of Royal building in the middle ages have shown that the Clock Tower at Westminster was not begun until 1365 and was finished in 1367. As regards the clock, there is a record on the Issue Roll of Thomas de Brantingham, May 1370, of a payment of 6d. a day to John Nicole 'Keeper of the great clock of the lord King within the Palace of Westminster'. Records have also been found of three more 14th-century clocks, one in the Castle of Queenborough, one in the Manor of Langley (1366/7) and one at Windsor Castle at a date between 1351 and 1354; all three ordered by Edward III. All were striking clocks according to records found for them.[132]

WILLARD BROTHERS. The four Willard brothers, Benjamin 1743, Simon 1748, Ephraim 1750 and Aaron 1752 were all noted clockmakers. Benjamin was apprenticed to Benjamin Cheney and later opened his own business in Grafton, Massachusetts in 1765 and later trained his three brothers. Of these, Simon is the most noted as the designer of the very popular and delicate banjo clock (q.v.), which, in the opinion of the author, is by far the most pleasing of all American designs. It is a shape much sought after by collectors, hence often reproduced, so great care should be exercised in buying a clock of this design. The Willards built up an extensive clock

199

503. *Willard Clock. Re-cased c. 1820. (Mr Walter M. Roberts)*

504. *Long case clock by Joseph Williamson, London, c. 1725, with back to back dials for mean time and the equation. The case is modern. (Professor Hans von Bertele)*

505. *The mean time dial of Williamson's clock.*

business in Connecticut, but made chiefly inexpensive brass movement clocks. Aaron introduced the Massachusetts shelf clock.[133] Fig. 503 shows a Simon Willard clock, which was originally a wall clock, and then re-housed.

WILLIAMSON JOSEPH, (?1669-1725). Little is known about the life of Joseph Williamson. Baillie says that he was apprenticed in 1683 and assuming that he was fourteen at that time, he would have been born in 1669, there is, however, no record of his apprenticeship in the Clockmakers' List of Apprentices issued in 1932. In his early days he worked for Daniel Quare (q.v.) and probably entered the Clockmakers' Company at a late date, when he set up on his own. He was appointed Junior Warden in 1721 and duly advanced to Master in 1724, dying in office in June, 1725. He was a mathematician and had good astronomical knowledge. The popularity of the equation clock (q.v.) in the late 17th and the early years of the 18th century, both in England and in Europe, particularly in France, led to his claiming its invention. The credit for this, in the author's opinion lies with Christaan Huygens (q.v.) (*See* EQUATION OF TIME). However, Williamson claimed to have made all the equation clocks produced in England up to 1719 and his letter, which appeared in the *Philosophical Transactions* for November-December, 1719 is quoted here:

'A letter of Mr Joseph Williamson, Watchmaker, to the Publisher, wherein he asserts his Right to the curious and useful invention of making Clocks to keep time with the Sun's Apparent Motion.

'Having been informed of a *French* Book lately published, wherein the Author speaks of making Clocks to agree with the Sun's Apparent Motion: and supposeth that it was a thing never thought of by any before himself: I was therefore willing

506. *An example of a wisdom clock.* (*Bib. Natl. Paris. MS.* 926, *fol.* 113)

by the advice of some of my Friends, to write this short Account of what I have performed in this matter myself.

'And in the first place I must take notice of the Copy of a letter in this Book, wrote by one P. Kresa, a Jesuit, to me *Mr Williamson*, Clockmaker to his Imperial Majesty: of a clock found in the late King *Charles the Second of Spain's* Cabinet, about the year 1699 or 1700 which sheweth both equal and apparent Time according to the Tables of Equation, and which went 400 days without winding up. This I am well satisfied is a clock of my own making; for about six years before that time, I made one for Mr Daniel Quare, for whom I then wrought mostly, which agrees with the Description that he gives of it, and went for 400 days. This clock Mr Daniel Quare sold, soon after it was made to go to the said King *Charles the Second of Spain:* and it was made so that if the *Pendulum* was adjusted to the sun's mean Motion, the Hands would show equal Time on two fixed Circles, on one the Hour, and the other the Minute . . . Soon after this clock was sent to *Spain*, I made others for Mr *Quare* which showed Apparent Time by lengthening and shortening the *Pendulum*, in lifting it up and letting it down again, by a Rowler in the form of an *ellipsis*, through a slit in a piece of Brass, which the Spring at the Top of the Pendulum went through. . . For one of those, and not the first, made with the rising and setting of the Sun, Mr Quare sold to the late King *William* and it was set up at *Hampton Court* in his lifetime, where it hath been ever since. . . So that I think that I may justly claim the greatest right to this contrivance of making clocks to go with Apparent Time; and I have never heard of any such clock sold in *England* but was of my own making, though I have made them so long.'

The incorrectness of this claim was demonstrated by the author in 1943.[134] (*See* EQUATION OF TIME and THOMAS TOMPION). All equation clocks made by Quare have the equation part separate from the main movement, connected by a rod and endless worm, suggesting that Quare made the move-

ment and Williamson the equation part, the two being then brought together. Those clocks made by Tompion have the equation part integral with the movement, the work of one man. The only clocks where the equation kidney acts directly on the suspension of the pendulum are of Williamson's independent production.[135]

Finally, we have a clock signed by Williamson where he has mean time on one face and backing onto it he has another dial showing apparent time from a central arbor, driven off the mean time movement (Figs. 504 and 505). To do this he had to reverse the direction of the hour and minute hands and so he introduced a true differential gear, such as we find in motor cars today, which, is perhaps, the first application of this principle.[6]

WING LANTERN CLOCKS. *See* LANTERN CLOCKS.

WISDOM CLOCKS. These clocks are called in French 'Horloges de Sapience' and the term applies to those early clocks which appear in medieval manuscripts and paintings. It originates in a manuscript which belonged to Marie, granddaughter of Charles I of France, who died in 1380. The book in which the miniature of the clock is to be found is called *L'Horloge de Sapience*[136,137] and is founded on the Book of the Wisdom of Solomon (Fig. 506). The clock would seem to be weight driven, as the ropes are seen passing into the supporting pedestal; indeed it is far too early to be spring driven. It has a 24 hour dial which in the illustration is rubbed; probably there was no hand, the dial revolving before a fixed pointer, as was customary in very early clocks. Top right are seen God the Father, the Son and the Holy Ghost, who presumably, through the angel, endowed the maker with the necessary knowledge. The monk on the left may be either the maker of the clock or the donor, or perhaps the writer of the book.

Another example of a wisdom clock is seen in Fig. 239. This is taken from a translation of a work written in 1327 and trans-

507. (*Above*) *Mahogany long case 'Yorkshire' clock from Ottley, Yorkshire, c.* 1800. (*The late Mr W. Gibson*)

508. (*Above*) *Escapement and pendulum arrangement in a Zaandam clock.* (*Science Museum, London*)

lated into Latin under the title *Horologium Sapienties* about 1355, and copied many times.[138] A clock was regarded as a symbol of temperance because of its restraint and control, hence a symbol of the virtues. In this example the monk seated on the left is Henri Suss, the author of the original work, and Wisdom comes to inspire him.

WÜRZBURG CLOCK. An early alarm clock with its little bell seen in Fig. 8 is in the Museum at Würzburg, and is sometimes referred to as the Würzburg clock.

YEAR CLOCK. A clock that goes for one year with one winding. A month clock goes for four times as long as an eight day clock (q.v.), i.e., 32 days, and a year clock goes for 12×32 days, i.e. 384 days. The earliest year clock known to the author is that by Hans Buschmann (q.v.), most year clocks are weight driven and it is surprising to see that this earliest example is spring driven. The author understands that, now at any rate, it has difficulty in running its full time. In England the first year clocks were made by Thomas Tompion (q.v.) for the original Observatory at Greenwich, in 1676. His first, and probably only, spring driven year clock is that now in the possession of Lord Mostyn, it was made *circa* 1697 for King William III. The clock illustrated under Daniel Quare (Fig. 387) is a year clock. These year clocks are rare, but some occasionally come onto the market. The author knows of a year clock by Vulliamy

509. *A modern astronomical clock.* 1959. (*Horological Journal, February,* 1962)

(q.v.), about 4 feet high; he utilised piano wire to suspend the weight, so as to get sufficient turns onto the winding drum.

YORK MINSTER CLOCK. *See* ATKINSON, Dr R. d'E.

YORKSHIRE CLOCK. Towards the end of the 18th and in the first half of the 19th century industrial prosperity was rapidly increasing and this led to a period where bulk was preferred to line and proportion. Fig. 507 is a typical Yorkshire clock *circa* 1800, which comes from Otley; the small door in the trunk is usually found in this type. The pillars of the hood and the feet of the base are turned and the dial is painted with a pastoral scene in the arch.

ZAANDAM CLOCK. A Dutch type, made at the end of the 17th century. The seconds pendulum is suspended from the back board and from it, just above the top plate of the clock, projects an L shaped arm. The verge pallet arbor (q.v.) has a horizontal arm attached to it, which is bent upwards at the end, this portion passes into a slot in the pendulum arm (Fig. 508). This is a style adopted by Huygens (q.v.). It will be noted that the frame construction of this clock is akin to that of a horizontal strip Gothic clock (q.v.).

ZODIAC. A zone in the heavens bounded by two circles about 9° on either side of the celestial equator, within which all the motions of the sun, moon and the planets take place. It is divided into twelve signs which are marked by twelve constellations. Aries the Ram ♈, Taurus the Bull ♉, Gemini the Twins ♊, Cancer the Crab ♋, Leo the Lion ♌, Virgo the Maiden ♍, Libra the Balance ♎, Scorpio the Scorpion ♏, Sagittarius the Archer ♐, Capricornus the Goat ♑, Aquarius the Water Carrier ♒, and Pisces the Fishes ♓. These twelve signs are each divided into 30°, giving 1°-360° starting from the vernal equinox (q.v.) and proceeding anti-clockwise.

In astrology (q.v.) the twelve signs are known as the twelve celestial houses. Fig. 509 shows a modern astronomical clock made in 1959 for the new building of the *Financial Times* in London. In the centre of the solar effigy is a representation of Sir Winston Churchill. It may be recalled that Mr Brenden Bracken was at one time Chairman of the *Financial Times* and he seems to have given in this way permanent recognition to his admiration for his war-time chief, in whose Cabinet he served. The dial revolves and the month, the hour and minute are read within the frame at the top. The lunar phase is seen through the aperture in the dial.

APPENDIX I

REFERENCE NUMBERS IN THE TEXT

1. *Old Clocks and Watches*, Britten, 6th Edition, p. 651. Spon, London, 1932

2. Haberdasher's Company, London

3. *Some Accounts of the Worshipful Company of Clockmakers*, Atkins and Overall, pp. 50 and 172. Privately printed, 1881

4. *Encyclopaedia Britannica*, 1947

5. *L'Horloge Astronomique de Strasbourg*, A. and T. Ungerer. Strasburg, 1922

6. *Some Outstanding Clocks over 700 Years, 1250–1950*, H. Alan Lloyd, 1958. Leonard Hill Ltd, London

7. *Uhren*, von Bertele/von Bassermann-Jordan, p. 166. Klinkhardt and Biermann, Brunswick, 1961

8. *Clockmakers of Wigan*, A. J. Hawkes, Wigan, 1950

9. *Antiquarian Horology*, December 1962, p. 14

10. *Uhren*, von Bertele/von Bassermann-Jordan, p. 186. Klinkhardt and Biermann, Brunswick, 1961

11. *Astronomiae Instauratae Mechanica*, Tycho Brahe. Wandsburgi, 1598, English edition pp. 29 and 30. Copenhagen 1946

12. *Jost Burgi, Kammeruhrmacher Kaisers Rudolf II*, von Drach, p. 15 ? Marburg n.d.

13. *Watchmakers and Clockmakers of the World*, G. H. Baillie, N.A.G. Press, London, 1947

14. *Beschreibung einer Astronomischen Uhr von F. David a S. Cajetano*, Joseph Rendler. Vienna, 1771

15. *Neues Raedergebaeude mit Verbesserungen und Zusatzen, Vienna*, Leipzig, 1793

16. *Dizionario degli Orologiani Italiani*, E. Morpurgo. La Clessidra, Rome, 1950

17. *La Clessidra*, A. Simoni. Rome, January, 1955

18. *Some Outstanding Clocks over 700 Years, 1250–1950*, H. Alan Lloyd, p. 32. Leonard Hill Ltd, London

19. *James Ferguson's Commonplace Book*. Edinburgh University Library

20. *Antiquarian Horology*, September 1962. J. B. Penfold

21. *Clockmaking in Oxfordshire, 1400–1850*. C. F. C. Beeson, p. 64. Antiquarian Horological Society, 1962

22. *Lloyd, Horological Journal*, April 1952

23. *Evolution of Clockwork*, Drummond Robertson, p. 78. Cassell, London, 1931

24. *Some Accounts of the Worshipful Company of Clockmakers*, Atkins and Overall, p. 184. Privately printed, 1881

25. *Buckingham Palace*, H. Clifford Smith, p. 266. Country Life, London, 1930

26. *L'Horloge Astronomique de Strasbourg*, A. and T. Ungerer, pp. 16 and 17. Strasburg, 1922

27. *Old Clocks and Watches*, Britten, 7th Edition, p. 366. Spon, London, 1956

28. *Horological Journal*, December 1950. Tides and the Time, H. Alan Lloyd

29. *Philosophical Transactions No. 143*. January 1683–4

30. *Suisse Horologère*, July 1955. Giovanni de Dondi's Horological Masterpiece, H. Alan Lloyd

31. *Tractatus Astraii Biblica Apostolica Vaticana, 1960*

32. *Clocks and Watches*, G. H. Baillie, p. 1. N.A.G. Press, London, 1951

33. *La Clessidra*, Rome. 12th/27th April 1962, Zinner quoted by D. W. Macrow, p. 90

34. Lynn Thorndike in *Archeion*, 1936, pp. 308–19; *Isis*, Vol. 10, 1928; *History of Magic*, Vol. III. p. 740

35. *Old Clocks and Watches*, Britten, 7th Edition, p. 6. Spon, London, 1956

36. *Some Accounts of the Worshipful Company of Clockmakers*, Atkins and Overall, p. 165. Privately printed, 1881

37. *Mercurius Politicus*. London, 21st/28th October 1658

38. *Oeuvres Complètes de Christiaan Huygens*. Soc. Hollandaise des Sciences, Letters Volume XXII

39. *Horological Disquisitions*, John Smith, p. 4. London 1694

40. *Clocks and Watches*, G. H. Baillie, pp. 87 and 88. N.A.G. Press, London, 1951

41. *Evolution of Clockwork*, Drummond Robertson, Chap. VI. Cassell, London, 1931

42. *The Marine Chronometer*, Gould. Potter, London, 1923

43. Conservatoire des Arts et Métiers, Paris. Cat. Sect. J. B. 1949, pp. 206 and 207

44. *Antiquarian Horology*, September 1961

45. *Heavenly Clockwork*, Needham, Ling and Price, Fig. 1 and p. 3. Cambridge University Press, 1960

46. *Horological Journal*, February 1962

47. *Horological Journal*, March 1941, and February 1942

48. *Select Mechanical Exercises*, Jas. Ferguson, F.R.S. London, 1773

49. *Les Habrechts*, T. Ungerer. Strasburg, 1925

50. *Horological Journal*, December 1958. H. v. Bertele

51. *Antiquarian Horology*, March 1955

52. *Les Habrechts*, T. Ungerer. Strasburg, 1925

53. *Uhren*, von Bertele/von Bassermann-Jordan, p. 185. Klinkhardt and Biermann, Brunswick, 1961

54. John Harrison's MS. 10.6.1730, paras 5 and 6. Clockmaker's Library

55. *L'Orologio da petto prima del Henlein*, Morpurgo. La Clessidra Rome, 1952

56. *The Diary of Robert Hooke, 1672–80*, Robinson and Adams. Taylor and Francis, 1935.

57. *Suisse Horologère*, October 1953. H. Alan Lloyd

58. *Evolution of Clockwork*, Drummond Robertson, pp. 148 and 149. Cassell, London, 1931

59. *Ottheinrich*, 1956, pp. 185 ff. Heidelberg University

60. *The Ingraham Story*, E. Ingraham Coy, Bristol, U.S.A.

61. *Horological Journal*, October 1953. H. Alan Lloyd

62. *Some Accounts of the Worshipful Company of Clockmakers*, Atkins and Overall, p. 168. Privately printed, 1881

63. *Esquisse d'une Histoire du Système Sexagesimal*, F. Therau Dangin, pp. 14 and 15. Paris, 1932

64. *The Dawn of Civilisation*, p. 67. Thames and Hudson, London, 1961

65. *Esquisse d'une Histoire du Système Sexagesimal*, F. Therau Dangin, pp. 44 and 45. Paris, 1932

66. *Die Uhrmacher von Winterthur u. ihre Werke*, Schenk. Statsbibliotek, Winterthur, 1959

67. *American Clocks and Clockmakers*, Dreppard, p. 73. Doubleday Inc., N.Y.

68. *The Equatorie of the Planets*, D. J. Price, p. 123. Cambridge University Press, 1955

69. *Encyclopaedia Britannica*, 1947. Vol. 2. p. 685

70. *Libros del Saber de Astronomica*, Manuel Rico y Sinoba. Madrid, 1866

71. *La Réparation des Pendules*, Jacquet and Gilbertini, p. 97, Ch.Rohr. Bienne, 1948

72. *Buckingham Palace*, H. Clifford Smith, p. 82. Country Life, London, 1930

73. *Old Clocks and Watches*, Britten, 7th Edition p. 446. Spon, London, 1956

74. *Jens Olsen's Clock*. O. Mortensen. Technological Institute Publishing Dept. Copenhagen, 1957

75. British Museum. Add. Ms. 17480.

76. *An Organ for the Sultan*. S. Mayes. Putnam, London, 1956

77. *Illustrated London News*, 18th December 1937

78. *Esquisse d'une Histoire du Système Sexagesimal*, F. Therau Dangin, pp. 23, 41, 44. Paris, 1932

79. *Esquisse d'une Histoire du Système Sexagesimal*, F. Therau Dangin, pp. 9, 43. Paris, 1932

80. *L'Orologio e il Pendolo*, Morpurgo. La Clessidra, Rome, 1957

81. John Harrison's MS. 10.6.1730, p. 4 and 5. Clockmaker's Library

82. *Buckingham Palace*, H. Clifford Smith, p. 255. Country Life, London, 1930

83. *Plough Count*, Cripps, p. 10. Allen and Hanbury, London

84. *Antiquarian Horology*. March 1963

85. *Horological Journal*, December 1960. H. H. Quill

86. *Some Accounts of the Worshipful Company of Clockmakers*, Atkins and Overall, p. 171. Privately printed, 1881

87. *Old Clocks and Watches*, Britten, 7th Edition, p. 269. Spon, London, 1956

88. *The Rittenhouse Orrery*, Rice. Princetown N.J., 1954

89. *Abouti's Guide Book. Egypt*. Coststsoumas and Co., Cairo, 1960

90. *Penloubet's Bible Dictionary*, p. 253. Winston and Co., Philadelphia, 1912

91. *Die Geschischte der Zeitmessung, Altaegyptische Zeitmessung*, L. Borchardt, p. 27. Walter de Gruyter and Co., Berlin, 1920

92. *Old Clocks*, H. Alan Lloyd. Benn, London, 1958

93. *Tercentenary Celebrations*, 1939, Turnbull, p. 15. University of St Andrews

94. *Anthology of Clocks and Watches*, C. A. Fox. Privately printed, Swansea, 1947

95. *Some Outstanding Clocks over 700 Years, 1250–1950*, H. Alan Lloyd, Pl. 32. Leonard Hill, London

96. *Horological Journal*, April, 1962. P. G. Coole

97. *Thomas Tompion his Life and Work*, R. W. Symonds, pp. 22–7. Batsford, London, 1951

98. *Thomas Tompion his Life and Work*, R. W. Symonds, p. 14. Batsford, London, 1951

99. *Dizionario degli Orologiani Italiani*, E. Morpurgo, p. 186. La Clessidra, Rome, 1950

100. *Alte Uhren und ihre Meister*, Bassermann-Jordan, p. 55. Diebner, Leipzig, 1926

101. *Receuil d'Ouvrages Curieux*, Grollier de Servière. Lyons, 1719

102. *Journal of the National Association of Watch and Clock Collectors*, U.S.A., December 1956/June 1957. Johann Philip Treffler, Bedini

103. *Antiquarian Horology*, September, 1962. C. Clutton

104. *Connoisseur Year Book*, Lloyd and Drover, London, 1954

105. *L'Horloge Astronomique de Besançon*, P. Brandibas. Goudry

106. *L'Horloge Monumentale de la Cathédral de Beauvais.* Prevot and Co., Beauvais, 1953

107. *Dizionario degli Orologiani Italiani*, E. Morpurgo. La Clessidra Rome, 1950. Marcine Library M.C. Coc. It. IV 4.1. folio 83v

108. *Antiquarian Horology*, March 1957, p. 31

109. *Buckingham Palace*, H. Clifford Smith. Country Life, London, 1930

110. *Some Accounts of the Worshipful Company of Clockmakers*, Atkins and Overall, pp. 184 and 194. Privately printed, 1881

111. *Some Accounts of the Worshipful Company of Clockmakers*, Atkins and Overall, p. 176. Privately printed, 1881

112. *Antiquarian Horology*, March 1954, p. 15

113. *Thomas Tompion his Life and Work*, R. W. Symonds, p. 118. Batsford, London, 1851

114. *Horological Journal*, December 1951, p. 796. Also *Antiquarian Horology*, March 1956

115. *Antiquarian Horology*, December 1954. MS Bod. 270b. f. 183v

116. *Ancient Egypt*, Manchip White, p. 24. Allen Wingate, London, 1952

117. *Official Guide Book to Cairo Museum* 1962, p. 37

118. *Die Geschischte der Zeitmessung, Altaegyptische Zeitmessung*, L. Borchardt. Walter de Gruyter and Co., Berlin, 1920

119. *Ancient Egypt, 1924.* Sloley, Ancient Clypsedra, p. 43

120. *Ancient Egypt, 1917.* Sloley, Ancient Clypsedra, p. 42

121. *Horological Journal*, August 1943. H. Alan Lloyd

122. *Encyclopaedia Britannica*, 1947. Vol. I, 916c; Vol. 2, 609a; Vol. 7, 310d

123. Vitruvius IC. VI

124. Vitruvius IXC. VIII

125. *Du Gnomon à la Montre*, Tardy. Paris, n.d. Sold by the author

126. *Antiquarian Horology*, December 1954, p. 56

127. Professor H. A. Harris. University of Wales

128. *Camden Society Papers, 1851*

129. *Horological Journal*, December 1942. H. Alan Lloyd

130. By permission of the Royal Society, London

131. *Old Clocks and Watches*, Britten, 6th Edition p. 25. Spon, London, 1932

132. *Antiquarian Horology*, December 1960. R. Allen Brown

133. *Connoisseur Encyclopaedia of American Antiques.* Amos G. Amery, p. 315

134. *Horological Journal*, December 1943, H. Alan Lloyd

135. *Antiquarian Horology*, December 1955, p. 127. von Bertele

136. Bibl.Natl. Paris, MS. 926, fol. 113

137. *Antiquarian Horology*, December 1954

138. *Antiquarian Horology*, March 1962

139. *Evolution of Clockwork*, Drummond Robertson, p. 198 ff. Cassell, London, 1931

140. *Time Measurement.* Science Museum, London. Pt. I 1955, Pt. II 1958

141. *Antiquarian Horology*, March 1954, p. 15

142. *The Clock of Big Ben*, Gilgrass. Joseph, London, 1946. Also *The Story of Big Ben*, Stationery Office, London and Messrs. E. Dent and Son

143. *Buckingham Palace*, H. Clifford Smith, Pl. 234. Country Life, London, 1930

144. As 143, plate 294. *Horological Journal*, December 1946. *Old Clocks and Watches*, Britten, 7th Edition, Pl. 157. Spon, London, 1956

145. *L'Horloge Astronomique de Messines*, R. Redslob. La Vie en Alsace, Strasburg, 1933

146. *Inventory by two Clockmakers, Jean Pavin and Thomas Merkley of King John Casimir of Poland, 1673*, Abbey St Germain de Prés. Zn Dziejon Poposkiejo Mecenatem, Artystysznegor, Warsaw, 1952

147. Description by P. Coole

148. Dr A. B. Dickie

149. *Galileo Galilei and Time Measurement*, Silvio A. Bedini, *Physics* Vol V. fasc. 2. Florence, 1963

150. *Horloges Astronomiques*, Ungerer, p. 373. Strasburg, 1931

APPENDIX II

DICTIONARY OF HOROLOGICAL TERMS

ENGLISH	FRENCH	GERMAN	ITALIAN
Arbor	Tige	Welle	Albero
Alarm clock	Réveil	Wecker	Sveglia
Astronomical clock	Horloge astronomique	Astronomische Uhr	Orologio astronomico
Balance spring	Spiral	Spiralfeder	Spirale
Barrel	Barillet	Federhaus	Bariletto
Beat	Battement	Schlag	Battito
Bell	Cloche	Glocke	Campana
Bezel	Lunette	Glasreif	Lunetta
Bob	Lentille du pendule	Pendellinse	Lente del pendolo
Bolt and shutter	Remontoir auxiliaire d'entretien combiné avec volets	Gegengesperr kombiniert mit Freigabe der Aufzuglöcher	Freno ad alette
Carriage clock	Montre de carosse	Reiseuhr	Orologio da carrozza
Centre seconds	Seconde au centre	Sekunde aus der Mitte	Secondi al centro
Chops	Suspension du pendule	Pendelaufhängung	Ganasce
Circular error	Erreur circulaire	Pendelschwingungsfehler	Errore di oscillazione
Clock	Horloge, Pendule	Standuhr	Orologio di medio calibro, pendola
Cock	Coq	Unruh-Kloben	Ponte
Conical pendulum	Pendule conique	Drehpendel	Pendolo conico
Contrate wheel	Roue de champ	Kronrad	Ruota di rincontro
Crown wheel	Roue de rencontre	Spindel-Hemmungsrad	Ruota corona
Crutch	Fourchette de pendule	Pendelgabel	Guida o forchetta del pendolo
Drum clock	Horloge tambour	Trommelförmige Dosenuhr	Tamburina
Escapement	Echappement	Hemmung	Scappamento
Escapement, anchor	Echappement à ancre	Ankerhemmung	Scappamento ad ancora
Escapement, chronometer	Echappement à détente	Chronometerhemmung	Scappamento chronometro
Escapement, cylinder	Echappement à cylindre	Zylinderhemmung	Scappamento a cilindro
Escapement, coup perdu see Escapement, single beat			
Escapement, dead beat	Echappement à repos	Ruhende Hemmung	Scappamento a colpo monto, o di Graham
Escapement, detached	Echappement libre	Freie Hemmung	Scappamento libero

Escapement, gravity	Echappement à gravité	Schwerkrafthemmung	Scappamento a gravita
Escapement, lever	Echappement à ancre libre	Freie Ankerhemmung	Scappamento ad ancora
Escapement, pin pallet	Echappement à ancre à chevilles	Stiftenankerhemmung	Scappamento a caviglie
Escapement, recoil	Echappement à recul	Rückfallende Hemmung	Scappamento a rinculo
Escapement, single beat	Echappemant à coup perdu	Hemmung mit verlorenem Schlag	Scappamento a colpo perduto
Escapement, verge	Echappement à verge	Spindelhemmung	Scappamento a verga
Equation of time	Equation du temps	Zeitgleichung	Equazione del tempo
Fusee	Fusée	Schnecke	Fuso, conoide
Fusee chain	Chaîne	Kette	Catena
Going barrel	Barillet tournant	Verzahntes Federhaus	Bariletto
Grandfather clock	Horloge à gaine	Bodenstanduhr	Orologio a colonna
Hands	Aiguilles	Zeiger	Lancette
Lantern pinion	Pignon lanterne à chevilles	Laternentrieb	Rocchetto a laterna
Locking plate	Roue de compte	Schlosscheibe	Spartitora
Mainspring	Ressort Moteur	Zugfeder	Molla
Maintaining power	Remontoir auxiliaire d'entretien	Gegengesperr	Remontorio ausiliare
Mantel clock	Pendule de cheminée	Stutzuhr	Pendola romana
Monumental clock	Pendule monumentale	Prunkuhr	Orologio monumentale
Motion work	Minuterie	Zeigerwerk	Minuterie
Movement	Mouvement	Uhrwerk	Movimento
Neck clock	Montre de cou	Halsuhr	Orologio da collo
Night clock	Pendule de nuit	Nachtuhr	Orologio notturno
Pallet	Ancre	Anker	Ancora
Pallet staff	Tige d'ancre	Ankerwelle	Albero d'ancora
Pendulum	Le Pendule	Pendel	Pendolo
Pendulum spring	Ressort de suspension	Pendelfeder	Molla di sospensione
Pillar	Pilier	Pfeiler	Pilastro
Pinion	Pignon	Trieb	Rocchetto
Pinion leaf	Aile de pignon	Triebflügel	Dente del rochetto
Pivoted detent	Bascule pivotante	Wippe	Bascula, scatto
Potence	Potence	Spindelrad-Kloben	No equivalent
Rack clock	Horloge à crémaillère	Sägeuhr	Orologio a sega
Rack and snail striking	Sonnerie à râteau et colimaçon	Schlagwerk mit Rechen und Stundenstaffel	Soneria a rastrello e a chiucciola
Regulator	Régulateur	Normaluhr	Regolatore
Religieuse	Réligieuse	Religieuse	Religiosa
Remontoire	Force constante	Konstante Kraft	Remontorio
Repeater	Horloge à répétition	Repetieruhr	Orologio a ripetizione
Roman strike	Sonnerie Romaine	Römische schlagwerk	Soneria romana

Saw clock *see* Rack clock

Seat board	Support de mouvement	Postament	Basamento
Silent clock	Pendule silencieuse	Uhr mit leisem Gang	Orologio silenzioso
Snail	Colimaçon	Stundenstaffel	Chiocciola
Strike/Silent	Sonnerie/Silence	Schlagen/nicht schlagen	Sona/non suona
Striking work	Sonnerie	Schlagwerk	Soneria
Table clock	Horloge de table	Tischuhr	Cappoccina
Teeth	Dents	Zaehne	Denti
Tidal clock	Horloge de marée	Ebbe- und Flutuhr	Orologio delle maree
Ting-Tang clock	Horloge à deux timbres	Uhr mit Bim-Bam Schlag	Orologio a due campane
Torsion pendulum	Pendule à torsion	Torsionspendel	Orologio con pendolo a Torsione
Train	Rouage	Laufwerk	Rotismo
Train, striking	Rouage de sonnerie	Schlag-Räderwerk	Rotismo della soneria
Train, chiming	Rouage du carillon	Glockenspiel-Räderwerk	Rotismo della soneria
Train, astronomical	Rouage astronomique	Astronomisches Räderwerk	Rotismo astronomico
Turret clock	Horloge de clocher	Turmuhr	Orologio da campanile
Up and down indicator	Indicateur de développement du ressort	Auf- und Abwerk	Indicatore
Wall clock	Cartel	Wanduhr	Orologio da muro
Wheel	Roue	Rad	Ruota

APPENDIX III

INDEX TO ENTRIES OCCURRING IN THE TEXT, BUT NOT UNDER THEIR OWN ALPHABETICAL HEADING